FRACTURE PREVENTION AND CONTROL

Proceedings of a Symposium
at the
1972 Western Metal and Tool Exposition and Conference

13 – 16 March 1972
Los Angeles, California

Edited by

David W. Hoeppner

Number 3 in the
American Society for Metals
Materials/Metalworking Technology Series

Library of Congress Catalog Card Number:
73–86453

Printed in the United States of America

PREFACE

The collection of papers contained herein is the result
of a symposium that was held in conjunction with Westec 1972.
The symposium was the result of the combined efforts of numerous persons. Mr. Tom Landig served as the symposium chair-
man and led the organization of the program. Mr. Keith Lamp-
son made contributions to the organization of the symposium
as well. Several committees aided in planning the program;
we are indebted to all those that made a contribution.

The symposium initially was organized to focus attention
on fracture mechanics as it relates to aircraft technology.
An attempt was made to introduce the audience to all of the
elements of fracture prevention and control. This theme extended to the papers and, thus, this volume attempts to draw
attention to the various factors that play a role in establishing structural integrity and/or flaw tolerance. Unfortunately, not all of the papers that were presented were
submitted for presentation in this volume. However, it is
believed that the papers contained herein will introduce the
concepts of fracture prevention and control to a large audience. The concepts covered herein are fracture testing, inspection and flaw detection capability, fracture of high-
strength materials, specification requirements for fracture
control, temperature and environment effects in fracture behavior, and applications of fracture toughness to design.
It is not intended that this volume be an end in itself but
only a continuation of the attempts that are being made to
make us all more aware of flaws and flaw tolerance and the
effects they have on structural behavior.

It is a pleasure to extend a word of appreciation to
all the authors and contributors to this volume and the symposium. A special acknowledgment is due to numerous person-

nel at American Society for Metals headquarters and the
United States Air Force. Both of these organizations provided stimulus to this endeavor. Personnel at American
Society for Metals provided encouragement and support for
the collection of papers into this volume.

    My personal hope is that this volume will aid in pro-
viding a little more knowledge and insight into fracture
prevention and control in order that our structures may be
even safer than they already are.

Columbia, Missouri   David W. Hoeppner
February, 1974

CONTENTS

FRACTURE TESTING

FRACTURE OF HIGH STRENGTH ENGINEERING MATERIALS

FRACTURE TESTING

THE USAF INTEREST IN FRACTURE TOUGHNESS SPECIFICATIONS

James W. Mar
Professor of Aeronautics and Astronautics
Massachusetts Institute of Technology.
Formerly Chief Scientist, United States Air Force

ABSTRACT

The structural designer is approaching the
textbook goal of an airplane structure which is
everywhere working at or near the limits of the
material. This has become possible because the
analyst, with his high speed computers, can optimize, and the shop, with its tremendous capabilities, can produce almost any shape or configuration the designer wishes to commit to paper.
The performance requirements, both initially and
after introduction into the inventory, are more
demanding than in the past, and coupled to all of
these factors are the fatigue life specifications
which were first introduced as contractual items
on the F-111 and C-5A airplanes. There is evidence
which indicates that static strength, aeroelasticity,
and fatigue are insufficient to give adequate
structural integrity. Damage tolerance is being
added as a requirement . The designer, therefore,
needs quantitative, reproducible values of fracture
toughness, and the concomitant properties related
to crack growth.

INTRODUCTION

The theme of this symposium is Fracture Prevention and Control. However, complete fracture prevention is not possible and even if possible would not be feasible. We, as engineers, realize that our objective in designing an airframe is to control the factors which lead to fracture and hence minimize the probability of catastrophic failure while the airplane is being used. This, of course, has always been our objective but as you will be able to judge at the end of this symposium, there is a new sense of urgency and concern with respect to the application of fracture prevention and control to aircraft. It is the objective of this paper to present views on why the United States Air Force is interested in fracture toughness specifications.

THE PRIMARY REQUIREMENTS FOR STRUCTURAL INTEGRITY

There is a series of military specifications which defines the general requirements imposed on the aircraft structure (1-3). Historically, the first airplanes were designed for static strength. Younger's 1939 book (4) has a chapter on design requirements which shows free body force diagrams of airplanes in pullouts, landing, and taxiing, etc. There is a brief mention of flutter but there is no discussion of fatigue. Niles and Newell's 1955 book (5), also makes no mention of fatigue. The emphasis for structural design was to build a structure for static strength. The 1938 specification does not contain any reference to flutter or fatigue. However, in an amendment, dated April, 1943, to X-1803A, (6), the appendix dealing with fittings was augmented with the phrase "proper consideration shall be made of stress concentrations, eccentricities and the possibilities of fatigue failures". As the designer learned to minimize structural weight while still

meeting the static strength requirement, the airframes began to encounter flutter difficulties. The 1940's and 1950's
were periods of intense research into flutter and other
aeroelasticity problems. With time, the designer was able
to meet both static strength and aeroelasticity requirements with efficient structures, i.e., with minimum weight
structures. The next problem which faced the structural
designer was fatigue. It is true that the good detail designer was always conscious of the meaning of stress concentrations and hence instinctively used generous radii on
filets. Nonetheless, the Comet fuselage fatigue experiences
and those of the Martin 202 wing fatigue created much interest in fatigue.

The three main criteria for structural integrity have
been static strength, aeroelasticity, and fatigue life. Of
these, the starting point for design has been static strength
because it is the easiest to tackle. Aeroelasticity calculations in fact cannot be made until the static strength
sizes the structure and the aeroelastician if he cannot meet
the flutter requirements without additional structure is
berated by management. Fatigue calculations also come later
in the design although the importance of stress concentrations is part of the psyche of every good detail designer.

THE PURSUIT OF HIGH STRENGTH MATERIALS

Since static strength has been considered the most important factor in structural integrity, the aircraft structural designer has placed great importance on tensile strength
and the metallurgists have responded with high strength materials. As an example, Table I shows the values for three different aluminum alloy extrusions. (7)

In the time period when the 7178 alloy became available,
the increases in ultimate strength were translated into weight
savings. Unfortunately, the fatigue and toughness capabilities of this alloy were not commensurate with the static

Table I: Comparison of Aluminum Alloy Extrusions

Alloy	Tensile Ultimate	Tensile Yield	% Elongation
2024-T4	62 Ksi	47 Ksi	12
7075-T6	86 Ksi	78 Ksi	7
7178-T6	91 Ksi	84 Ksi	5

Table II: Fracture Toughness Comparison

Alloy	Tensile Yield	Fracture Toughness	Rel. Crack Size
2024-T4	47 Ksi	45 Ksi $\sqrt{inch}$	1 inch
7075-T6	78 Ksi	28 Ksi $\sqrt{inch}$	.14 inch
7178-T6	84 Ksi	25 Ksi $\sqrt{inch}$	.095 inch

strength and the Air Force suffered some rather bad experiences. These were sufficiently traumatic so that the 7178
is now banned from new Air Force airplanes. As shown in
Table I the decrease in toughness is evident in the lower
elongation but at that time the quantification of toughness
by fracture mechanics was not well understood and hence was
not used.

     With today's knowledge, the decrease in per cent elonga-
tion is quantified in terms of the critical crack size. The
basic equation in fracture mechanics is

where
$$\underline{a} = \lambda \left(\frac{K_{Ic}}{s} \right)^2$$

$\underline{a}$ = critical crack length
K_{Ic} = fracture toughness
s = tension stress
λ = dimensionless parameter

This equation states that catastrophic, i.e., rapid crack
growth, will occur when the crack length is $\underline{a}$. The conditions leading to "$\underline{a}$" being the critical size are determined
by the operating stress level, $\underline{s}$, a geometric parameter, λ,
and the plain strain fracture toughness, K_{Ic}. It is generally
agreed that K_{Ic} is a basic material parameter and as can be
seen by the equation, K_{Ic} has the rather peculiar dimensions
of psi $\sqrt{\text{inch}}$ if stress is in psi. The evaluation of the three
aluminum alloys in terms of K_{Ic} is shown in Table II. The
column labeled "relative crack size" indicates that 2024-T4
can safely sustain cracks which are ten times larger than
can 7178-T6. Everyone can appreciate that finding a crack
one inch long is much easier than finding one only one-tenth
of an inch long. Table II also reveals why 7075-T6, while
not banned, is losing favor in critical tensile applications.

     The complete preoccupation with high strength also was
evident in the metallurgical research. There were many theories
developed for explaining the disparity between theoretical

strength and actual strength.   At the heart of all these theories
was the theory of dislocations, and strengthening mechanisms
based upon precipitation hardening, Fisher hardening, cross
slip, etc., were developed. (8)   Many generations of metallurgists did their theses on subjects of this kind.

THE INSUFFICIENCY OF THE REQUIREMENTS - RECENT EXPERIENCES

Some recent experiences have raised questions about the
sufficiency of the static strength, aeroelasticity, and fatigue
life requirements to produce adequate structural integrity.

The C-5A airplane is the first transport airplane procured by the USAF with a contractual life guarantee of 30,000
flight hours to a scatter factor of 4.   A full scale specimen
of the wing and fuselage has successfully sustained the static
application of 150% of design limit load in three critical
design conditions and failure occurred in the wing at 132% of
design limit load in a fourth design condition.   Late last
summer the number one engine of a C-5A which was preparing
to take off separated from the wing, fortunately before the
airplane had started its take-off roll.   Figure 1 is a photomicrograph of the cross section of the titanium strut which
failed.   Fatigue induced striations can be seen over about
one inch of the "T" of the member.   The Air Force Program Office
and Lockheed were aware that the struts were marginally adequate for fatigue and this particular strut had been X-rayed,
but the people looking at the X-ray had not seen the crack.

Figure 2 is a picture of a crack found in one of the C-5A
full scale fatigue articles.   This crack which emanated from
a taperlok fastener hole originated at the faying surface.
The C-5A wing structure is divided in the chordwise direction
by a number of planks and these planks give the C-5A wing
a damage tolerance capability.

The F-111 airplane was the first Air Force fighter airplane procured to a contractual life requirement of 4000 hours

 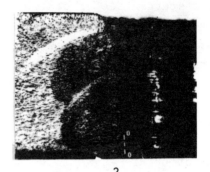

1   2

Fig. 1.   Cross section of titanium strut that failed
Fig. 2.   Crack in C-5A full scale fatigue article

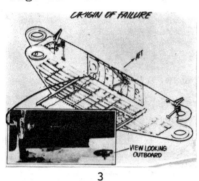 

3   4

Fig. 3.   Point of failure in F-111 carry through box
Fig. 4.   Location of failure surface in F-111 wing

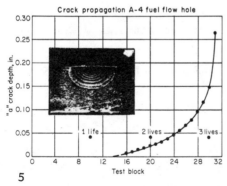 

5   6

Fig. 5.   Fatigue striations and plot of crack growth
Fig. 6.   Flaw in F-111A wing pivot fitting

to a scatter factor of four. Full scale specimens of the F-111
have successfully completed all of the prescribed static and
fatigue tests. However, there were a number of traumatic experiences encountered.

In August of 1968, the fatigue article of the F-111 wing
carry through box (9) failed after only a few hundred hours
of testing. At the time of failure, the crack had grown to a
length of about 3/4 of an inch. Figure 3 shows the point in
.the structure at which the failure occurred. (10) It was determined that the origin of failure was a taperlok fastener
hole and that the early failure was due to a combination of
inadequate hole preparation for the taperlok and a high stress
concentration. The solution involved both redesign and major
changes in manufacturing.

At just over 12,000 hours (3 lives), the initial fatigue
test of the wing pivot fitting failed. (10) Figure 4 shows
the location of the failure surface. This failure was caused
by the early initiation of a crack due to the excessive stress
concentration caused by the presence of a fuel flow hole in
the stiffening flange shown in the figure. There is shown in
Figure 5 a photomicrograph of the fatigue striations and a
plot of the growth of the crack with the application of the
fatigue loadings. The optimum solution to this particular
problem is the adhesive bonding of a boron/epoxy doubler to
the exterior surface of the wing pivot fitting. This solution
has successfully sustained its fatigue tests.

In December of 1969, a F-111A on a practice weapon de-
livery mission suffered the loss of its left wing and crashed.
It was determined that the aircraft was operating well within
its design envelope. Investigation disclosed the presence of
a flaw in the wing pivot fitting. Figure 6 is a picture of
this flaw. (11) Metallurgical study led to the conclusion that
the flaw had been in this airplane upon roll-out from the factory, and that the inspection procedures then being used were
not capable of detecting such a flaw. The solution has been

the imposition of a cold proof test of every F-111. (9)

This flaw and the loss of an airplane it caused marks the beginning of the fracture mechanics era in Air Force airplanes. Excellent and authoritative accounts of the F-111 cold proof test program are to be found in references 6, 9, 10 and 11.

THE INSUFFICIENCY OF THE REQUIREMENTS - FACTORS LEADING TO

The experiences previously cited raise the question of why the present static strength, aeroelasticity, and fatigue life requirements have not produced airplanes with adequate structural integrity. It is not that the designer and analyst are not capable enough (on the contrary, the thesis will be developed that they are too capable for the present requirements).

The requirements have been developed in a historical manner. The legislated factor of safety for ultimate loads is 1.5 and has been 1.5 since the beginning of specifications. It is submitted the true or real factor of safety is much lower for present day airplanes, because the 1.5 factor of safety was promulgated when design load factors were higher, when different materials were used, when the designer used a slide rule, and when tracings were made in ink of every drawing.

It is germane to compare, in Table III, Air Corps Specification No. X-1803-A of 1938 to the present MIL-A-8866A in the matter of maneuver load factors.

Let us oversimplify an example to make a point. Before the advent of high speed computers, the designer would design, e.g., the wing to the 1.5 factor of safety at three or four wing stations. In between these stations, the designer interpolated conservatively such that the factor of safety was substantially larger than 1.5. With the high speed computer, the designer can almost design every square inch of the wing to the factor of safety of 1.5. Thus it is maintained that the true factor of safety of a modern airplane is significantly less than for previous generations of airplanes.

An index of the structural efficiency of an airframe is the structural weight fraction, which is the ratio of the structural weight to the gross weight. Table IV tabulates this index for a series of transport aircraft and fighters.

Even though the C-5 and F-111 show structural weight fractions larger than their predecessors, the increases were evidently not sufficient. It is difficult to justify a priori just what the structural weight fraction should be. The modest variations shown in Table IV are the result of the designer working within the static, aeroelastic, and fatigue life requirements. These requirements do not account in any meaningful manner for the differences in the performance envelope of the aircraft. In this connection, the next generation of fighter aircraft will have thrust-to-weight ratios of about 1.5 as compared to the present fighters which have ratios of about 0.5. Figure 7 shows a stylized depiction of the maneuvering capability of an airplane with a thrust-to-weight ratio of 1.5 in comparison to that for a fighter with a thrust-to-weight ratio of 0.5. At the boundaries shown the respective airplanes can sustain a 5g maneuver without loss of airspeed or altitude. Inside the boundaries the aircraft can pull 5g and still have excess energy which can be translated into instantaneous rates of climb. As can be seen, the next generation of airplanes can perform this kind of a maneuver over a substantially larger portion of the sky. Thus, the exposure to high loads will be substantially larger but the static, aeroelastic and fatigue life requirements as now stated do not account for this aspect of the increase in performance.

The designers and analysts have learned to produce minimum weight structures which satisfy the three requirements of static strength, aeroelasticity, and service life. On a per pound basis or a per square foot basis, there is more analysis done than previously. In 1972, the computer gives one the capability to analyze any structure which can be committed to a piece of paper. This in conjunction with the very versatile manufacturing

Table III: Maneuver Load Factors

Type	Maneuver Load Factor		
	X-1803-A, 1938	MIL-S-5700, 1954	MIL-A 8861A, 1960
Pursuit(fighter)	8	7.33	7.33
Bomber	3.67	3.00	3.00
Transport	3.67	2.50	2.50
Factor of safety	1.5	1.5	1.5

Table IV: Structural Weight Fractions

Model	Structural Weight Fraction	Year of First Flight
C-130	.23	1955
C-133	.27	1956
C-141	.26	1963
C-5	.33	1968
F-100F	.25	1953
F-105	.27	1955
F-106	.28	1956
F-4	.30	1958
F-111	.33	1964

methods makes it possible to create structures which are minimum weight throughout the airframe. This means there are high
stresses everywhere. Consequently, repairs and changes in design details are very difficult to accomplish because the original design is optimized so delicately that changes cannot be
tolerated.

With the new analytical and manufacturing capabilities,
the designer has also found sufficient confidence to raise the
design stress levels. By increasing the tension allowable
stress levels from 60 ksi to 80 ksi, it was possible to decrease structural weight by 8%. Increased shear allowables
yielded a weight reduction of 23% and an increase in the hoop
stress from 14 ksi to 18 ksi saved another 4% of the structural weight. In this same system, improved machining techniques coupled with optimization carried out by computer iterations reduced weight by about 10%.

CURRENT TRENDS

As a result of these and other factors, the Air Force is
in the process of revising its specifications. The ASIP (Aircraft Structural Integrity Program) is to be issued as a Military Standard. Presently it is being referred to as MIL-STD-
XXX, and is under the cognizance of the Structures Division
of the Directorate of Airframe Subsystems Engineering, which
is part of the Aeronautical Systems Division located at Wright-
Patterson Air Force Base.

The new specifications contain the explicitly stated
assumption that an undiscovered flaw of a prescribed size
exists in the most critical part of the structure. The designer must then demonstrate that this undiscovered flaw shall
not grow to critical size during some specified period of
time. This kind of a specification is feasible only because
fracture mechanics supplies the analytical tools whereby the
analyst can quantify crack growth and critical crack size.

However, fracture mechanics is still a relatively immature
discipline and much remains to be done.

The material data base likewise requires much work. This
is the role which must be played by the material producers.
The structural designer is now saying "we want strong and tough
materials". Implicit in this statement are many other requirements. This can be illustrated by two more figures. Figure 8 is a plot of the fracture toughness variation found by
General Dynamics on a 2 x 3 ft piece of D6ac steel. A structural designer faced with the new specification and this kind
of a variability is understandably unenthusiastic about fracture mechanics.

Crack growth is governed by fatigue crack growth rate
(da/dn), the growth of the crack per cycle and ΔK, the amplitude of the change in stress intensity at the tip of the crack.
Figure 9 is a plot of typical data obtained by General Dynamics
on D6ac steel. This kind of data is generally plotted on log-
log graph paper. A stress analyst will find it difficult to
reconcile margin of safety calculations which are carried to
three significant figures with data which is correlated by the
metallurgists on a log-log plot!

Table V shows the variations in fracture toughness of
6Al-4V annealed titanium forgings found by the Air Force in
a recent program. Again, the variation in K_{Ic} presents the
designer with a problem which is especially difficult at this
time because of the relatively small amount of accrued experience.

Finally, the lessons to be found in structural experiences
of the past few years are being taken to heart. Figure 10 is
a plot of critical crack size and design limit stresses for a
number of airplanes. It is interesting to note that the three
airplanes which have had major structural problems all lie below a certain line. It is also very comforting to note that
the B-1 and F-15 by this measure are even better than the F-4.

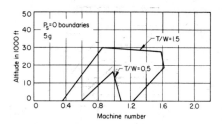

Fig. 7.   Maneuvering boundaries

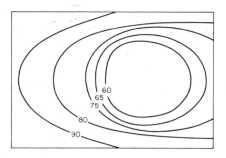

Fig. 8.   Fracture toughness variation on 2-ft by 3-ft
          D6ac steel

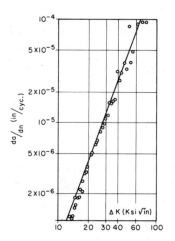

Fig. 9. $\frac{da}{dn}$ data for D6ac steel

Table V: Fracture Toughness of Ti-6Al-4V Forgings

| | No. of Tests | Low K_{Ic} | Av. K_{Ic} |
		Ksi $\sqrt{\text{inch}}$	
A	19	47.6	64.8
B	10	64.0	73.6
C	23	50.4	61.1

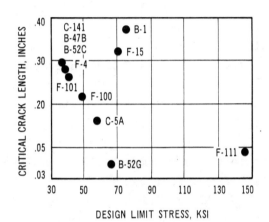

Fig. 10. Critical crack lengths

SUMMARY

All aspects of the (ASIP) Aircraft Structural Integrity
Program are presently under intensive review. It is interesting to realize that the MIL-A-8860 series of specifications
came into existence in May of 1960 and superseded the MIL-S-
5700 specifications. The MIL-S-5700 came into existence in
December of 1954 and this superseded C-1803-E. The USAF ASIP
was conceived in 1958, and originally published as ASD Technical Note 61-141 and later was formalized in ASD Technical
Report 66-57, dated January 1968. In May of 1970 TR 66-57
was issued with revisions. Currently, the ASIP is to be placed
in the form of a military standard and is presently referred
to as MIL-STD XXX. MIL-STD XXX has undergone many drafts and
has been reviewed by an ASIP Industry Advisory Group as well
as by the Aircraft Industries Association.

The new specifications and standards, with their increased emphasis on the assumed existence of undetected flaws,
are a response to the problems of the immediate past. But in
conjunction with the historical perspective, the new ASIP documents reveal areas for research. The Advanced Metallic Structures ADP (Advanced Development Program) under the Structures
Division of the Air Force Flight Dynamics Laboratory is investigating the impact of fracture mechanics on the design of
future airplanes. The Air Force Materials Laboratory is preparing a Handbook for the Standardization of Non-destructive
Testing Methods and is also investigating new NDI methods as
well as evaluating the efficiency of present procedures. But
at the heart of all of these activities are the two material
parameters, fracture toughness and da/dn, rate of crack growth.
We, the users, need reliable data; the material producers
supplying the material should bear much of the responsibility.
Admittedly, fracture toughness and da/dn are difficult, as
well as more expensive, to obtain. However, these data are
crucially important to the design of airplanes with adequate
structural integrity.

Acknowledgments. The author wishes to express his appreciation to individuals at the General Dynamics Corporation, Fort Worth; the Lockheed Corporation, Marietta; the F-15 System Program Office, the Air Force Materials Laboratory and the Directorate of Airframe Subsystems Engineering, Wright-Patterson Air Force Base, for supplying data and assistance in the preparation of this paper.

REFERENCES

1. MIL-A-8860A, "Airplane Strength and Rigidity, General Specification for."

2. MIL-A-8866A, "Airplane Strength and Rigidity, Reliability Requirements, Repeated Loads, and Fatigue."

3. MIL-A-8870A, "Airplane Strength and Rigidity, Flutter, Divergence, and Other Aeroelastic Instabilities."

4. Younger, John E. "Structural Design of Metal Airplanes," McGraw Hill, 1935.

5. Niles and Newell, "Airplane Structures," Vol. I, Wiley 1954, 4th Edition.

6. X-1803-A Stress Analysis Criteria, Appendix A, Basic Flight Criteria, November 15, 1938.

7. Military Handbook 5, "Strength of Metal Aircraft Elements," March 1959.

8. McLean, D. "Mechanical Properties of Metals," Wiley 1954.

9. Hinders, U.A. "F-111 Design Experience - Use of High Strength Steel," AIAA Paper No. 70-884, July 1970.

10. Dietz, W.C. "Fracture Mechanics Considerations in Design Problems in Aircraft Structures," Naval Postgraduate School, October 1971.

11. Buntin, W.D. "Concept and Conduct of Proof Test of F-111 Production Aircraft," Presented to Royal Aeronautical Society, 27 October 1971.

FRACTURE TESTING GUIDELINES FOR ENGINEERS

H. S. Pearson

Pratt & Whitney Aircraft, Advanced Development
Center, West Palm Beach, Florida. Formerly with
Lockheed-George Co., Marietta

P. F. Packman

Materials Science Department, Vanderbilt University
Nashville, Tennessee

ABSTRACT

Fracture testing of notched or precracked high-
strength metallic materials is one of the most rapidly
changing subjects in engineering. Several papers,
books, and specifications describe fracture testing
procedures and specimen designs; some of these are
in conflict in significantly important parameters.
This paper, therefore, reviews these documents and
refers the reader to the most applicable one for each
specific test.

The ASTM Specification for K_{Ic} testing is discussed and is recommended for use; however, other
specimens and procedures are covered for those who
might desire to use some other type specimen. The
area of plane stress (K_c) testing is discussed in
some detail, as are various specimens that can be
used for screening purposes.

Testing for stress corrosion crack propagation
for either determining a threshold value (K_{Iscc}) or

crack growth with time (da/dt) are discussed. Cyclic
crack growth testing is not well standardized throughout industry although generally industry agrees on
many aspects of this type test. Therefore, testing
for da/dn is discussed in considerable detail.

    This paper is intended for engineers and scientists engaged
in developing and specifying tests for determining fracture
toughness properties of materials. It also can be used as a
primer for the test engineer who is just becoming involved in
fracture testing. It is not intended as a specification document for testing, since there are many such documents available.
Therefore, test techniques will not be discussed in detail;
instead, the reader will be referred to current documents in
the literature. Ideally, one should be able to go to the
various specifications available in the literature without the
need for a guide such as this; however, the state-of-the-art
of fracture testing is rapidly changing and many documents
exist specifying techniques that have been superseded or revised.
For example, Ref 1 - 5 are partially sequential documents, all
giving information on plane strain fracture testing. On the
surface it would appear that one can simply use the ASTM
specification (3) and ignore the others. This is not alto-
gether true since much information, especially on other types
of specimens, is included in the other references. Many
tests that must be performed to meet present requirements are
not covered by any specification in the literature. The
design of these tests requires a considerable amount of ingenuity
    Before proceeding into fracture testing, let us review
some of the basics of fracture mechanics. Derivation of the
Griffith equation was based on perfectly linear elastic behavior. (6) This formulation was later revised to include
small-scale yielding. (7,8) The basic assumption in the small-
scale-yielding premise is that the crack length is much larger

than the plastic zone. When this assumption is violated, formulations tend to break down.

The initial fracture mechanics theory was based on a two-dimensional elasticity formulation. Later, when the third dimension was added, complications arose. Primarily, the adding of the third dimension includes the entire region between the idealized limits of plane strain, $\epsilon_z = 0$, and plane stress, $\sigma_z = 0$. In reality, in many materials the condition of plane strain is approximated in thick parts and the condition of plane stress is approximated in thin parts. Between these two limiting cases are conditions loosely referred to as "transitional" or "mixed mode fractures." The generation of fracture toughness data by test is complicated by this plane-strain/plane-stress situation. It is reasonably simple to determine the plane-strain fracture toughness, K_{Ic}; however, when specimen conditions are such that plane-strain conditions are not assured, the results become difficult to interpret and are often vague.

We shall discuss plane-strain testing for K_{Ic}, then mixed-mode testing, and finally screening tests that are intended to obtain toughness values for either plane-strain or plane-stress regions. Another important aspect of fracture testing is the determination of crack growth, both with respect to time and applied load cycles. These areas will be discussed in detail; however, it is extremely important that the reader understand the basics of fracture testing in both the plane-strain and plane-stress regions before proceeding into the more complicated crack-growth area, since crack growth occurs for either plane-strain or plane-stress conditions.

SPECIMENS USED FOR K_{Ic} TESTING

K_{Ic} is reported to be a material constant; therefore, one should be able to test and determine its value. However,

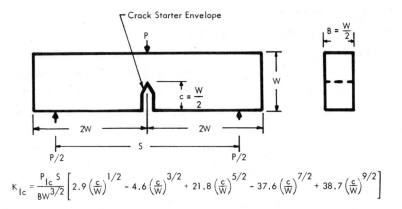

$$K_{Ic} = \frac{P_{Ic}\,S}{BW^{3/2}}\left[2.9\left(\frac{c}{W}\right)^{1/2} - 4.6\left(\frac{c}{W}\right)^{3/2} + 21.8\left(\frac{c}{W}\right)^{5/2} - 37.6\left(\frac{c}{W}\right)^{7/2} + 38.7\left(\frac{c}{W}\right)^{9/2}\right]$$

Fig. 1.   Bend specimen (3-point loading) for determination of K_{Ic}

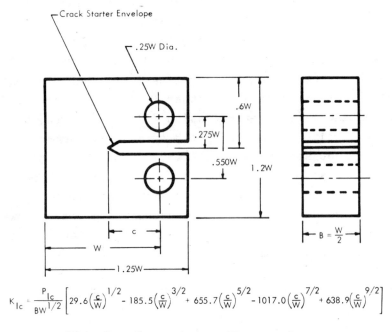

$$K_{Ic} = \frac{P_{Ic}}{BW^{1/2}}\left[29.6\left(\frac{c}{W}\right)^{1/2} - 185.5\left(\frac{c}{W}\right)^{3/2} + 655.7\left(\frac{c}{W}\right)^{5/2} - 1017.0\left(\frac{c}{W}\right)^{7/2} + 638.9\left(\frac{c}{W}\right)^{9/2}\right]$$

Fig. 2.   Compact tensile specimen

the determination of K_{Ic} is affected by many variables in
the test procedures. It is therefore best to think of K_{Ic}
as a material parameter similar to the 0.2% offset yield
stress. Yield stress is determined by a specific set of
test criteria. Normally a specific size specimen is used
and the test procedure is quite specific. The 0.2% offset
has no physical significance; it is simply a point of reference from which one laboratory can obtain data that correlate with data obtained from another laboratory. Thus
these data can be empirically used in design. Similar considerations also hold for K_{Ic}; if tests are conducted per
the ASTM standard, (3) values are obtained that are in
agreement with values obtained in other laboratories, and
the test engineer, stress analyst, and designer are using
a compatible set of K_{Ic} values for a given material.

It is therefore recommended that anyone desiring to
determine K_{Ic} should use either the three-point bend or
compact tension specimens shown in Fig. 1 and 2. More research and development has gone into these two specimens
than any of the others. The selection was made by ASTM
Committee E24 based on the experience of many individuals
working in this field. Many of the pitfalls one can encounter in fracture testing are specified in Ref 3.
Among the factors entering into the selection of these
specimens, both accuracy of test result and cost of specimen preparation and testing were considered.

The compact tension specimen, Fig. 2, requires the
least amount of material and is relatively inexpensive to
test. The bend specimen requires somewhat more material,
but may be slightly cheaper to machine and test. These
factors should be weighed, dependent on the material and
the availability of test equipment. Both specimens must
be fatigue precracked. The compact tension specimen must
be precracked in tension -- tension fatigue, whereas the
three-point bend specimen may be precracked in either three-

point bending or as a cantilever beam. It is therefore
possible to precrack the latter specimen with much less
sophisticated equipment than is required for the compact
tension specimen. Before attempting such a test one must
be thoroughly familiar with the limitations and procedures
described in Ref 3.

The question that may be asked is: "Why should a
three-point bend test be used when four-point bend is less
sensitive to specimen alignment, thus there is less chance
for error in test results?" The ASTM Committee selected
the three-point bend specimen primarily because most
laboratories are not equipped with the high-capacity testing machines necessary to test four-point bend specimens.
For four-point bending the equation used for determinations
of K_{Ic} should be taken from Ref 2; however, this equation
has not been evaluated as extensively by test as that for
the three-point bend specimen. The test procedure should
follow that outlined in Ref 3 for the three-point bend
specimen.

Another specimen that has received considerable attention in the past is the round-bar precracked specimen shown
in Fig. 3. The obvious advantages of this specimen are
that there are no edge effects, there is an equal stress
field around the crack, and the specimen is relatively
inexpensive to machine and test. However, this specimen
is extremely difficult to precrack with a concentric crack.
Usually, an eccentric crack is formed and in some areas
around its periphery the crack may not initiate. This leads
to inaccuracies in test results. For these reasons, this
specimen is not recommended for determination of K_{Ic}. It
is, however, a good specimen for screening purposes without
the fatigue precrack, as will be discussed later. Initially,
the specimen was tested without a fatigue precrack for determination of K_{Ic}, and the results obtained were usually
higher than those obtained from a precracked specimen, the

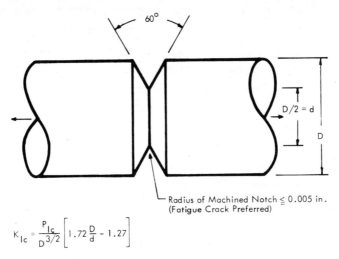

$$K_{Ic} = \frac{P_{Ic}}{D^{3/2}}\left[1.72\frac{D}{d} - 1.27\right]$$

Fig. 3. Circumferentially notched or fatigue cracked round bar for K_{Ic} determination

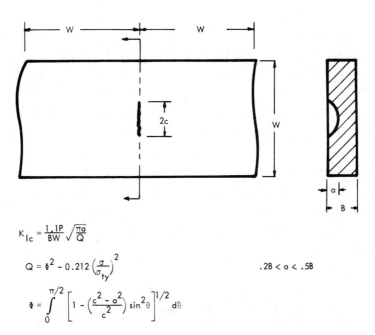

$$K_{Ic} = \frac{1.1P}{BW}\sqrt{\frac{\pi a}{Q}}$$

$$Q = \Phi^2 - 0.212\left(\frac{\sigma}{\sigma_{ty}}\right)^2 \qquad .2B < a < .5B$$

$$\Phi = \int_0^{\pi/2}\left[1 - \left(\frac{c^2 - a^2}{c^2}\right)\sin^2\theta\right]^{1/2}d\theta$$

Fig. 4. Surface cracked specimen for determination of K_{Ic}

amount of difference being somewhat dependent upon material
properties. The equation for calculation of K_{Ic} from data
resulting from test of this specimen is discussed in Ref 2.

The surface-crack specimen shown in Fig. 4 has been
used extensively in the past few years in fracture testing.
The specimen originated as an approximation to actual
service-induced cracks. (9,10) For this reason it is very
valuable; it is not, however, recommended for K_{Ic} testing,
since the K values obtained are usually slightly higher
than values obtained from either the compact tension or
the three-point bend specimen. Additionally, there is no
general agreement on the equations to be used for determining K from the surface-crack specimen. When this specimen
is used, K_{Ic} should be obtained by one of the standard test
methods, the surface-flaw specimen then should be tested
and the answers correlated. This procedure is extremely
useful in crack growth testing, as will be discussed later.
The surface-flaw specimen also is good for screening tests.
McEowen and Hughes (11) report they can test this specimen
very economically and use it for screening purposes. The
primary risk in using a specimen with actual flaws for either
a screening test or for data correlation is that the size
of the flaw relative to the size of the specimen, especially
the thickness of the specimen, can affect the K value obtained. Numerous researchers have added correction factors
to the basic Irwin equation (12) for the surface-crack specimen, but none of these are generally agreed upon by industry;
thus caution should be used. It should be mentioned that
in addition to the normal EDM starter notch, a spark discharge technique has been developed to initiate starter
flaws. (13,14)

Another specimen commonly used for K_{Ic} testing is the
double-cantilever beam or constant-K specimen shown in Fig.
5. Initially this was proposed for a K_{Ic} specimen, but present use is primarily concentrated in crack growth, environ-

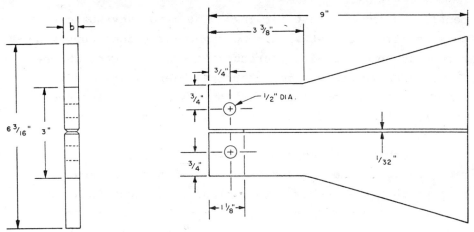

Fig. 5.   Double cantilever beam specimen geometry

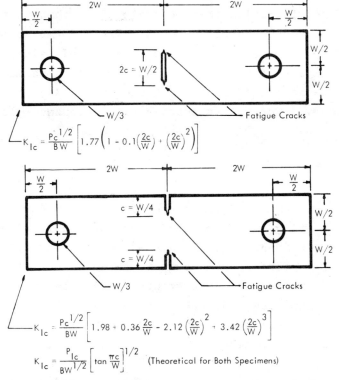

$$K_{Ic} = \frac{P_c^{1/2}}{BW}\left[1.77\left(1 - 0.1\left(\frac{2c}{W}\right) + \left(\frac{2c}{W}\right)^2\right)\right]$$

$$K_{Ic} = \frac{P_c^{1/2}}{BW}\left[1.98 + 0.36\frac{2c}{W} - 2.12\left(\frac{2c}{W}\right)^2 + 3.42\left(\frac{2c}{W}\right)^3\right]$$

$$K_{Ic} = \frac{P_{Ic}}{BW^{1/2}}\left[\tan\frac{\pi c}{W}\right]^{1/2} \quad \text{(Theoretical for Both Specimens)}$$

Fig. 6.   Center and edge cracked tensile specimens for
determination of K_{Ic}

mental and crack arrest testing. The major advantage of
this specimen is that with proper geometric configuration
K remains constant with increases in crack length; therefore, crack growth can be determined over a large region
without changing the K formulation. Normally, side grooves
are used with this specimen to force the crack growth in a
straight line.

Numerous other specimens have been used, or can be
used, to determine K_{Ic} for materials. There is, however,
no need to use a specimen that might yield questionable
results when other specimens, accepted by industry and
standards groups, are available. The exception is an
attempt to simulate an actual failure on a part. In this
case, the configuration that most closely resembles the
part being examined should be used. The K formulation is
of secondary importance as long as the same K values are
used in analysis of the part and the similar specimen. A
value of K so obtained should not be labeled K_{Ic} since K_{Ic}
is now reserved for values obtained in accordance with
E399. (3)

SPECIMENS USED FOR DETERMINATION OF EITHER K_{Ic} OR K_c (MIXED MODE)

The most common specimen used in the past for either
K_{Ic} or K_c testing is the center-crack (or double-edge cracked)
specimen shown in Fig. 6. This specimen configuration has
been used for years in widths up to three or four feet for
obtaining K_c values or crack growth resistance curves for
specific thicknesses. At one time it was believed that the
center-crack specimen could be used to obtain both K_{Ic} and
K_c from a single specimen. This was attempted, and in the
literature a number called "pop in" has been associated with
K_{Ic} and the failure with K_c. Later work, however, revealed
that different size requirements are necessary for K_{Ic} than
K_c. The K_{Ic} specimen requires a minimum thickness and the

K_c speciman requires a minimum width. It is possible to meet both criteria; however, for most engineering materials, if both criteria are met, the specimen is extremely large and the load required to test it to failure considerably exceeds the capacity of most conventional testing machines. Although the concept is valid, it is generally impractical to obtain both K_{Ic} and K_c from a single specimen; therefore, this type specimen is not recommended for K_{Ic} testing. The center-crack specimen is preferred for K_c testing, at least at the present time, since efforts to determine K_c from small specimens of different configurations have not been successful.

There is now general agreement on the K equations for a center-crack specimen (Fig. 6). The major question still unresolved is with regard to the width correction. This subject is discussed in Ref 2 in comments by Feddersen. There are several procedures for testing the center-crack specimen to obtain K_c, but it is difficult at this time to say which is the preferred test technique since there is no standard technique. The authors prefer the technique presented in Ref 15, although other methods are discussed in the literature and probably are as valid.

A single-edge notch specimen (Fig. 7) also has been used for K testing. Although this specimen primarily is used for screening purposes, other variations of the single-edge notch (different dimensions) have been used for screening. The K equations are discussed in Ref 2. ASTM Committee E24 had written a specification for both the center-crack and edge-notch specimens. (4) Originally, this specification was intended to be used in K_{Ic} or K_c determinations; however, due to problems and disagreements within industry, the specification now is a screening test and does not refer to any K formulations.

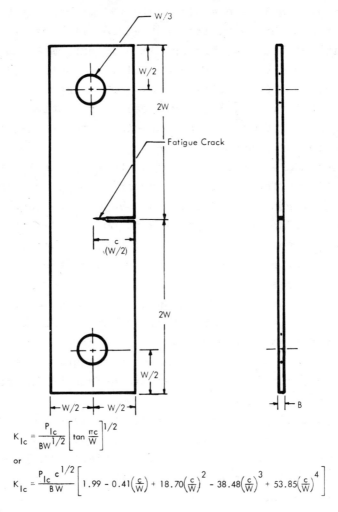

$$K_{Ic} = \frac{P_{Ic}}{BW^{1/2}} \left[\tan \frac{\pi c}{W} \right]^{1/2}$$

or

$$K_{Ic} = \frac{P_{Ic} \, c^{1/2}}{BW} \left[1.99 - 0.41\left(\frac{c}{W}\right) + 18.70\left(\frac{c}{W}\right)^2 - 38.48\left(\frac{c}{W}\right)^3 + 53.85\left(\frac{c}{W}\right)^4 \right]$$

Fig. 7.   Single edge cracked tensile specimen for determination of K_{Ic}

SPECIMENS FOR SCREENING TESTS

Quite often it is impractical to test specification-type fracture specimens due to the expense and time required. It is possible to evaluate the relative toughness of a material by using simplified specimens. This type of evaluation may be used in preliminary materials selection, (16,17) in alloy or process development research, or in quality control. Probably the best-known screening test specimen for toughness is the simple impact specimen shown in Fig. 8. This specimen has been used for many years and is covered by an ASTM specification. (18) In some cases, it is possible to extrapolate from an impact test result to a K_{Ic} number. Although this has been done successfully, the extrapolation can lead to error resulting from plasticity effects. Such error is therefore dependent on specimen size. To get a qualitative idea of the size effect, the required thickness for a K_{Ic} specimen can be calculated, and if this exceeds the size for the impact specimen, no reliable correlation can be obtained. Even in the presence of gross plasticity, the impact specimen is a good specimen for screening from one batch of material to another or from one material to another as long as the strength of the materials being compared is similar, i.e., a highly ductile material cannot be compared with a highly brittle material because of the differing effects of specimen size and basic material behavior differences.

Edge-notch specimens or notch-tensile specimens have been quite valuable for ranking materials, for example during the materials selection phase of the SST. (16,17) Alcoa (19)* has effectively used a single-notch tensile specimen for obtaining relative toughness values for materials. The Alcoa test is reported to be sensitive to the

*Also see Chapter 6 in this book.

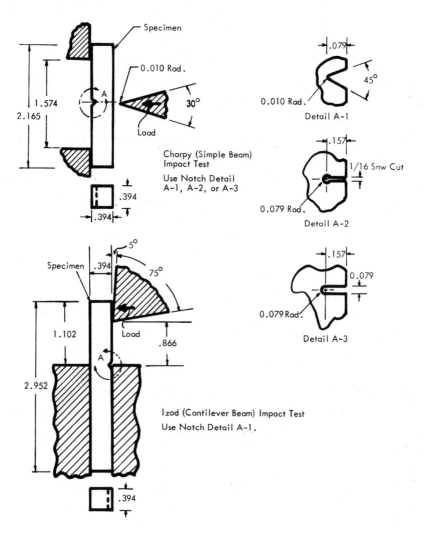

Fig. 8. Typical impact tests

testing machine and technique, and extreme care must be taken
to obtain a quantitative measure of the relative toughness.
Unfortunately, there are no standards for notch specimens
other than Ref 4, which specifies a three-inch wide specimen. Therefore, a choice of both size and notch configuration is available. Fig. 9 shows a typical notch specimen
where three different notch configurations are possible. Before using this specimen, a thorough study should be made of
the work of Sachs and Sessler (20) and the behavior of notch
strength ratio versus theoretical stress concentration factor,
K_t, as shown in Fig. 10. It is possible to have a mild notch
and to obtain an increase in strength due to the existence of
the mild notch. A specimen with a mild notch can lead one to
a completely different answer from that obtained from one
having a sharp notch or crack. It would therefore seem ad-
visable to always use a sharp notch for fracture screening.
In many cases the minimum notch radius is a function of shop
capability. It is much better to have a slightly milder
notch and have it repeatable than to have a very sharp notch
and have a different radius from one specimen to another.

For thick materials, possibly the best screening specimen would be a notch round similar to that shown in Fig. 3.
The diameter can be controlled to a size large enough to
obtain the simulation of K_{Ic} or smaller size to obtain a
ranking parameter. Similar to the impact specimen, as the
diameter approaches 2.5 $(K_{Ic}/\sigma_{ty})^2$ the number obtained from
the K equation will approximate K_{Ic}. The value of K obtained
will always differ from K_{Ic} because of the effect of notch
acuity. Screening type tests also can be used effectively
in failure investigations where material limitations pre-
clude use of standard specimens. For maximum effectiveness
one should test standard specimens versus the screening test
specimen being used on known material of the same type as
that being investigated. Then a screening test value from
the failed part can be used to estimate the toughness of the
failed part.

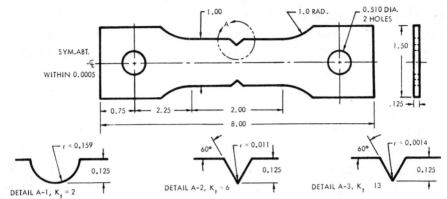

Fig. 9. Typical notch-tensile specimen configurations for three different stress concentrations

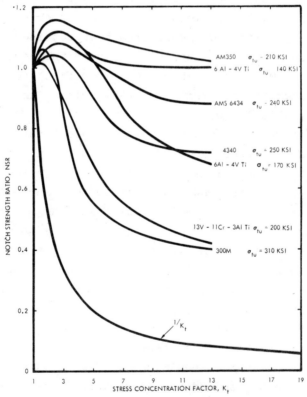

Fig. 10. Effect of stress concentration on notch strength ratio of 0.063-in. thick sheet specimens of several titanium alloys and steels at room temperature (From Sachs and Sessler, Ref 20)

K_{Iscc} DETERMINATION

The term K_{Iscc} is used for the threshold value above
which stress corrosion crack propagation occurs in a specified corrosive environment. To understand K_{Iscc}, we should
look briefly at conventional stress corrosion cracking.

First, an initiation stage requiring months or years
takes place; second, the crack propagates to failure. Although many theories have been proposed to explain this
initiation and propagation, no one theory has been proven,
and it is generally agreed that different processes cause
the initiation stage and the propagation stage.

The standard way to evaluate the stress corrosion cracking characteristics of a material is by applying a constant
tensile stress to a specimen, and then subjecting the specimen to a corrosive environment. The schematic shown in Fig.
11 is normally used to select a nominal design stress below
the threshold level indicated in the figure.

Tiffany (21) eliminated the initiation stage of stress
corrosion by testing a precracked specimen. To eliminate
the need for costly equipment, Brown (22) developed a precracked cantilever beam specimen loaded with dead weight on
a lever arm. The data analysis from these specimens presented the problem that, with an existing crack, the initial
crack length was a variable in the test, and the stress
versus time analysis could not be applied. The data could
be analyzed by using fracture mechanics concepts, since
crack length is included in the formulation. This approach
(shown in Fig. 12) plots the initial applied stress-intensity
level for a given test specimen versus the time to failure.
Several materials were analyzed by Tiffany, Brown, and others,
and it was found that some, such as titanium alloys, are susceptible to crack propagation under corrosive environments when
they are not susceptible to crack initiation. In a sense, this
observation intensified activity directed at screening materials for sustained load flaw growth resistance. All materials

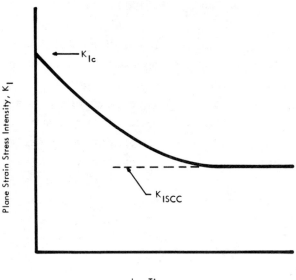

Fig. 11.   Schematic showing stress corrosion cracking test
            results

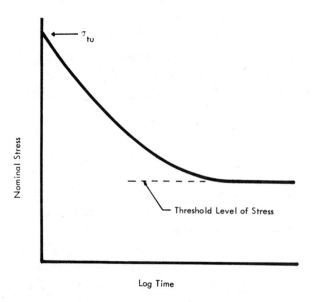

Fig. 12.   Presentation of precracked stress corrosion test data

previously believed to be insensitive to stress corrosion cracking were now suspect. Many testing programs were initiated to check susceptibility of materials to sustained load flaw growth. Since there were no standard precracked specimens, and most investigators using precracked stress corrosion specimens were schooled in fracture mechanics principles, specimens were of the fracture mechanics type and were made thick to obtain plane-strain conditions. K_{Ii} was determined versus time, as shown in Fig. 12. The curve should originate from zero time at K_{Ic}, decrease with time, and approach a threshold value for K_I. This threshold was designated K_{Iscc} ("scc" is an abbreviation for stress corrosion cracking). Note that K_{Ic} is a material property (as qualified earlier), while K_{Iscc} is a function of the environment and the time defined for cutoff.

K_{Iscc} is used exactly like the normal threshold value for stress corrosion cracking, i.e., if the operational level of K_I is below K_{Iscc}, no problems will arise from stress corrosion cracking. Conversely, if the operational K_I is above K_{Iscc}, failure will occur with time. Determination of K_{Iscc} can be made using any type of precracked tensile or bending specimens for which a stress analysis of K can be performed. The most common specimens used are shown in Fig. 13. The specimen is loaded to a predetermined value, then is subjected to the environment. The most common environment is a 3.5% solution of salt in distilled water. Alternate immersion testing is normally used.

The cantilever beam specimen is the most commonly used because of the simplicity of Brown's test method using a built-up system. Many specimens can be tested without requiring expensive equipment.

Recently, the WOL (wedge opening loading) specimen has gained favor. (23) This specimen evolved from the work of Manjoine, (24) as did the compact tension specimen shown in Fig. 2. Therefore, these specimens are similar. The

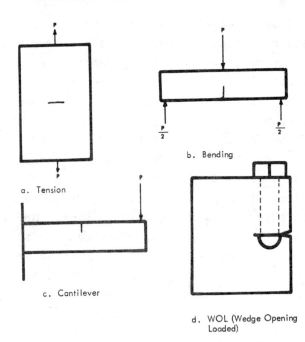

Fig. 13. Typical specimens used for determination of K_{Iscc}

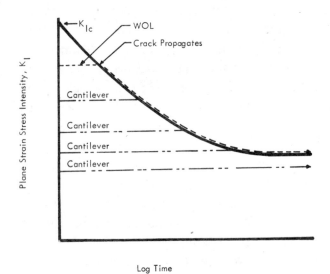

Fig. 14. Comparison of test results from cantilever and WOL test specimens

advantages of the WOL specimen are: (<u>a</u>) load is applied without any external force, i.e., with a bolt separating the two cantilever arms of the specimen; and (<u>b</u>) the crack opening displacement remains constant while the load drops, enabling the determination of K_{Iscc} with one specimen rather than several. The main problem with this specimen is that the load must be measured with either a gaged bolt or a clip gage.

Comparing the results from a WOL specimen with those from a cantilever specimen (Fig. 14), it is observed that the cantilever specimen is loaded to a fixed K_I level, where it remains until failure. Several specimens are required to establish the curve. The WOL specimen remains at the initial load until the crack propagates. When propagation occurs, the load is automatically reduced, since the double cantilever arms are effectively increased in length. This process is repeated until crack propagation ceases. By measuring the crack length at intervals and calculating the K_I at these intervals, a curve can be plotted. After crack propagation has ceased for a sufficient time, the specimen is pulled apart to enable measurement of an accurate crack length. The K_{Iscc} then is calculated from the final crack length. Load is calculated at each increment corresponding to the measured crack lengths by using geometry and the initial load value.

Two additional problems exist. In fairing in the curve to the K_{Ic} value, an adjustment may have to be made. If the specimen selected does not yield K_{Ic} in the normal manner, the values of K obtained for the corrosion environment should be adjusted according to the difference between K_{Ic} and the measured K at failure from the corrosion specimen. The shape of the K_I-versus-time curve is a function of crack growth with time, da/dt, and is not normally used in this form. Therefore, the K-versus-time curve is only a tool to arrive at K_{Iscc}.

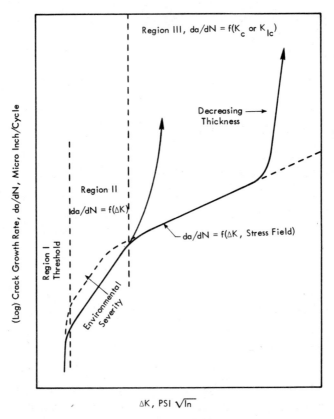

Fig. 15.   Model of crack growth behavior as a function of
           stress intensity

CYCLIC CRACK GROWTH, da/dn

Crack propagation in fatigue can be treated by linear
fracture mechanics by considering each cycle separately.
Thus, we have a multiple of single static tests. During
each loading cycle, the specimen is subjected to a change
in stress intensity, Δ, that can be calculated from the
fracture mechanics equations for the specimen type being used,
using maximum and minimum stress. Fatigue loadings are
normally reported in terms of mean stress and alternating
stress; therefore, the corresponding fracture mechanics term
would be mean K level and alternating K or ΔK.

Several equations have been proposed for presenting
crack growth rate (da/dn) versus ΔK data. These differ
basically as to whether the mean K is included in the equation
as a variable, (25,26) or the equation is written for a
specific mean K or specific fatigue stress ratio, R (27,28).
It is important to note that most of the proposed equations
assume a linear relationship on a log-log plot of some crack
growth parameter versus ΔK. This straightline relationship
has been experimentally verified by a number of investigators such as Hudson and Scardina. (29) If constants are
determined for one of the relationships and data are extrapolated (by the use of the constants) into different regions
of crack growth, considerable error can result. This does
not mean that the data generated are in error, but merely
that the extrapolation is invalid. The intent is to qualify
the linear log-log relationship to exist only within certain
regions of the da/dn versus ΔK curve, as shown in Fig. 15.

Region I on Fig. 15 is a threshold below which little
or no crack growth occurs. The point of argument here is
whether or not any crack growth occurs.

Region II is the flat fracture region. Crack growth
in Region II appears to be independent of specimen thickness.
The plane-strain condition is induced by the matrix of stress

and strain present. For <u>failure</u> conditions a specimen would
have to be relatively thick for plane-strain conditions to
be present. An approximate criterion is $B \geq 2.5 \ (K_{Ic}/\sigma_{ty})^2$. (3)
For <u>lower</u> applied K, it is proposed that the plane-strain con-
dition is approximated when $B \geq 2.5 \left(\dfrac{K_{max}}{\sigma_{ty}}\right)^2$. The K_{max} is the
maximum applied value of K. For example, for 7075-T6 aluminum
with K_{Ic} = 30 ksi $\sqrt{inch}$ and σ_{ty} = 70 ksi, the required thickness for a K_{Ic} test is 0.45 inch. For a K_{max} of 10 ksi $\sqrt{inch}$,
a thickness, B = 0.051 inch, will produce plane-strain conditions. This simple approach is proposed rather than a more
complex analysis of the stresses associated with the crack
tip in varying thicknesses. Such an analysis will produce
the same results, i.e., plane-strain conditions are approximated in thin materials for low applied K levels.

Region III of Fig. 15 is dominated by the final fracture
conditions, either K_{Ic} or K_c. The crack growth rate approaches
infinity as K approaches the critical value. This region
is of little practical value since very few cycles are incurred
during this region; it could be neglected with little loss
in usable information. It is proposed that the lower boundary
of Region III is the crack growth curve obtained for mixed
mode crack growth. The length of this curve would be controlled by the material thickness, i.e., the crack growth
curve for a specific thickness would leave this line slightly
before the failure event. Available test data do not allow
the determination of whether this is a single line or whether
it is slightly thickness dependent; this, however, is not
important for present state-of-the-art conditions.

The flat fracture region, Region II, is important since
the usable life of structure requiring crack growth tolerance
is expended before Region III crack growth occurs. Large
environmental effects on Region II crack growth have been
reported. It has been proposed that environment has little
effect on the threshold (30) and Walker (31) showed that the

effect is minimized as mixed mode fracture occurs. The
termination of Region II growth may be affected by environment, i.e., the region lines may shift slightly.

Before attempting any crack growth testing one must
determine which portion of the crack growth curve is required.
Test data collected in the vicinity of a transition may be
misleading, as any slope can be fit into a transition region
dependent on the testing range. Thus it becomes obvious
that data cannot be extrapolated beyond the test range.

The economics of testing cannot be overlooked. It is
much cheaper to test in the high crack growth region than
in the low crack growth region; therefore, most testing has
been done in this region. But as previously pointed out it
is impossible to extrapolate from testing in the high da/dn
range to the low da/dn range; therefore, testing must be in
the low da/dn range if crack growth in this range in service
is anticipated.

Once the use of the crack growth information has been
established, the engineers can proceed to design the test
program. The type of specimen used to obtain the data is
unimportant, but a valid K solution must exist for the
specimen being used. For this reason most testing has been
done with the center-crack specimen or the compact-tension
specimen; stress intensity solutions for these configurations are generally accepted. Also, some testing has been
accomplished using the part-through-crack specimen, since
that specimen simulates service-induced flaws. Often the
designer must relate the da/dn data to behavior of a part-
through flaw.

Specimen size requirements for a crack growth specimen
are not necessarily the same as those for a K_{Ic} test. For
example, a very thin specimen should be used to obtain crack
growth data at low ΔK values. For low crack growth rates,
the K values used allow plane-strain to be obtained in a
thin specimen. It is easier to maintain a straight crack

front in a thin specimen during the propagation. If a thick
specimen is tested in this range, errors are possible because
of the shape of the crack front; the crack moves faster in
the center of the specimen than on the edge and measurements
made on the edge of the specimen indicate slower crack growth
than is actually occurring. If crack growth characteristics
of the slant-fracture mode are to be determined, the thickness in question should be tested. A center-crack specimen
probably should be used, since the edge-crack specimen K
formulation is not proven for slant-fracture failures.

The techniques for crack growth testing are far from
standardized; in fact probably each laboratory has its own
procedures. However, there are a number of common variables
that must be considered before attempting crack growth testing. These variables are stress ratio, test environment,
rate of cyclic load application, testing temperature, plasticity effect at the crack tip, etc. The environmental
effects and cyclic load application are interrelated, because for environment to affect crack propagation there must
be sufficient time available for the environment to reach
the crack tip. Therefore, on the extremes of one cycle per
day or 4,000 cycles per second, tests would presumably show
extreme environmental effects and no environmental effects,
respectively (for an environmentally-sensitive material).
Stress ratio is an important factor. Most test data are
generated between $R = +0.1$ and $R = +0.3$; but frequently in
application, especially for aircraft, the actual spectrum
encountered contains a range of R values. The present equations accounting for stress ratio effect in crack rate growth
are not completely established and it is not known if equations can accurately account for stress ratio effects in all
materials. This is especially true for negative stress ratios.
The best estimate now appears to be that stress ratios below
$R = -0.1$ should be discarded for fatigue crack growth. In
any test program, however, it should be determined if the

material in question <u>does</u> obey the present equations for
stress ratio effects.

Laboratory air is not a definitive environment since
it can range from 0 to 100% relative humidity; therefore,
it is not recommended that testing be conducted in laboratory
air. If, however, it is done, then humidity should be
monitored and recorded. The baseline in humidity for test
reference is being evaluated on a current Air Force contract.
Wei (32) showed that Ti-6Al-4V is affected by humidity content in the parts per million. Therefore, it is questionable that dry air or dry inert gas would be an acceptable
atmosphere for reference. Possibly the best reference would
be a high humidity atmosphere, such as 80% or above. This
atmosphere can be obtained by surrounding the specimen with
a chamber and putting in either air or an inert gas after
it is bubbled through water. This environment is repeatable
and is in fact more representative of actual conditions than
a dry test would be. Further information on this subject
should be available at the conclusion of the Air Force contractual work.

SUSTAINED CRACK GROWTH, da/dt

Where a flaw can be loaded higher than K_{Iscc}, the possibility of crack growth with time exists. To evaluate this
condition we need to determine the crack growth with respect
to time under specific sets of environmental/stress conditions. This type of testing is very similar to K_{Iscc} testing except that here we want to determine the crack growth
rate as a function of time. Here again we can use any specimen having a known K solution although the most common is
the tapered cantilever beam specimen shown in Fig. 5. The
specimen must be placed in the required environment and periodic measurements of the crack growth versus time must be
made. No standard test techniques exist.

The stress condition is a primary variable for da/dt testing. If plane-strain exists at the crack tip, the test and analysis of results are straightforward; however, for mixed mode conditions, complications arise. Significantly different growth rates for different stress conditions may be obtained; therefore, caution must be used if mixed mode conditions exist. For example, it is possible to test a compact tension type specimen at a thickness K condition of mixed mode and measure mixed mode crack growth. Then if constant displacement is used, load is reduced and plane-strain conditions may be reached before crack growth stops. It is reasonable to assume that if the environmental effect is minimized for da/dn under mixed mode conditions, the da/dt under mixed mode conditions would be small. If the structure under test is a relatively thin sheet, there will probably be little effect of environmental crack growth except at the very low stress levels. At very low stress levels it is possible to have plane-strain conditions in thin sheet material; however, for this situation (low stress) the material would probably be operating close to or below the K_{Iscc} level. Therefore, there is little concern for environmental crack growth in thin sheet applications.

REFERENCES

1. "Fracture Toughness Testing and its Applications," ASTM
    STP No. 381, American Society for Testing and Materials,
    1965

2. W. F. Brown, Jr. and J. E. Srawley, "Plane Strain Crack
    Toughness Testing of High Strength Metallic Materials,"
    ASTM STP No. 410, American Society for Testing and
    Materials, December 1967

3. "Proposed Method of Test for Plane-Strain Fracture Tough-
    ness of Metallic Materials," ASTM Standards, American
    Society for Testing and Materials, Part 31, 1969, p 1099-
    1114
    (Editors note: See part 31, 1973 for a more up to date
    version of this specification.)

4. "Recommended Practice for Sharp-Notch Tension Testing
    of High-Strength Sheet Materials," ASTM Standards, Amer-
    ican Society for Testing and Materials, Part 31, Desig-
    nation E-338, 1968

5. Review of Developments in Plane-Strain Fracture Toughness
    Testing, ASTM STP 463, American Society for Testing and
    Materials, 1971

6. A. A. Griffith, Phil Trans Roy Soc (London), Ser A, 221,
    163-198 (1920)

7. G. R. Irwin, "Onset of Fast Crack Propagation in High
    Strength Steel and Aluminum Alloys," NRL Report 4763,
    Proceedings, 1955 Sagamore Conference on Ordnance
    Materials, Vol II, Syracuse University Press, N.Y., 1956

8. E. Orowan, Weld Res Suppl, 20, 157 (1955)

9. J. E. Srawley and C. D. Beachem, "The Effect of Small
    Surface Cracks on Strength," Proceedings of the Seventh
    Sagamore Ordnance Materials Research Conference, Report
    No. MeTE 661-611/F, Syracuse University Research Insti-
    tute, 1960, p IV-169

10. J. E. Srawley and C. D. Beachem, "Fractures of High Strength
    Sheet Steel Specimens Containing Small Cracks," Evalua-
    tion of Metallic Materials in Design for Low Temperature
    Service, ASTM STP 302, American Society for Testing and
    Materials, 1961, p 69

11. L. J. McEowen and B. G. Hughes, "RFT -- A Practical Ap-
    proach to Fracture Toughness Determination," preliminary
    data, Republic Steel Corporation, 1971

12.   G. R. Irwin, J App Mech, 84E, 4 December 1962

13.   A. T. D'Annessa and J. S. Owens, J Mater, 3, 2 (June 1968)

14.   P. F. Packman, H. S. Pearson, J. S. Owens, and G. B.
      Marchese, "The Applicability of a Fracture Mechanic - NDT
      Design Criterion," AFML TR-68-32 (May 1968)

15.   H. S. Pearson, "Fracture Testing of Notched or Precracked
      High-Strength Metallic Materials," Lockheed report

16.   G. B. Espey, M. H. Jones, and W. F. Brown, Jr., "The
      Sharp Edge Notch Tensile Strength of Several High-
      Strength Steel Sheet Alloys," Proceedings of the American
      Society for Testing and Materials, Vol 59, 1959

17.   G. B. Espey, M. H. Jones, and W. F. Brown, Jr., "Factors
      Influencing Fracture Toughness of Sheet Alloys for Use
      in Lightweight Cryogenic Tankage," Evaluation of Metallic
      Materials in Design for Low-Temperature Service, ASTM STP
      302, American Society for Testing and Materials, 1961

18.   "Notched Bar Impact Testing of Metallic Materials," ASTM
      Designation E23-66, ASTM Standards, Part 31, 1967, p 284-
      311

19.   J. G. Kaufman and M. Holt, "Fracture Characteristics
      of Aluminum Alloys," Alcoa Research Laboratories Tech-
      nical Report No. 18, 1965

20.   G. Sachs and J. G. Sessler, "Effects of Stress Concen-
      tration on Tensile Strength of Titanium and Steel Alloy
      Sheet at Various Temperatures," ASTM STP 287, American
      Society for Testing and Materials, 1960, p 122

21.   "Progress in Measuring Fracture Toughness and Using
      Fracture Mechanics," Mater Res Stand, Vol 4, 1964, p 107

22.   B. F. Brown, "A New Stress-Corrosion Cracking Test for
      High-Strength Alloys," Mater Res Stand, Vol 6, No. 3,
      March 1966, p 129

23.   S. R. Novak and S. T. Rolfe, "Modified WOL Specimen for
      K_{Iscc} Environmental Testing," J Mater, 4, (3), 701-728 (196⋅

24.   M. J. Manjoine, J Basic Eng Trans, ASME, June 1965, p
      293-298

25.   R. G. Forman, V. E. Kearney, and R. M. Engle, J Basic
      Eng Trans, ASME, 89,3,459-464 (1967)

26. E. K. Walker, "The Effect of Stress Ratio During Crack
     Propagation and Fatigue of 2024-T3 and 7075-T6 Aluminum,"
     Effects of Environment and Complex Load History on Fatigue
     Life, ASTM STP No. 462, American Society for Testing and
     Materials, 1970

27. P. C. Paris and F. Eldogan, "A Critical Analysis of Crack
     Propagation Laws" J Basic Eng Trans ASME, 85, 1963

28. H. H. Johnson and P. C. Paris, "Sub-Critical Flaw Growth,"
     Engineering Fracture Mechanics, Vol 1, June 1968, p 3-45

29. C. M. Hudson and J. T. Sardina "Effect of Stress Ratio on
     Fatigue-Crack Growth in 7075-T6 Aluminum-Alloy Sheet"
     Engineering Fracture Mechanics Vol 1, Pergamon Press,
     1969, p 429-446

30. P. C. Paris, informal talk to ASTM Committee E-24, Atlanta,
     Georgia, March, 1971

31. E. K. Walker, "A Study of the Effect of Environment on
     the Propagation of Fatigue Cracks," Lockheed-California
     Company Report LR 22077, December 1968

32. R. P. Wei and D. L. Ritter, "Influence of Temperature
     on Fatigue Crack Growth in Mill Annealed Ti-6All-4V,"
     Lehigh University publication preprint, 1971

THE ROLE OF NONDESTRUCTIVE INSPECTION
IN FRACTURE MECHANICS APPLICATIONS

D. E. Pettit and W. E. Krupp
Lockheed California Company,
Rye Canyon Research Laboratory

ABSTRACT

Fracture mechanics analysis requires a statistical definition of the largest flaw that can escape
detection during inspection. The impact of this
requirement on design assumptions, selection of
materials, fabrication methods, and inspection
intervals is discussed. Common methods for flaw
detection are listed, stressing reliability aspects
associated with instrumentation, test environment,
human factors, and field versus laboratory inspection results. Considerations involved in developing a typical experimental program to define
quantitative flaw detection limits are presented.
The importance of integrating nondestructive examination considerations into design, material
selection, and manufacturing is discussed.

BACKGROUND

In modern aircraft systems, increased demands are being
imposed for improved performance, greater reliability, longer
design life, and reduced maintenance costs and down time, all

without an appreciable cost impact. One approach has been the use of a worst case design analysis (i.e., initially flawed structure assumed) to attempt to satisfy these requirements.

Conceptually, the use of a worst case analysis to insure a highly reliable structure is not new, but the recent evolution of current fracture mechanics concepts has now provided a quantitative basis for the worst case analysis. While fracture mechanics is often considered a design tool, it can only be used effectively if it interfaces with other disciplines such as materials, manufacturing, and inspection. As shown in Fig. 1, a key to the successful implementation of fracture mechanics analysis is definition of the starting point for the analysis, i.e., definition of the largest initial flaw that could be present.

In the early applications of fracture mechanics, the structures being analyzed were fabricated from high strength materials that possessed relatively low fracture toughness. The structures in question, e.g. spacecraft pressure vessels, were of a configuration that readily allowed stressing of critical flaw locations above the projected operating stress levels. [1] As a result, proof testing could be successfully used to eliminate the possible presence of flaws larger than those that would cause fracture at the proof test load. As the use of fracture mechanics was extended to higher toughness materials and more complex structural configurations, the applicability of proof testing as a method of defining the initial flaw size decreased. Thus, alternate methods were required, i.e., nondestructive inspection (NDI) methods had to be relied upon to determine the maximum possible initial flaw size.

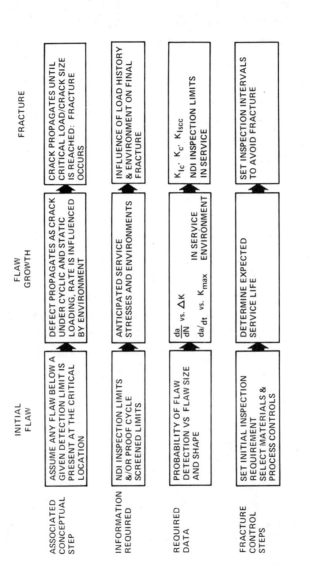

Fig. 1.   Conceptual fracture mechanics considerations

WHAT IS A DEFECT?

Defects in a variety of types, sizes, and shapes arise from many sources as shown in Table 1. (2) As a result, a given inspection may be concerned primarily with detecting specific types of defects, depending on whether the inspection is being conducted to verify the acceptance of a mill product, to verify that a given processing sequence has not introduced defects into the material, or to verify that no defects have been developed during a portion of the service life. These defects are normally classified as either volume or planar defects, planar defects being basically two dimensional rather than three dimensional in shape. Of these two cases, planar defects such as tight cracks are the most difficult to detect and normally the most important in a fracture mechanics analysis. Cracks or planar defects may occur as through-the-thickness flaws (normally relatively large), embedded flaws, or as part-through-the-thickness or surface flaws.* In a typical fracture mechanics analysis, the surface flaw is often the anticipated initial defect type. In subsequent discussion the surface flaw will be used as an example, but the general concepts discussed are applicable to all types of defects.

---

*A variation of the surface flaw often encountered in service is the corner crack at the edge of a hole or other geometric discontinuity.

Table 1.

Typical Material Defects

Defects Existing in Mill Products

Chemical contamination
  Inclusions, dirt
  Segregation
  Laminations
Internal defects
  Porosity
  Pipes
  Cracks
Surface defects
  Cracks, tears
  Laps, pits
  Scratches
  Distortion

Defects Produced by Processing

Metal removal
  Cracks
  Tool marks, gouges
Heat treatment
  Cracks
  Distortion
  Decarburization
  Incomplete transformations

Defects Produced by Processing (continued)

Metal finishing
  Cracks in coating, base metal
  Pits, blisters
  Lack of adhesion, insufficient thickness
  Hydrogen embrittlement
  Surface contamination
Joining
  Weld defects - Cracks
    Incomplete fusion, residual stress
  Fasteners - Tears, galvanic corrosion

Defects Produced in Service

Mechanical damage
  Particle damage, tool marks
  Improper repair, maintenance
  Fatigue cracks
  Fretting
  Creep
Environmental damage
  Corrosion
  Stress corrosion, corrosion fatigue
  Bacterial degradation
  Thermal degradation

DESCRIPTION OF A DEFECT - DO WE ALL
SPEAK THE SAME LANGUAGE?

The description of a defect may have different meanings to individuals of differing backgrounds. In fracture mechanics analysis, the extent of a defect is defined by the parameter that enters into the stress intensity equation. For a surface flaw, this parameter is the normalized crack depth, a/Q, where a is the crack depth and Q is a crack shape parameter incorporating a plasticity correction. The parameter Q is in turn a function of the ratio of crack depth to surface crack length, a/2C. The key question from a fracture mechanics viewpoint thus becomes, "What is the smallest crack, as defined by the a/Q value, that can reliably be detected by NDI?" At this point communications often hit a snag.

Current NDI inspection procedures typically include x-ray, magnetic particle, penetrant, ultrasonics, and eddy current methods. Each of these methods is sensitive to different flaw parameters. For example, penetrant and surface wave ultrasonics are primarily sensitive to surface crack length while shear wave ultrasonics, eddy current, and x-ray are flaw area (and volume) dependent. Unfortunately, none of these flaw parameters correspond to the a/Q value desired by the fracture mechanics analyst. As a result, a request by fracture mechanics personnel to verify the detectability of flaws in terms of a/Q has meaning to them, but not the NDI personnel. As an example, consider the two typical design values for a/Q, 0.1 and 0.03, and two typical surface flaw shapes, a/2C = 0.5 and 0.1, shown in Table 2. As can be seen, a given a/Q value can correspond to a wide range of crack lengths and depths, the variation in the flaw area being somewhat less than the variation in the crack length dimensions. Thus it becomes necessary to either assume a value for the crack shape parameter or perform extensive NDI to define minimum a and 2C

Table 2.

Variation of the Geometric Characteristics of Surface
Flaws as a Function of Normalized Flaw Depth

Normalized flaw depth, a/Q, inch	Flaw aspect ratio, $a/2C$	Flaw depth, a, inch	Flaw surface length $2C$, inch	Flaw area, A, inch^2
0.1	0.5	0.25	0.50	0.39
	0.1	0.10	1.05	0.33
0.03	0.5	0.075	0.15	0.035
	0.1	0.031	0.31	0.030

values; an extremely challenging task for marginally detectable
flaws. One possible procedure might involve assumption of a
worst case, i.e., a shallow crack (a/2C = 0.1) if the NDI
method being used is crack area sensitive, or a semi-circular
crack (a/2C = 0.5) if a surface crack length sensitive NDI
method is being used. (3) In either case, direct communication between fracture mechanics and NDI personnel is required
to agree upon the inspection method and design crack parameter that is being used for a given situation.

DETECTABILITY -- WHAT DOES IT MEAN?

After an agreement has been reached on the flaw size
parameter of interest and appropriate NDI methods have been
selected, a second problem must be dealt with, that of detectability. In the past, detection limits have been described as the flaw size that normally could be detected.
An unstated but widely understood assumption was that the
detectable flaw size varied with the experience of each inspector. (4,5) Typical values of detectable flaw sizes that
have been quoted (6) for processing and fatigue crack defects
are shown in Table 3 (note that defect shape is not specified).
However, since the aim of a fracture mechanics analysis is to
quantify the worst flaw case, the starting point or NDI detection limit must be quantitatively defined. The detection
limit for fracture mechanics applications is typically defined as the largest flaw that can escape detection for a
given statistical basis. (7)

Development of a statistically reliable flaw size detection limit is normally no easy task in that the influences
of many parameters must be considered in developing the NDI
detection limits, including:

(a) Material characteristics: grain size, amount and distri-
     bution of second phase particles, other metallurgical
     parameters

Table 3.
Estimates of Minimum Detectable Surface Crack
Lengths (Inches) for Part-Through Flaws in a Magnetic Steel (6)

NDT Technique	Surface crack Processing	Fatigue	Internal flaw Void	Crack	Weld lack of penetration	Disbond
		Test Specimens (Polished)				
Visual (b)	0.050	0.030	(a)	(a)	(a)	(a)
Ultrasonic	0.005	0.005	0.015	0.080	0.030(c)	0.300
Magnetic particle	0.030	0.030	0.300	0.300	(a)	(a)
Penetrant	0.010	0.020	(a)	(a)	(a)	(a)
Radiography	0.020	0.020	0.010	0.030	0.030(c)	0.300
Eddy current	0.010	0.010	(a)	(a)	(a)	(a)
		Production Parts (Smooth-Fine Machined)				
Visual	0.100	0.060	(a)	(a)	(a)	(a)
Ultrasonic	0.010	0.010	0.030	0.160	0.060(c)	0.600
Magnetic particle	0.060	0.060	0.600	0.600	(a)	(a)
Penetrant	0.020	0.040	(a)	(a)	(a)	(a)
Radiography	0.040	0.040	0.020	0.060	0.060	0.600
Eddy current	0.020	0.020	(a)	(a)	(a)	(a)

(a) Not applicable. (b) With use of magnifier. (c) Not possible for tight crack.

(b) Flaw type: volume defect, planar defect, surface defect or embedded defect

(c) Stage in processing: surface condition and finish, effect of previous processing steps, residual or applied stresses

(d) Part configuration: thickness, presence of abrupt geometric changes, accessibility of critical regions

(e) Method of developing defects for calibration: electrical discharge machining, quenching, welding, fatigue

(f) Human factors: variation in inspector experience, person-to-person variations in interpreting results, use of production versus laboratory personnel

(g) Equipment or procedure: variations in methods of calibrating equipment, variations between equipment of the same type but from different vendors, variations in inspection procedures and sequencing

(h) Inspection environment: conditions in the laboratory, factory, or in the field on an assembled component

(i) Detection limit criteria: probability limit and confidence level required

While the list of variables to be considered is imposing, many of them can be eliminated or reduced to secondary importance for a given inspection. For example, standard calibration blocks used to optimize NDI procedures can be prepared using the same material and configuration as the part of interest. The most critical type of defect, often a tight surface crack, can be assumed for optimization and service inspections, since other types of defects (volume) should be more readily detectable. For a given NDI method some geometric variables are of only secondary importance, such as component thickness for penetrant inspection. Thus by considering the flaw types of interest and the NDI method being considered for a particular inspection, the major variables can be identified and incorporated into the NDI detection limit verification test plan. (8)

Perhaps the most dangerous pitfall in the development of an NDI detectability verification program is the failure to recognize that the method, personnel, and inspection environment must simulate the actual conditions to be encountered in the production and/or service situation. (9) For example, Table 3 presented typical flaw detection sizes that could be specified by NDI research personnel, and indeed the limits quoted may be applicable in a laboratory situation if the flaw locations are known. However NDI detection limits based on laboratory data often are not representative of production inspections and are certainly not representative of service inspections. Estimated variations in these limits are presented in Table 4 for laboratory, production, and field service conditions.

Previously, quantitative flaw size detection limits have not been required test data. However, new government specifications require a statistically based demonstration of flaw detection limits for fracture critical design applications. (8,9) After the factors previously discussed have been weighed and an experimental verification program formulated, specimens similar in design detail to the fracture critical parts must be manufactured. Ideally, tight planar cracks of various size and shapes will be generated by fatigue, with cracks randomly dispersed from specimen to specimen, crack locations not revealed to test personnel, and a few specimens containing no cracks used as controls. The entire group of specimens should be inspected on a routine basis, similar to the production situation (details of a typical experimental program are given in Ref 10). In this manner valid NDI data can be obtained to provide a basis for an accurate quantitative assessment of true flaw detection limits for a given situation.

Table 4.
Estimated Variations in Flaw Detection Limits by Type of Inspection
(Numbers in Inches)

NDI Technique	Surface crack		Internal flaw	
	Processing	Fatigue	Void	Crack
Test Specimens, Laboratory Inspection				
Visual (b)	0.050	0.030	(a)	(a)
Ultrasonic	0.005	0.005	0.015	0.080
Magnetic particle	0.030	0.030	0.300	0.300
Penetrant	0.010	0.020	(a)	(a)
Radiography	0.020	0.020	0.010	0.030
Eddy current	0.010	0.010	(a)	(a)
Production Parts - Production Inspection				
Visual	0.10	0.25	(a)	(a)
Ultrasonic	0.13	0.12	0.2	0.12
Magnetic particle	0.10	0.15	(a)	(a)
Penetrant	0.06	0.06	(a)	(a)
Radiography	0.20	(c)	0.05	(c)
Eddy current	0.10	0.20	(a)	(a)
Cleaned Structure - Service Inspection				
Visual	0.25	0.50	(a)	(a)
Ultrasonic	0.20	0.20	0.15	0.20
Magnetic particle	0.25	0.40	(a)	(a)
Penetrant	0.05	0.05	(a)	(a)
Radiography	0.50	(c)	0.15	(c)
Eddy current	0.20	0.25	(a)	(a)

(a) Not applicable. (b) With use of magnifier. (c) Not possible for tight crack.
Assumed conditions: High-strength magnetic steel part 1-inch thick with 63 RMS surface finish.

RELIABILITY: HOW MUCH IS ENOUGH?

A variety of flaw size parameters exist that can be used
to evaluate the detection limits of various NDI methods.
Typical parameters include surface crack length, crack depth,
normalized crack depth, crack area, and crack area/thickness.
The major difficulty in comparing the results of various NDI
methods used to inspect the same specimens centers on selection of the flaw parameter used in statistical comparisons,
since each of the NDI methods is sensitive to a different
flaw size parameter. For example, penetrant results are sensitive to surface crack length but relatively insensitive to
crack area or thickness. X-ray, on the other hand, is very
dependent on crack volume rather than surface crack length
per se. As a result it is possible to bias the results somewhat in favor of a given method by the selection of the flaw
parameter used in the comparison. Here again careful selection of the prime flaw parameter is required.

Once the flaw parameter of interest has been determined
for a given application, the statistical basis for verification must be defined. Various methods of data presentation
and analysis have been used. One method is summarized in
Fig. 2. (11) The use of a percent detected parameter involves the combination of data in arbitrary flaw size intervals. A statistical flaw detection limit is determined by
conducting a suitable statistical analysis on each interval
of data, as shown in Fig. 3. This procedure has two drawbacks, however. First, it treats all data within a flaw
size interval as equal; that is, it does not differentiate
between flaw sizes near the upper or lower flaw size boundary
of the interval. The statistically based detection limit is
therefore sensitive to the ranges of flaw size selected.
Secondly, it does not account for the flaw size distribution

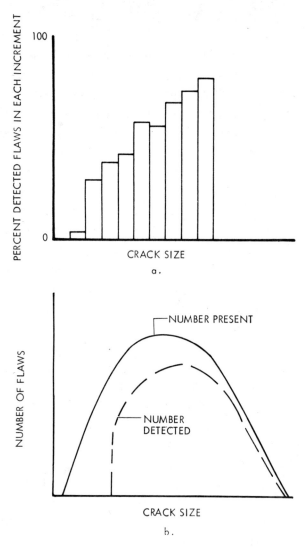

Fig. 2.- Typical basic data presentation

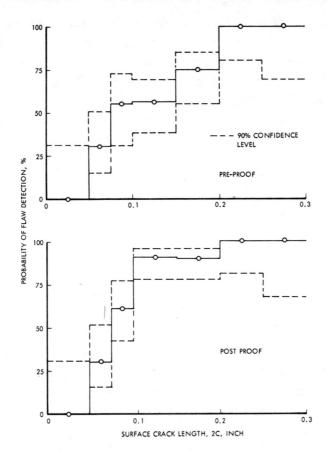

Fig. 3. Probability of detection of randomly located surface cracks in 2219-T87 aluminum

within each interval. These drawbacks can be minimized by
decreasing the size of the intervals examined provided an
adequate number of data points exist. The current requirements (7) for a statistical B value detection limit (90 percent probability with a 95 percent confidence level of detecting a crack larger than specified) results in performance
of a large number of separate inspections for each critical
case. As shown in Fig. 4, well over 29 data points are required to give a 95 percent confidence level of a 90 percent flaw detection probability, even though 100 percent of
the flaws in each sample are detected.

IS IT ALL REALLY WORTH IT?

The requirement (8) that statistically based quantitative flaw detection limits be used in fracture mechanics
analysis will have a large impact on subsequent aircraft
programs. This will obviously require additional expenditures
of time and money for large structures where many critical
materials, part configurations and manufacturing processes
are involved. The question will be raised, is this really
worth all the time and expense? The answer must be "yes" if
total program costs are assessed, including maintenance, in-
service down time and the high cost in men and materials
caused by the unnecessary loss of a single modern-day aircraft.

This cost impact can be minimized by a firm interface
between the designer, materials, manufacturing, inspection
and maintenance personnel, increased communications and joint
formulation of the necessary controls and precautions for
critical programs. Only through such a team effort can the
potential advantages of marrying fracture mechanics analysis
and NDI be realized.

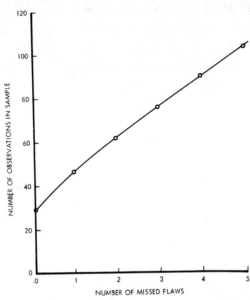

Fig. 4. Required sample size for "B" value basis as a function
of maximum number of missed flaws permitted

    <u>Acknowledgments</u>. We would like to thank Dr. D. W. Hoeppner, Mr. Ken Kleinberg, and Mr. John Crocker of Calac and Mr. Hugh Pearson of Gelac (now with Pratt and Whitney Co., West Palm Beach, Florida) for their valuable discussions in the area of NDI applications.

REFERENCES

1. National Aeronautics and Space Administration, "Fracture Control of Metallic Pressure Vessels," NASA Space Vehicle Design Criteria (Structures), NASA Sp-8040, May 1970

2. W. E. Krupp, "Application of Fracture Mechanics to Assurance of Structural Integrity for Safe-Life Aircraft Components," Lockheed-California Company, LR 24527, July 1971

3. D. E. Pettit and D. W. Hoeppner, "Fatigue Flaw Growth and NDI Evaluation for Preventing Through Cracks in Spacecraft Tankage Structures," NASA CR-1285600, September 1972

4. E. O. Lowerson, Jr., "Statistical Method for Evaluating Penetrant Sensitivity and Reproducibility," Materials Evaluation, March 1972, p 67

5. E. F. Thomas and W. E. Kloster, "F-111/NDI/Human Factors Reliability Program," 1971 ASM Materials Engineering Congress, Detroit, Michigan, October 1971

6. W. H. Lewis and W. H. Sproat, "A Review of Nondestructive Testing for Aerospace Applications," Lockheed-Georgia Co., ER-11051, January 1971

7. H. A. Wood, "Fracture Control Considerations in Aircraft Structural Design," in this book

8. U. S. Air Force, "Aircraft Structural Integrity Program, Airplane Requirements," MIL-STD-1530, September 1972

9. U. S. Air Force, "Inspection Program Requirements, Nondestructive for Aircraft and Missile Materials and Parts," MIL-I-6870C, July 1970

10. P. Hodgetts, "Results of Product Inspection of Titanium Test Specimens Using Longitudinal Wave Pulse Echo Ultrasonics," Los Angeles Division, North American Rockwell, TFP-72-677, June 1972

11. P. Packman, H. Pearson, J. Owens, G. Marchese, "The Applicability of a Fracture Mechanics-Nondestructive Testing Design Criterion," AFML-TR-68-32, 1968

THE EFFECT OF TEMPERATURE AND ENVIRONMENT
ON SUBCRITICAL-CRACK GROWTH

R. P. Wei

Lehigh University

Department of Mechanical Engineering and Mechanics

Bethlehem, Pennsylvania

ABSTRACT

The integrity and service lives of engineering structures depend, to a large extent, on the sub-critical-crack growth resistance of the component materials. Subcritical-crack growth can occur under both sustained and cyclically varying loads, and can be strongly influenced by temperature and chemically aggressive environments. Methods for evaluating the subcritical-crack growth resistance of high strength alloys, based on fracture mechanics, will be discussed. The influences of different loading and environmental conditions (both chemical and thermal) on subcritical-crack growth will be reviewed. The application of subcritical-crack growth data for fracture prevention and control will be considered.

INTRODUCTION

The general aim of this symposium is directed at the prob-lems of fracture prevention and control, and at developing guidelines for the formulation of viable fracture control

programs. These fracture control programs include specifications of those properties of engineering materials that determine their crack growth resistance; specifically, fracture
toughness and subcritical crack growth resistance. Fracture
toughness defines the load bearing capacity of a structural
component in the presence of cracks or crack-like defects and,
hence, the strength of the component. Subcritical crack growth
resistance, on the other hand, governs the rate of degradation
of the load bearing capacity of such a component through crack
growth and establishes its useful life or durability. Although the principal thrust of this symposium is being directed
at the consideration of fracture toughness, the importance of
subcritical crack growth in fracture prevention and control
in engineering structures must not be ignored.

To provide a better perspective, a more detailed consideration of the respective role of fracture toughness and subcritical crack growth resistance in determining structural
integrity and durability will be made. Fracture toughness
measures the tolerance of a material for cracks under load,
and as such, defines the condition for failure, or the onset
of unstable fracturing. Quantitative definition of fracture
toughness has now been established, through the formalism of
fracture mechanics analysis, in terms of the critical stress
intensity factor (K_{Ic} or K_c) or the critical strain energy
release rate $\mathcal{G}_{Ic}$ or $\mathcal{G}_c$. (1-3) These parameters can be readily
measured in the laboratory and serve to define a failure locus
as illustrated in Fig. 1. (For simplicity, failure by general
yielding will not be considered here.) For a crack of given
size, a specific critical stress for failure of a material is
defined by its failure locus; for example, a_1 and σ_1. Conversely, for a given stress, a critical crack size is similarly defined: σ_2 and a_2. The strength of the structural
component is therefore defined by the size of the crack that
is present and the material fracture toughness. In principle,
the region to the left of the failure locus represents the

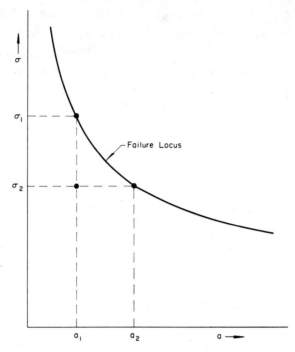

Fig. 1.   Schematic representation of failure locus

"safe" region. For example, it should be safe to load a
structure containing a crack of size a_1 to some stress level,
say σ_2 (where $\sigma_2 < \sigma_1$), since a_1 is smaller than the critical
crack size a_2 corresponding to the applied stress σ_2. (A
crack that is smaller than the critical size for the prevailing
applied stress is commonly termed a "subcritical crack".)
This safety is predicated on the assumption that the loading
is static and that the crack will not grow during service.
It is well known, however, that cracks can and do grow during service under both sustained (static) and cyclically varying loads. The progressive enlargement of the crack, termed
subcritical crack growth, eventually leads to structural
failure. While fracture toughness establishes the condition
for failure and the strength of a structural component, its
service life or durability is principally a function of the
subcritical crack growth resistance of the material. It is
clear, therefore, that considerations of subcritical crack
growth constitute an essential part of fracture prevention
and control.

In this paper, some of the phenomenological aspects of
the subcritical crack growth problem are reviewed; current
test methods and the application of subcritical crack growth
data to fracture prevention and control are discussed. General considerations of subcritical crack growth and of testing approaches will be made first. More specific considerations of the influences of various environmental and loading
variables on subcritical crack growth will then be made. The
consequences of these influences in terms of the validity and
usefulness of data for design and in terms of structural performance will be discussed.

GENERAL CONSIDERATIONS

Design practices based on fracture mechanics generally
assume the pre-existence of cracks or crack-like defects or

the early initiation of cracks, in structural components, and
that the lives of these structural components are determined
by subcritical crack growth. These assumptions have been well
justified by service experience (see Ref 4, for example).
Primary emphasis in recent years, therefore, has been placed
on studies of subcritical crack growth.

Subcritical crack growth can be broadly grouped into
four categories according to the type of loading and the external chemical environment.

1. Sustained load crack growth in inert environments
    (vacuum, inert gases, etc.).
2. Fatigue crack growth in inert environments.
3. Sustained load crack growth in aggressive environ-
    ments, or stress corrosion cracking.
4. Fatigue crack growth in aggressive environments, or
    corrosion fatigue.

The first two of these are purely mechanical in nature, while
the latter two entail mechanical and environmental interactions. All four categories of crack growth are affected by
temperature, reflecting the temperature dependence of the
kinetics of chemical and deformation processes that control
crack growth. (5-12) Because thermal and chemical environments are invariably present during service, these factors
have received and are being given a great deal of attention.
(11,12)

Many variables can influence the subcritical crack growth
behavior of materials or structural components. Some of the
significant variables are as follows (13):

Mechanical Variables

For sustained load crack growth:
- Applied stress or stress-intensity factor, σ or K.
- State of stress.
- Residual stress and prior loading.

For fatigue crack growth:

- Maximum stress or stress intensity factor, σ_{max} or K_{max}.*
- Cyclic stress or stress intensity range, $\Delta\sigma$ or ΔK.*
- Stress ratio, R*, that is, ratio of minimum to maximum stress or stress intensity factor in one cycle.
- Cyclic load frequency, f.
- Cyclic load wave-form (for constant-amplitude loading).
- Load interactions in variable amplitude loading.
- State of stress.
- Residual stress.

Geometrical Variables

- Crack size, and relation to component dimensions.
- Crack geometry.
- Component geometry adjoining crack.
- Stress concentrations associated with design.

Metallurgical Variables

- Alloy composition.
- Distribution of alloying elements and impurities.
- Microstructure and crystal structure.
- Heat treatment.
- Mechanical working.
- Preferred orientation of grains and grain boundaries (Texture).
- Mechanical properties (strength, fracture toughness, etc.)

---

* These parameters are interrelated. Only 2 of the 3 need to be specified.

Environmental Variables
- Temperature, T.
- Types of environments.- gaseous, liquid, liquid metal, etc.
- Partial pressure of damaging species in gaseous environments, p_i.
- Concentration of damaging species in aqueous or other liquid environments, C_i.
- Electrical potential, ϕ.
- pH.
- Viscosity of environment, η.
- Coatings, inhibitors, etc.

Many of these variables have been examined.(11,12) Only selected examples will be used here to illustrate the effects of these environmental and loading variables.

The application of fracture mechanics to subcritical crack growth studies is now well established. In this approach, the crack-tip stress intensity factor K or stress intensity range ΔK is used to characterize the mechanical crack driving force. (7-10,14) The assumptions, utility and restrictions of this approach have been discussed in detail elsewhere. (7-10,14) Currently two different approaches are used for studying subcritical crack growth and material evaluation, within the general framework of fracture mechanics:
- Threshold - Life
- Kinetics of Crack Growth

In the first approach, attention is directed at measuring the life of test specimens or of structural components, or at determining the "threshold" stress intensity level below which crack growth is presumed not to occur.* In the second approach,

---

* For the purpose of this discussion, the "threshold" K shall be defined as the asymptotic value of K as the rate of crack growth approaches zero.

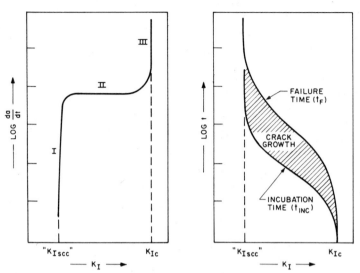

Fig. 2. Schematic representations of the crack growth kinetics
          and time-to-failure under sustained loads (15)

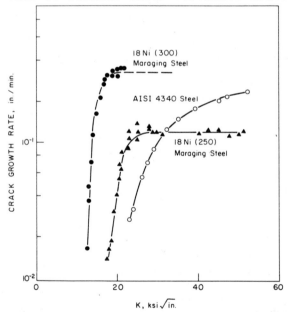

Fig. 3. Influence of gaseous hydrogen on sustained-load crack
          growth in some high strength steels at room tempera-
          ture (16)

the kinetics of crack growth (that is the growth rate response
to the mechanical crack driving force K or ΔK) is determined.
An example of these two different approaches for stress corrosion cracking is illustrated schematically in Fig. 2. Because of the fact that kinetic information is of greater
fundamental value, and that threshold and life data can be
determined directly, in principle at least, from the crack
growth kinetics, the second approach is currently more in
vogue. A more detailed discussion of these two approaches has
been given in a recent paper by Wei, Novak and Williams. (15)
To date, however, no standard test methods have been established.

SUSTAINED LOAD CRACK GROWTH

Fig. 3 illustrates sustained load crack growth in a highly
aggressive environment (gaseous hydrogen at ~ 1 atm. and room
temperature). (16) The rate of crack growth is strongly dependent on K, exhibiting stage I and stage II behavior as illustrated in Fig. 2. Stage II crack growth is nearly independent of the mechanical crack driving force, and is presumed
to be rate limited by the associated chemical process(es). The
results indicate that crack growth is strongly dependent on the
material (or, metallurgical variables). Comparison of the rate-
limited growth rate of AISI 4340 steel indicates the strong
effect of environment; the respective rates of crack growth in
dehumidified hydrogen, distilled water, and dehumidified argon
being approximately 2×10^{-1}, 4×10^{-2} and 10^{-5} in./min. (16,17)
(Crack growth in dehumidified argon has been shown to be con-
trolled by creep at the crack tip.) (6)
The rate of crack growth can depend strongly on temperature, Fig. 4. (18) In saturated environments and in distilled
water, crack growth in high strength steels is characterized
by an apparent activation energy of about 9 kcal/mole in the

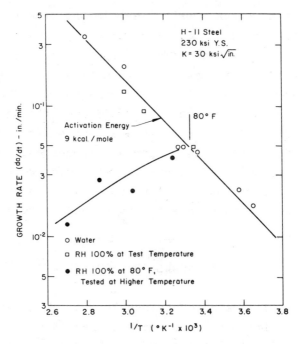

Fig. 4.   Influence of temperature on sustained-load crack growth in water and water vapor environments (18)

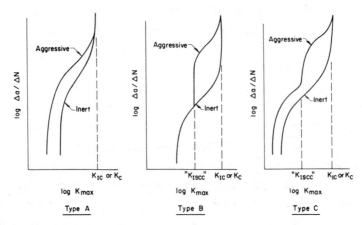

Fig. 5.   Types of fatigue crack growth behavior (10)

rate limited region. (6,17,18) In gaseous hydrogen, the apparent activation energy is about 4 to 5 kcal/mole. (16,19) In a
partially saturated environment, the temperature dependence is
quite different, and is supposed to be related to the adsorption
kinetics. (18)

FATIGUE CRACK GROWTH

Fatigue crack growth is much more complicated. In addition to the metallurgical, environmental and geometrical variables, crack growth is influenced by a broad range of mechanical variables, some of which can interact with the environment. Many of the observed effects of loading variables can
be traced directly to environmental interactions. (7,10) On
the basis of experimental data gathered over the past several
years, environment-enhanced fatigue crack growth may be grouped
into three basic types, and be discussed in relation to the
apparent K_{Iscc}, Fig. 5. (7,10) Type A behavior is typified
by the aluminum-water system. Environmental effects result
from the interaction of fatigue and environmental attack.
(7,10) Type B behavior is represented by the hydrogen-steel
system. (20) Environmental crack growth is directly relatable
to sustained load crack growth, with no interaction effects.
(7,10,20) Type C represents the behavior of most alloy-
environment systems. Above K_{Iscc}, the behavior approaches
that of Type B, whereas, below K_{Iscc}, the behavior tends
toward Type A, with the associated interaction effects.

Extensive work on the aluminum alloys (Type A behavior)
indicates that practically all aluminum alloys are susceptible
to environment-enhanced fatigue crack growth (see Refs 7 and
21). The environmental effect is a function of thickness or
state of stress. There is no effect of frequency for crack
growth in an inert environment, and a small effect in fully
saturated and aqueous environments. The effect of frequency

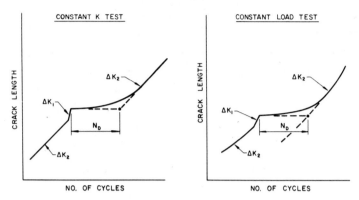

Fig. 6.   Schematic illustration of delay in fatigue crack
          growth and definition of N_D (30)

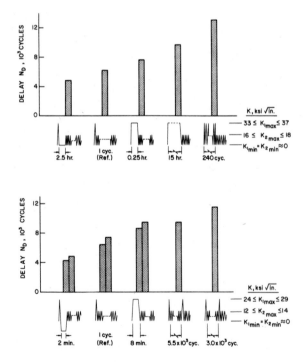

Fig. 7.   Delay in fatigue crack growth produced by various
          simple load sequences (30)

can be very large in partially saturated environments and is related to the partial pressure of water vapor. (7,22,23) The influence of temperature can be quite strong and depends on the mechanical crack driving force ΔK. (7,24)

Work on Type B systems (7,17,25,26) indicates that fatigue crack growth in an aggressive environment depends on frequency, stress or stress intensity level, stress ratio and wave-form. The influences of all of these loading variables may be accounted for, to a fair degree of approximation, by the simple superposition model proposed by Wei and Landes (20) which relates fatigue and sustained load crack growth.

In recent studies by Barsom (27) and Gallagher (28), it was found that environment-enhanced fatigue crack growth below K_{Iscc} in certain steels is a function of both frequency and wave-form. Environmental effect was a maximum for a specific frequency and approached zero at higher and lower frequencies. (27,28) Environmental effect was observed only for certain wave forms (such as sine and triangle) and not for others (such as square waves). (27) These peculiar effects were not observed for an aluminum alloy. (29)

The effects of load interactions in variable amplitude loading are very complex and can be very large. (30,31) Delay in fatigue crack growth, as defined in Fig. 6, can be affected by a broad range of loading variables, Fig. 7 (30,31), and by temperature and service environments. (32) These effects are significant to design and need to be fully explored.

DATA UTILIZATION AND PROBLEMS

Ideally, it is desirable to characterize the subcritical crack growth behavior in terms of all of the pertinent variables.

$$da/dt = F_1 (K, T, p_i, C_i, \ldots \ldots)$$

and $$\Delta a/\Delta N = F_2 (K_{max}, R, f, T, p_i, C_i, \ldots \ldots)$$

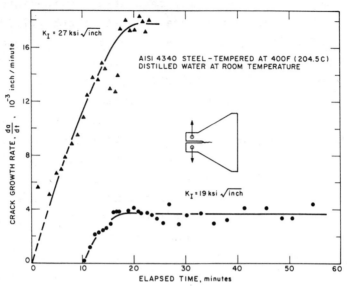

Fig. 8. Sustained-load crack growth under constant K_I showing
         incubation, crack acceleration and steady-state stages
         of crack growth (33)

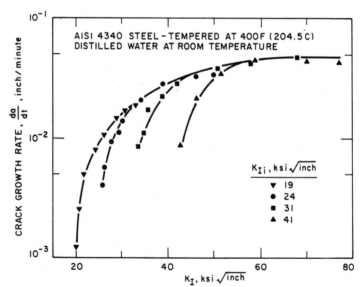

Fig. 9. Kinetics of sustained-load crack growth showing the
         effect of initial K_I (17)

Obviously, such a complete characterization is not feasible
and cannot be justified. Data, therefore, must be obtained
under certain restricted conditions consistent with the intended service applications. Having obtained the requisite data,
one can integrate the rate equations, in principle, to determine
the service life or an appropriate inspection interval. The
lower limit of integration is usually defined on the basis of
nondestructive inspection (NDI) capabilities; the upper limit
being defined by either fracture toughness or a pre-determined
allowable crack size, consistent with inspection requirements.

This procedure presupposes that there is a one-to-one or
unique relationship between the rate of crack growth and the
mechanical crack driving force, with all other variables constant. This is indeed the case for steady state crack growth.
The possible occurrence of nonsteady state crack growth, however, cannot be ignored. Nonsteady state crack growth has,
in fact, been observed and reported.(6,15,25,33) Wei et al
(15) indicated that sustained-load crack growth occurred in
six stages:

- Crack growth on rising loading
- Transient crack growth
- "Incubation"*
- Crack acceleration
- Steady state crack growth
- Onset to failure or crack growth instability.

The incubation period, and periods of crack acceleration and
steady state growth are illustrated in Fig. 8. (33) The consequences of nonsteady state crack growth are as follows
(Fig. 9):

---

* Incubation is defined as that period during which the crack
  growth is much less than 10^{-6} inch per minute.

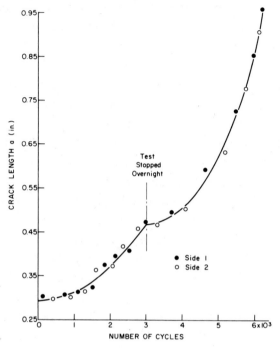

Fig. 10. Fatigue crack growth curve showing nonsteady-state behavior (25)

- Erroneous rates of crack growth may be inferred from limited or replicated tests at the same load.
- Erroneous K_{Iscc} may be deduced from the kinetics data, as well as from "life" tests.

An example of nonsteady state crack growth in fatigue is shown in Fig. 10. (25) Nonsteady state crack growth at the start of the test and following an overnight shutdown can be readily seen. Errors in growth rate and life determinations similar to those for sustained loading can be expected. In addition, serious errors in growth rate determinations and life estimates can result from load interaction effects and from the coupled environmental influences if these effects are not properly considered in testing and in making design estimates.

SUMMARY

In this paper, the respective roles of fracture toughness and subcritical crack growth resistance in determining the strength and durability of structural components are considered. The strength of a structure is governed principally by fracture toughness, while its durability is determined primarily by the subcritical crack growth resistance of the component materials.

Subcritical crack growth can be affected by a broad range of environmental, metallurgical and mechanical (loading and geometrical) variables. The effect of environment (both chemical and thermal) can be very large, and reflects interactions with a broad range of loading variables. Load interaction effects under variable-amplitude loading can be very large also and are affected strongly by the environment. The occurrence of nonsteady state crack growth under both sustained and fatigue loading can confound data development utilization. In the development of a viable fracture prevention and control program, many of these factors must be carefully considered.

Acknowledgment. Support for the work reported in this paper by the American Iron and Steel Institute, the Office of Naval Research under Contract N00014-68-A-0514, and The National Aeronautics and Space Administration under Grant NGL39-007-040 is gratefully acknowledged.

References

1. G. R. Irwin, in Structural Mechanics, Pergamon Press, 557 (1960)

2. Fracture Toughness Testing and Its Applications, ASTM STP 381 (1965)

3. W. F. Brown, Jr. and J. E. Srawley, ASTM STP 410 (1966)

4. C. F. Tiffany and J. N. Masters, ASTM STP 381, 249 (1965)

5. Che-Yu Li, P. M. Talda and R. P. Wei, unpublished results, Applied Research Laboratory, U. S. Steel Corporation (1966)

6. J. D. Landes, "Kinetics of Sub-critical Crack Growth and Deformation in a High Strength Steel," Ph.D. Dissertation, Lehigh University (1970)

7. R. P. Wei, J. Eng'g. Fract. Mech., 1, 633 (1970)

8. H. H. Johnson and P. C. Paris, J. Eng'g. Fract. Mech., 1, 3 (1968)

9. R. P. Wei, Proceedings of Conference - Fundamental Aspects of Stress Corrosion Cracking, Ohio State University, NACE, 104 (1969)

10. A. J. McEvily and R. P. Wei, Proceedings - International Conference on Corrosion Fatigue, University of Connecticut, 1971 (to be published)

11. Proceedings of Conference - Fundamental Aspects of Stress Corrosion Cracking, Ohio State University, NACE (1969)

12. Proceedings - International Conference on Corrosion Fatigue, University of Connecticut, 1971, NACE (to be published)

13. R. P. Wei and M. O. Speidel, Proceedings - International Conference on Corrosion Fatigue, University of Connecticut, 1971, NACE (to be published)

14. P. C. Paris, Fatigue - An Interdisciplinary Approach, Syracuse University Press, 107 (1964)

15. R. P. Wei, S. R. Novak and D. P. Williams, in AGARD Conference Proceedings No. 98, Specialists Meeting on Stress Corrosion Testing Methods (1971)

16. R. P. Wei and S. J. Hudak, unpublished results (1970)

17. J. D. Landes and R. P. Wei, "The Kinetics of Subcritical Crack Growth under Sustained Loading," Int'l. J. Fract. Mech. (to be published)

18. H. H. Johnson and A. M. Willner, Appl. Mat'l. Res., $\underline{4}$, 34 (1965)

19. D. P. Williams and H. G. Nelson, Met. Trans., $\underline{1}$, 63 (1970)

20. R. P. Wei and J. D. Landes, Mat'ls. Res. and Std., ASTM, $\underline{9}$, 25 (July, 1969)

21. J. A. Feeney, J. C. McMillan and R. P. Wei, Met. Trans., $\underline{1}$, 1741 (1970)

22. F. J. Bradshaw and C. Wheeler, Appl. Mat'l. Res., $\underline{5}$, 112 (1966)

23. A. Hartman, Int'l. J. Fract. Mech., $\underline{1}$, 167 (1965)

24. R. P. Wei, Int'l. J. Fract. Mech., $\underline{4}$, 159 (1968)

25. G. A. Miller, S. J. Hudak and R. P. Wei, J. of Mat'ls., to be published (1972)

26. R. Bucci, "Environment Enhanced Fatigue and Stress Corrosion Cracking of a Titanium Alloy Plus a Simple Model for Assessment of Environmental Influence of Fatigue Behavior," Ph.D. Dissertation, Lehigh University (1970)

27. J. M. Barsom, Proceedings - International Conference on Corrosion Fatigue, University of Connecticut, 1971, NACE (to be published)

28. J. P. Gallagher, "Corrosion Fatigue Crack Growth Behavior Above and Below K_{Iscc}," NRL Rept. 7064, Naval Research Laboratory, Washington, D. C. (May, 1970)

29. S. J. Hudak and R. P. Wei, Discussion, Proceedings - International Conference on Corrosion Fatigue, University of Connecticut, 1971, NACE (to be published)

30. O. Jonás and R. P. Wei, Int'l. J. Fract. Mech., $\underline{7}$, 116 (1971)

31. R. P. Wei and T. T. Shih, "Delay in Fatigue Crack Growth," to be published (1972)

32. R. P. Wei, "Influences of Temperature and Environment on Delay in Fatigue Crack Growth," to be published (1972)

33. S. J. Hudak and R. P. Wei, "Nonsteady-State Crack Growth under Sustained Loading," to be published (1972)

FRACTURE OF HIGH STRENGTH ENGINEERING MATERIALS

MICROSTRUCTURE AND FRACTURE TOUGHNESS

B. L. Averbach
Professor of Metallurgy
Massachusetts Institute of Technology
Cambridge, Massachusetts

ABSTRACT

The critical stress intensity factor, K_{Ic}, in high strength materials and the mode of fracture are influenced by the morphology of second phases and inclusions. The fracture toughness can be enhanced by the presence of a grain boundary envelope that is tougher than the matrix; in this case, K_{Ic} may be increased even if the fracture is intergranular. On the other hand, if the grain boundary precipitate is brittle, K_{Ic} is reduced. Precipitates within the grains affect the propagation of intragranular cracks and the fracture toughness. At high hardness levels the nature of the inclusions also has a significant effect on the fracture behavior. Fracture toughness can be improved by reducing the number of inclusions (e.g., by vacuum-processing) or by encapsulating harmful inclusions in a more favorable covering. The interplay of these microstructural features is discussed for several high-strength titanium, aluminum, and steel alloys.

INTRODUCTION

The ability of a material to resist fracture is con-
veniently described in terms of the critical stress intensity factor, K_{Ic}, or equivalently, the critical crack
propagation energy, G_{Ic}. For a given material the value
of K_{Ic} decreases as the yield stress, σ_y, increases and in
practice it is necessary to consider either K_{Ic} or the
defect parameter, $\delta = (K_{Ic}/\sigma_y)^2$, at a particular level of
the yield stress. The quantity δ is proportional to the
size of the plastic zone which precedes the crack front,
and it is also related to the allowable defect size. In
materials that exhibit considerable flow, and this can
occur even under conditions of plane strain fracture, the
critical crack size is considered to be in the range
$a_c \approx (0.1-0.5)\delta$. In very brittle materials with a minimal
flow zone the critical crack size is of the order of the
grain diameter, with $a_c \approx 0.01\delta$. The quantity δ is thus a
convenient indicator of the relative fracture toughness of
various materials; δ has dimensions of inches and is readily
visualized as a quantity which is proportional to the critical flaw size.

There is no direct way to calculate K_{Ic} from first
principles. However, there are experimental indications of
some of the microstructural factors that influence the fracture toughness. Several of these microstructural features
are reviewed herein and attempt is made to derive some general approaches that may be helpful in selecting materials
with the best resistance to crack propagation.

Our working model (1) is illustrated in Fig. 1, which
shows a propagating crack preceded by a region of plastic
flow. The plastic flow zone can be very small, but we believe that it is always present. Local stress concentrations
are produced within this flowed region by slip or twin bands

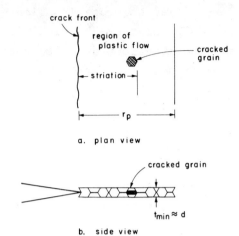

Fig. 1.   Model of propagating crack for K_{Ic} (min)

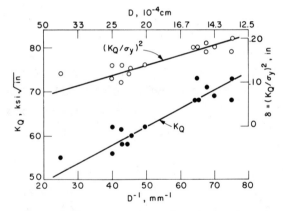

Fig. 2.   Effect of grain size on fracture toughness.
Ti-5.2Al -5.5V -0.9Fe -0.5 Cu, equiaxed α in aged β
matrix, intergranular fracture; $\sigma_y \approx$ 165 ksi.
(Greenfield and Margolin)

and microcracks are formed in properly oriented grains ahead
of the crack front. The microcracks link up because of the
additional stress concentrations and propagate backwards to
join the main crack front. The crack thus propagates in
intermittent steps, and such a mechanism is consistent with
striations which are often observed on crack surfaces. (2)

The minimum region that can sustain plastic flow is one
grain thick. Since most of the work in propagating the crack
goes into plastic flow, rather than into new surface formation, there is a lower limit to the value of the crack propagation energy. We have estimated the lowest values for G_{Ic}
and K_{Ic} for iron, titanium, and aluminum, and these are listed
in Table 1. These values refer only to transgranular fracture.
The minimum values for intergranular fracture will only be
slightly less since most of the work still goes into plastic
flow rather than into the new surfaces, even when the crack
propagates along the grain boundaries. These minimum values
of K_{Ic} will be achieved at the very highest yield strengths
attainable for each material, under conditions where the critical crack size is of the order of one grain diameter. As an
example, recent measurements on the bearing steel, 52100, at
a hardness of R_c = 63 yielded values of K_{Ic} = 15 ksi$\sqrt{\text{inch}}$.
This is in reasonable agreement with our estimate of the min-
imum value of iron. Using estimated upper limits for the
yield strength of each material, it is apparent that the minimum defect parameters for these materials are quite similar,
of the order of 0.07 inch.

In the next sections the influence of microstructure on
K_{Ic} for high strength titanium, aluminum, and steel alloys
is considered. At the end the principle generalizations are
summarized in the hope that this will provide some guidance
in choosing materials to minimize the propagation of fracture.

Table 1.

Estimated Minimum Values of K_{Ic}
for Transgranular Fracture

Material	Interfacial Energy dynes/cm	lb/in.	G_{Ic} (min) lb/in.	K_{Ic} (min) ksi$\sqrt{in}$.
α-Fe	4000	0.023	16	20
Ti	2300	0.013	9	13
Al	1350	0.0076	5	7

Note: 2γ = interfacial energy
       γ = surface tension

	Max yield, ksi	$\delta = (K_{Ic}/\sigma_y)^2$ in.
Fe	300	0.067
Ti	200	0.065
Al	100	0.07

THE INFLUENCE OF MICROSTRUCTURE

Most high strength materials are dependent on the precipitation of second phases and on phase transformations to
achieve high strengths. The influence of microstructure in
each class of materials is considered in the following
sections.

Titanium alloys. Recent work on the alloy Ti-5.2Al-
5.5V-0.9Fe-0.5Cu (3) has shown how the fracture toughness of
α-β titanium alloys can be varied by heat treatment. The
relative fracture toughness, K_Q, determined from fatigue-
cracked Charpy V-notch specimens is shown as a function of
grain size in Fig. 2 for structures consisting of equiaxed
α in a matrix of aged β. Although the fracture toughness
is plotted as a linear function of the grain diameter, D^{-1},
the data fit a $D^{-1/2}$ plot equally well. The D^{-1} function was
preferred because the fracture was intergranular and 2/D is
a measure of the total grain boundary area.

Electron photomicrographs showed that there was a fine
precipitate, about 0.2μ thick, at the β-β grain boundaries.
Thus even though the structure was the typical equiaxed α
in an aged β structure, the fracture path was determined by
the presence of grain boundary films of α. The yield strength
of all of the alloys shown in Fig. 2 was the same, approximately 165 ksi, and it is apparent that in this instance it
was possible to increase the fracture toughness without a
change in the corresponding yield strength.

The same series of alloys was heat treated to produce
a structure that consisted of a precipitate of α that completely outlined the β matrix. A small amount of α was also
present in a Widmanstatten structure. The fracture in this
case, Fig. 3, appeared to be sharply dependent on the thickness of the grain boundary α. For thicknesses below 3μ there
was no apparent toughening. At a thickness of 5 μ there was
an increase of almost 50% in the value of K_Q.

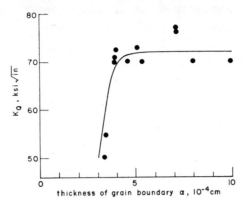

Fig. 3. Effect of thickness of α at grain boundaries of aged
         β. Ti-5.2Al -5.5V-0.9 Fe-0.5Cu, intergranular fracture;
         σ_y ≈ 165 ksi. (Greenfield and Margolin)

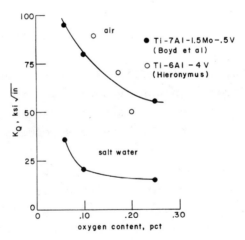

Fig. 4. Effect of salt water and oxygen content on fracture
         toughness

It is thus possible to obtain a substantial increase
in fracture toughness if the grain boundaries are enveloped
by a phase that is tougher than the matrix. The thickness
of the second phase is critical. If the layer is too thin,
plastic flow in the envelope will be inhibited and there will
be no increase in toughness. As the layer becomes thicker,
the resultant fracture toughness will become equivalent to
that of the grain boundary phase. The substantial variations
in K_Q at the same yield strength in this case appear to be a
consequence of the interplay between the grain size and the
precipitate effects.

The effects of oxygen on the fracture toughness of two
titanium alloys (4,5) are shown in Fig. 4. It is apparent
that both the fracture toughness, Fig. 4, and the defect
parameter, Fig. 5, are reduced sharply with increasing oxygen
contents, and a maximum value of 0.13% oxygen has been proposed for Ti-6Al-4V. The influence of testing in salt water
is also shown in Fig. 4 and 5, and it is evident that the
resistance to crack propagation in these titanium alloys is
lowered considerably in the presence of salt water. It has
been suggested* that the effects of oxygen and the interplay
of oxygen content with salt water environments are associated
with the presence of minute coherent precipitates of an inter-
metallic compound that increase in quantity as the oxygen
content increases. The local strains associated with these
coherent precipitates could then account for both the reduction in fracture toughness and the sensitivity to salt
water.

The distribution of the α and β phases in the microstructure also can affect the fracture toughness. Recent
data on Ti-6Al-4V forged conventionally and forged 120°F
above the β-transus are summarized in Table 2. (6) The
usual forging, below the β-transus, results in a structure

---

* Private communication, Dr. Frank Crossley, Lockheed.

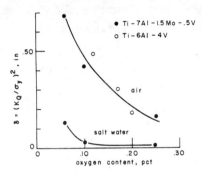

Fig. 5.   Effect of salt water and oxygen content on defect size

Table 2.
Effect of Forging Conditions on Fracture
Toughness of Ti-6Al-4V

Specimen Orientation	σ_y, ksi	Elongation, %	K_{Ic}, ksi$\sqrt{in.}$	$\delta = (K_{Ic}/\sigma_y)^2$, in.
Forged Conventionally				
Longitudinal	133	16	48	0.13
Transverse	132	10	49	0.14
Short Transverse	139	16	44	0.10
Forged 120°F Above β-transus				
Longitudinal	131	12	71	0.29
Transverse	136	16	71	0.27
Short Transverse	132	11	74	0.31

Note: Data from Petrak

of equiaxed α in an aged β matrix. On forging above the β-transus the structure is mainly acicular β, probably with some α in the grain boundaries. The alloys were heat treated to the same yield strength, and it is interesting to note that the acicular β structure had a substantially higher fracture toughness. There was little apparent directionality in the mechanical properties.

These studies indicate that there are opportunities for improving the fracture toughness in titanium alloys by heat treating the material to develop a more or less continuous precipitate of α at the grain boundaries. The α phase is relatively tough and it is thus possible to obtain an excellent combination of properties by taking advantage of the high yield strength of the β matrix and the excellent toughness of the α phase. On the other hand, increasing oxygen contents result in a serious deterioration of the fracture toughness, and the presence of sea water can be very deleterious. The β alloys will become more prominent as alloys with higher yield strength are sought. It will be necessary to explore the influence of oxygen content and the influence of phase changes on aging in order to achieve satisfactory levels of fracture toughness in a reproducible fashion.

Aluminum alloys. The fracture toughness of aluminum alloys has been investigated in some detail. We will confine our discussions here to the high strength alloys of the types 2000 and 7000. Data for several of these alloys as a function of heat treatment are summarized in Table 3. (7) Some of the data were obtained by means of tear tests, and values of K_Q rather than K_{Ic} are shown in the case of the thinner sheet. It is interesting to note that the 7000 series alloys exhibit consistently higher values of fracture toughness even at higher yield strengths (for the alloys indicated in the table).

Table 3.

Fracture Toughness of High Strength

Aluminum Alloys

Alloy	Plate Thickness, in.	σ_y, ksi	Elongation, %	(a) K_Q ksi$\sqrt{\text{in.}}$	$(K_Q/\sigma_y)^2$ in.
2024-T4	0.063	48.2	20.3	62	1.7
-T6		53.2	9.5	39	0.55
-T81		69.8	6.6	30	0.19
-T86		72.4	6.4	22	0.09
7075-T6	0.063	74.9	11.2	40	0.29
-T73		60.3	10.6	53	0.78
7079-T6	0.063	68.6	10.9	53	0.60

Alloy	Plate Thickness, in.	σ_y, ksi	Elongation, %	(b) K_{Ic} ksi$\sqrt{\text{in.}}$	$(K_{Ic}/\sigma_y)^2$ in.
2024-T851	0.25	65.2	10	26	0.16
7075-T6	0.125	78	11	28	0.13
-T651	0.25	78.2	13	33	0.18
7079-T651	0.25	74.7	11	25	0.11
	1.375	75	16	34	0.21
-T6	1.0	65	12	31(c)	0.21

Notes:

(a) Tear tests, Kaufman and Holt.

(b) Center notched tensile, Kaufman and Holt.

(c) Compact tension K_{Ic}, Bates and Clark.

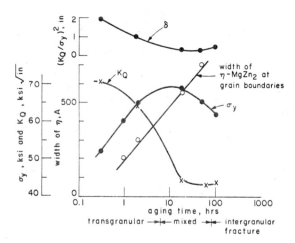

Fig. 6.   Effects of aging time at 150°C for 7075 Al alloy,
solution treated 482°C, WQ. (Kirman)   Precipitate
within grains is η' -MgZn₂ at all times

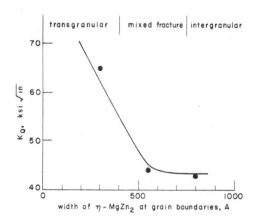

Fig. 7.   Influence of grain boundary precipitate MgZn₂ on
fracture toughness.   (Kirman)

The effects of heat treatment on the properties of a
7000 alloy have been investigated recently. (8) The influence
of aging time is summarized in Fig. 6. At an aging temperature of 150°C, microstructural studies indicated that the
very earliest precipitate was the transition phase η'-MgZn$_2$.
This precipitate thickened during the aging and was located
entirely within the matrix grains. However, at aging times
greater than one hour, a precipitate of the equilibrium phase
η'-MgZn$_2$ was observed to form at the grain boundaries. The
thickness of the grain boundary phase increased with aging.
The yield strengths increased to a peak on aging at approximately ten hours, but the fracture toughness was markedly
lower in the overaged alloys than in the underaged materials.

It should be noted that this behavior represents the
condition where the grain boundary phase is more brittle than
the matrix. If the brittle precipitate is very thin, the
resultant crack on yielding produces a stress concentration
that is too small to cause general crack propagation. However, at sufficient thicknesses of the precipitate, the resultant cracks produce high local stress concentrations and
intergranular fracture, at a reduced value of fracture toughness, occurs. The influence of the thickness of the grain
boundary precipitate is shown in Fig. 7.

The importance of inclusions in high strength alloys is
shown by the effect of iron content (9) on the fracture
toughness (Table 4). The lower fracture toughness in the
high iron alloys was attributed to the fracturing of the iron-
aluminum particles, which were arranged in a stringer pattern.

High strength steels. The following discussion is focused
on the fracture toughness of steels with yield strengths
greater than 200 ksi. Some of the crystallographic features
of the fracture in martensite have been studied in this laboratory. (10) Figure 8 shows transmission electron micrographs
of fracture in martensite containing 0.3% carbon. After an

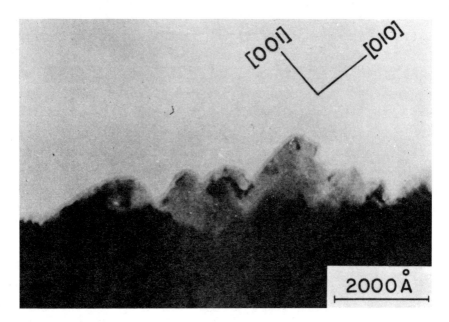

Fig. 8(a).   Fracture edge in 0.3C martensite tempered at 260°C

Fig. 8(b).   Fracture edge in 0.3C martensite tempered at 480°C

Table 4.

Effect of Iron Content on Fracture Toughness

of Al-5.8Zn-2.5Mg-0.7Cu-0.3Mn

Iron Content, %	σ_y, ksi	Elongation, %	K_{Ic} ksi$\sqrt{\text{in.}}$	Test Direction
0.05	70	5	34	Longitudinal
0.30	72	12	31	
0.75	66	4	18	
0.05			25	Transverse
0.30			18	
0.75			16	
0.05			21	Short Transverse
0.35			15	
0.75			13	

Note: Data from Peel and Forsyth

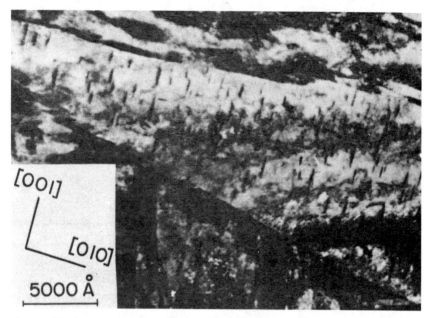

Fig. 9(a).   ε-carbide in martensite tempered at 260°C

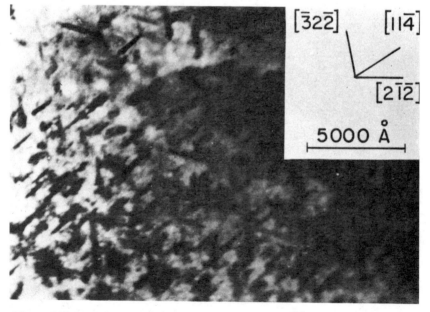

Fig. 9(b).   Cementite in martensite tempered at 340°C

iced brine quench from 900°C (1650°F), followed by tempering
at 260°C (500°F), it is evident that fracture proceeded by
localized cleavage on {100} faces. The morphology of the
hexagonal ε-carbide platelets within the martensite grains
after tempering at 260°C is shown in Fig. 9(a). The ε-carbide
platelets are parallel to {100} martensite planes. A typical
fracture edge in martensite tempered at 480°C (900°F) is
shown in Fig. 8(b). Cementite platelets precipitated on
tempering above 260°C and these platelets were generally
parallel to the {110} martensite planes (Fig. 9b). However,
there was also a significant precipitation of cementite along
the crystallite boundaries during the early stages of cementite
formation. This formation of cementite films may account for
the well-known 500°F embrittlement.

The fracture path in martensite is broken up into a large
number of very small segments. The segments tended to be along
simple crystallographic directions that depended on the tempering temperature and these data are summarized in Table 5. On
tempering at 260°C (the hardness was R_c 43) there was considerable cleavage on {100} martensite planes, and it is significant to note that ε-carbide also precipitated on the same
planes. On tempering at 340 and 480°C there was an additional
tendency to fracture along {110} planes, and this was probably
caused by the cementite platelets on these planes.

The general trends in fracture toughness for a few classes
of high strength steels are summarized in Fig. 10. The effects
of alloy content are evident in that the maraging steels have
higher fracture toughness values than the corresponding mar-
tensitic steels. The combined tempering and aging mechanisms
in the maraging steels are significantly different than in the
higher carbon martensites. It should be noted that the transverse properties of the high strength steels are particularly
affected by the inclusion content. Vacuum melting and vacuum
pouring frequently result in an improvement in the transverse
fracture toughness, and particularly in the transverse ductility.

Table 5.

Fracture Modes of 0.3% C Martensite

Treatment	Precipitate	Fracture Planes
As-quenched	-------	{100}
Tempered 260°C (500°F)	ε-carbide parallel to {100}M	{100} {321} {211}
Tempered 340°C (650°F) and 480°C (900°F)	Cementite, parallel to {110}M and at crystallite boundaries	{110} {100}

Note: Data from Lindborg and Averbach

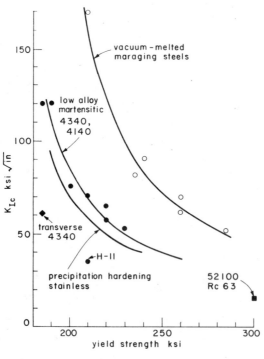

Fig. 10.   Fracture toughness of high strength steels

The influence of inclusions becomes especially important in steels at hardness levels in the vicinity of R_c 60. The bearing steel, 52100, is frequently used at hardnesses in the range R_c 60-65. A typical value of the fracture toughness at R_c 63 is about 15 ksi√inch (Fig. 10). In service these materials fail by rolling contact fatigue, and the load-life relationship suggests that this type of failure follows laws which are similar to those found in fatigue crack propagation studies.

The influence of the inclusion content on the fracture toughness has recently been studied for 4340, at a tensile strength of 285 ksi. (11) Figure 11 indicates that substantial increases in the inclusion content produced relatively small decreases in the value of K_{Ic}, even when the tests were made in the transverse direction. On the other hand, the effects of inclusion content on the fatigue life of 52100 bearings, (11) at a hardness of about R_c 65, was very marked (Fig. 12). The critical defect size in 52100 is of the order of 0.0005 inch, which is in the size range for the larger oxide microinclusions. This effect is well recognized, and there has been considerable emphasis on the use of vacuum treatments in the steelmaking practice for 52100. The most successful bearing steels usually have few large oxide inclusions.

There have been some indications that there are other methods that may be useful in reducing the hazards associated with inclusions in the steels of very high hardness. It has been observed that sulfide inclusions do not play a significant role in the fatigue failure of 52100 bearings. Recently, it has been shown that relatively small increases in the amount of sulfur can result in a situation where the oxide inclusions are encapsulated within sulfide particles. The effects of the oxide inclusion then are minimized and the

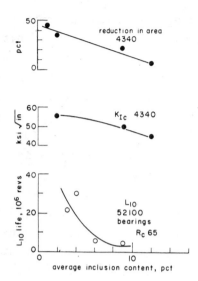

Fig. 11.   Effect of inclusions on transverse properties of 4340
           at 285 ksi and on bearing life at 52100 at R_c65.
           (Hauser and Wells)

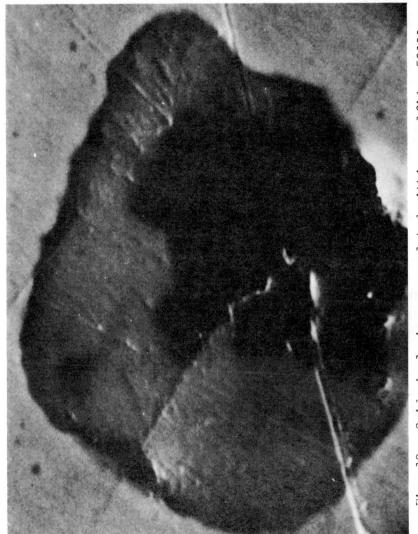

Fig. 12. Oxide inclusion encapsulated within a sulfide, 52100 bearing steel. Scanning electron microscope, original magnification 4300X

fatigue behavior improves. It should be emphasized that merely adding sulfur to a steel is not a guarantee that the oxide inclusions will be encapsulated. It is necessary to have the sulfur in the molten steel at a stage in the steelmaking process where there is sufficient opportunity for the manganese sulfide to agglomerate with and coat the oxide particles. There has been considerable speculation on the reasons for this behavior. Metallographic observations have shown that the sulfides are quite soft and generally have sharp corners and edges. Furthermore, the oxides are brittle and easily cracked and it is possible that the resultant local stress concentrations act as fracture initiation sites. The soft, smooth, well-rounded sulfide particles probably produce negligible stress concentrations and are thus far less dangerous. Alternate explanations in terms of differential expansion and tessellated stresses also have been proposed. (12)

Figure 12 shows a scanning electron micrograph of an oxide inclusion encapsulated within a sulfide particle. This inclusion was typical of those observed in a 52100 bearing steel with a sulfur content that was slightly higher than normal. The total number of inclusions was typical of that in the usual vacuum-processed material. The high sulfur steel produced bearings with good resistance to spalling fatigue. This work is still in process and the initial results are encouraging.

CONCLUSIONS

This limited discussion indicates that there is considerable scope for the raising of the fracture toughness at high yield strengths. One method is the introduction of a tough grain boundary envelope. On the other hand, if the precipitated phases are hard and brittle, it is best to

avoid grain boundary envelopes and to attempt to disperse
the precipitate in the form of small rounded particles within
the grains.

There is a good case to be made for the avoidance of the
larger microinclusions, particularly oxides, in steels at
high hardness levels. Excessive inclusion contents reduce
the transverse ductility and promote fracture initiation.
The most recent approach is to attempt to neutralize the
effects of inclusions by encapsulating them in a harmless
coating, such as manganese sulfide. This concept may be
applicable in a general way to other materials as the yield
strengths are pushed to higher values.

References

1. B. L. Averbach, Fracture, Vol 1, Ch 7, 441-472 (Academic Press Inc., New York), (1969)

2. R. C. Bates and W. G. Clark, Jr., Trans. ASM 62, 380 (1969)

3. M. A. Greenfield and H. Margolin, Met. Trans. 2, 841 (1971)

4. J. D. Boyd, et al, Battelle, February (1970); DMIC, August 29 (1971)

5. W. S. Hieronymus, Aviation Week and Space Technology, p 42, July 26 (1971); DMIC, August 29 (1971)

6. G. J. Petrak, University of Dayton, January (1971); DMIC, August 29 (1971)

7. J. G. Kaufman and Marshall Holt, ALCOA Research Laboratories, Tech Paper No. 18 (1965)

8. I. Kirman, Met. Trans. 2, 1761 (1971)

9. C. J. Pal and P. J. E. Forsyth, Royal Aircraft Establishment (September 1970); DMIC, September 29 (1971)

10. U. H. Lindborg and B. L. Averbach, Acta Met. 14, 1583 (1966)

11. J. J. Hauser and M. G. H. Wells, Crucible Materials Research Center, February (1970); DMIC, June 17 (1970)

12. D. Brooksbank and K. W. Andrews, J.I.S.I. 206, 595 (1968)

FRACTURE TOUGHNESS TESTING, INCLUDING
SCREENING AND QUALITY CONTROL TESTING,
IN THE ALUMINUM INDUSTRY

J. G. Kaufman
Aluminum Company of America
Alcoa Research Laboratories
New Kensington, Pennsylvania

ABSTRACT

The fracture toughness of aluminum alloys is
reviewed by alloy type and strength level, and the
effects of orientation and specimen size on K_{Ic}
are discussed. The alloys developed within the
past few years where particular attention was de-
voted to optimizing the strength-toughness combination are described, i.e., 2124, X7050, and X7475.
The paper also discusses the trends in the development of minimum values of plane-strain fracture
toughness, K_{Ic}, for aluminum alloys, the problems
which this introduces in quality control, and the
possible role of screening tests in dealing with
fracture minima.

INTRODUCTION

It is the purpose of this paper to provide a review of
the status of fracture toughness testing and evaluations in
the aluminum industry. This will include: (a) a review,

by alloy system, of the toughness levels observed for commercial alloys; (b) alloys developed recently, specifically with high toughness in mind; (c) data illustrating the influence of specimen orientation on test results; (d) the status of moves to generate minimum values of fracture-toughness parameters, such as K_{Ic}, for design purposes and material procurement; and (e) the role that screening tests for fracture toughness may play in the quality control testing of materials.

This review is timely because of the rapid pace with which fracture data have been developed over the past three years since test method standardization was reasonably well set, (1,2) and the attention that has been given during that time to developing aluminum alloys with outstanding combinations of strength and toughness. Together with this has come the increased interest in establishing minimum levels of toughness for the benefit of designers, with the attendant consideration of applying this to material procurement documents. This activity has represented a significant technical focus, and the ambitious scope of this presentation is to present the state of the art and anticipate future trends in this area within the aluminum industry.

In developing the data presented herein, the test methods developed by ASTM are the baseline. Specifically, plane-strain fracture toughness data that do not conform (except as specifically noted) to the validity requirements in ASTM Method E399[1] were not considered. It is recognized that such methods are not yet perfect and some data showing the range of values that can be obtained even within the scope of the method are presented. However, it should be a "standard" of the metals industry that in dealing with procurement documents, the best available standardized methods are utilized. That theme will be recurrent in this presentation.

COMMERCIAL ALUMINUM ALLOYS

The Aluminum Association groupings of aluminum alloys by major alloying constituents provide a meaningful as well as a convenient way of surveying the toughness of aluminum alloys. (3) This system may be summarized for wrought alloys as shown in Table 1. Also shown are representative alloys in each group. Discussion of the alloy types below will not follow the numerical order of the system, but rather the pattern of properties.

The 1XXX (>99.00% Al) and 3XXX (Al-Mn) series of alloys may be quickly dispensed with in any discussion of linear elastic fracture mechanics because they have very low strengths, and hence are not used in many strength-critical applications. They are extremely ductile, even in strain-hardened tempers. No further comment on these alloys is necessary except to note that even if we wished to treat these alloys by fracture mechanics techniques, we could not, because there is no recognized test for directly measuring fracture mechanics indices for them. The 4XXX alloys are specialty items, and warrant no further comment.

Most of the alloys in the 5XXX (Al-Mg) series are similar to the 1XXX and 3XXX series, in that they too have low strengths and high ductility, but several of the highest strength alloys in this class, notably 5083 and 5456, are used in very critical applications and so warrant some attention before moving on to the higher strength alloys. Both 5083 and 5456 are approved for pressure vessels (4) and cryogenic service to temperatures as low as -452°F, and both (particularly 5083) have been used in extremely critical applications such as tanks for transporting liquefied natural gas (LNG). No direct and formally acceptable measurement of K_{Ic} or K_c has been made of these materials in the annealed (-0) temper in which they are usually used in critical applications. This is because of their high toughness; even very large scale

Table 1.

Basic Characteristics of Aluminum Alloys

Series	Principal Alloying Element	Principal Strengthening Mechanism*	Typical Examples	Approximate Range of Yield Strengths+, ksi
1XXX	None	CW	1100	4 to 22
2XXX	Cu	PH	2014, 2024	25 to 65
3XXX	Mn	CW	3003	6 to 36
4XXX	Si	PH	4032, 4043	15 to 46
5XXX	Mg	CW	5052, 5083, 5456	6 to 37
6XXX	Mg-Si	PH	6061, 6063	13 to 55
7XXX	Zn	PH	7075, 7079 (Cu Bearing)	68 to 91
8XXX	Other	--	7005, 7007 (Cu Free)	45 to 65
9XXX	Unassigned			

* CW – Cold Work

  PH – Precipitation Hardening

+ In commonly used tempers

test sections have resulted in cross-section yielding which precluded precise measurements. Nelson and Kaufman (5,6) have estimated values of K_{Ic} for 5083-0 conservatively from 40 to 55 ksi$\sqrt{inch}$ and K_c for 1 inch 5083-0 plate, substantially in excess of 100 ksi$\sqrt{inch}$ at room temperature and subzero temperatures. DeMoney, Lake, and Eiber (7) estimated K_c for 5083-0 from burst tests of tanks at -220°F to be about 120 to 140 ksi$\sqrt{inch}$, but even in this instance the material exhibited large scale yielding on the net section. For purposes of design, these conservative estimates have been used to judge whether or not the structures are safe and, since the design stresses are usually less than 20 ksi, very large critical cracks can be tolerated. As interest has extended to the thickness range of 4 to 8 inches, closer estimates of K_{Ic} and K_c seem needed, but to this time all attempts (even tests of 8-inch thick notch-bend specimens) have yielded fully plastic behavior.

In the strain-hardened tempers, the high strength 5XXX alloys are not as tough as in the annealed temper. However, even 3-inch thick specimens were not sufficient to provide plane-strain conditions and valid K_{Ic} measurements of 5083 in the H321 temper. (8)

Tests by other investigators have confirmed these results. From the results of dynamic tear tests of plate of several thicknesses of the 5XXX series of alloys, Judy et al of the Naval Research Laboratory have stated that the critical crack size for plate up to 3 inches in thickness is "huge", (9) and the use of fracture mechanics in designing the structures of these alloys is discouraged.

In the 6XXX series of alloys, 6061-T6 is the workhorse. Alloy 6063 is more easily extruded, but has lower strength and is not usually used in strength-critical applications; it is extremely tough, however. Alloys similar to 6061, such as 6005 and 6351, and even higher strength versions, such as

6066, also are available, but not widely used. Plane-strain
fracture-toughness tests of 6061-T6, most of which have been
invalid from one standpoint or another, have generally indicated values in the range of 28 to 35 ksi$\sqrt{\text{inch}}$. (8) This
alloy has a relatively sharp-kneed tensile stress-strain
curve, and a low strain-hardening coefficient, so there appears to be a tendency for fracture toughness tests to appear
valid even when relatively large amounts of plastic deformation take place. Because of its intermediate strength and
relatively high toughness, fracture mechanics considerations
are not important in many applications, and so there has not
been extensive fracture testing of this material.

The 2XXX and 7XXX series of alloys have received the
most attention from the fracture-mechanics standpoint. (10,11)
After solution-heat treatment and artificial aging, these
alloys provide yield strengths from about 45 ksi up to 90 ksi,
and have been widely used in a number of aerospace and missile
applications where fracture mechanics considerations are important. Ranges and average values of K_{Ic} from plane-strain
fracture toughness tests of plate of some of these alloys
are summarized in Fig. 1. Values for extruded shapes and
forgings are generally in the same ranges, although the
directional variations may be somewhat different.

When K_{Ic} data are plotted as a function of yield strength,
as in Ref 10, some general trends are evident, namely:

(a). For each type of alloy and temper, there is a
general trend for toughness to decrease with increase in yield
strength;

(b). The 7XXX series have a slightly more favorable
combination of strength and toughness than the 2XXX series;

(c). Within the 7XXX series, the Cu-free alloys (e.g.,
7005, 7007) have lower strength and higher toughness than
the Cu-bearing alloys (e.g., 7075, 7079); and

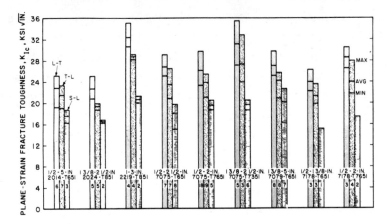

PLANE-STRAIN FRACTURE TOUGHNESS, K_{Ic}, OF ALUMINUM ALLOY PLATE

Fig. 1.   Plane-strain fracture toughness, K_{Ic}, of aluminum alloy plate

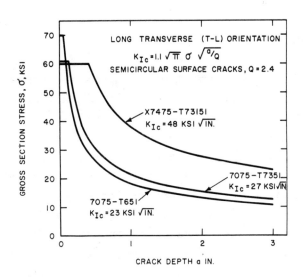

Fig. 2.   Critical crack size calculations for aluminum alloy plate

(d). There is evidence, though not always consistent,
that 7XXX series alloys in the T6-type temper have a combination of strength and toughness which is superior to that of
7XXX series alloys in the T7X-type temper. With regard to
this point, however, the toughness of the T7X-type temper of
a given alloy is generally higher than that of the T6-type
temper of the same alloy. Since the T7X-type temper generally has higher resistance to stress-corrosion cracking, it
is more commonly used in toughness-critical applications.

Among the 2XXX series of alloys, 2024 is one of the most
commonly used and it is available in two types of temper (T3
and T8) which provide such widely different properties as to
make it seem like two separate alloys. In the T3 (or T4)
type temper (solution heat-treated and naturally aged), 2024
products have yield strength levels around 50 ksi and relatively high toughness, with K_{Ic} equal to or greater than 30
ksi$\sqrt{\text{inch}}$. In the T8-type temper, 2024 products have higher
yield strengths (65 ksi) and superior corrosion resistance,
but also markedly lower fracture toughness ($K_{Ic} \approx$ 20-25
ksi$\sqrt{\text{inch}}$). Because of the lower toughness of the latter,
it is sometimes not possible to take full advantage of its
higher strength and corrosion resistance.

Among the 7XXX series, 7075 has been the most widely
used, first in the T6-type temper, but more recently in the
T7X-type tempers which provide higher toughness along with
greater resistance to stress-corrosion cracking. Higher
strength alloys like 7001 and 7178 have given way to tougher
alloys once the implications of their low fracture toughness
was understood. The Cu-free alloys, like 7005 and 7007, are
tougher and more readily welded than other 7XXX alloys, but
have not found wide application because they too are susceptible to stress-corrosion cracking under fairly common
service conditions.

Table 2.

Comparison of K_{Ic} Values for Conventional
and Premium Toughness Aluminum Alloy Products

	Average K_{Ic}, ksi$\sqrt{in.}$		
	L-T	T-L	S-L
Conventional 2014-T651 Plate	23	22	18
Alcoa 417 Process 2214-T651 Plate	36	30	24
Conventional 2024-T851 Plate	23	19	16
Alcoa 417 Process 2124-T851 Plate	29	24	23
Conventional 7075-T651 Plate	27	23	18
Conventional 7075-T7351 Plate	31	27	20
Conventional X7050-T7351 Plate	37	31	27
Alcoa 467 Process 7475-T7351 Plate	50	48	33
Conventional 7075-T7352 Forgings	31	25	20
Alcoa Premium Strength 7175-T736 Forgings	34	32	27

PREMIUM-TOUGHNESS PRODUCTS

As indicated earlier, the last several years have seen
a significant move toward the development of alloys specifically for their high toughness. The development of 7075-
T73 might be thought of as among the first in this direction,
but it is a historical fact that achieving higher levels of
resistance to stress-corrosion cracking was the true impetus
behind that development. The higher fracture toughness of
the T73 over that of the T6 temper was a secondary benefit.

In more recent years, however, a number of alloys for
which toughness was one of the prime considerations have come
forth, notably 2124 (12) and 2214 among the 2XXX series and
X7050, (13) 7175, and X7475 (14) among the 7XXX series. The
improvement in the toughness resulting from these developments is shown in Table 2. In most cases, the improvement
in toughness is accomplished with no significant sacrifice
in strength. In fact, the strengths of 7175-T736 forgings
are 10 to 15 per cent greater than those of 7075-T7352 forgings, so there is a significant improvement in both strength
and toughness.

Almost all of the moves toward higher toughness alloys
started with the use of relatively high purity material in
which the iron and silicon contents have been reduced to a
practical but relatively low level. (15) In the most successful cases, however, this has been combined with important
fabrication process improvements. The use of ultrapure material can result in even further increase in toughness, but
this extremely high purity is achieved at a considerable sacrifice in castability and fabricability, and no serious consideration is being given to these ultrapure versions.

Alloy X7475 is worthy of particular note. (14) Toughness
was the prime objective in its development, and the toughness
levels achieved are exceptional. In fact, one of the principal

problems in evaluating the material has been achieving valid measures of its fracture toughness. From the data generated to date, it appears that with strength levels in the same order as those of 7075, K_{Ic} levels ranging from 1½ to 3 times those of 7075 are achieved. The implications of this in terms of critical crack sizes is shown in Fig. 2. The long-sought goal of having the toughness levels of 2024-T3-type products coupled with the strengths of 7075-T6-type products seems to have been achieved.

INFLUENCE OF VARIABLES IN SPECIMEN ORIENTATION AND TESTING PROCEDURE ON PLANE STRAIN FRACTURE TOUGHNESS

There are six principal orientations from which fracture toughness specimens may be taken from conventional rectangular products, as shown in Fig. 3 with the new ASTM standard identification system. While there is a tendency on the part of some to consider that the toughness of a material be represented by a single K_{Ic} value, the toughness actually varies significantly depending upon the crack orientation and path, and so a specific orientation should be assigned to all values which are published. As the representative data in Fig. 3 show, values of K_{Ic} in ksi$\sqrt{inch}$ are highest for most aluminum alloy products when the crack plane is normal to the longitudinal direction and crack growth is either across or through the thickness (L-T or L-S). In many cases, toughness is greater with the crack moving through the thickness (L-S or T-S) than across (L-T) or along (T-L) the plate. Values are lowest when the crack plane is parallel to the principal plane of the product, that is, normal to the thickness direction (S-L or S-T); it makes little difference whether the crack is traveling along or across the product.

The L-T, T-L, and S-L orientations are nominally considered to be the standard for most testing, though it is

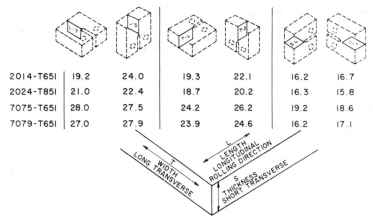

Fig. 3.   Influence of specimen orientation on K_{Ic} for aluminum alloy plate

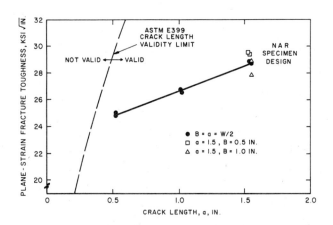

Fig. 4.   Influence of crack length on values of K_{Ic} for 2124-T851 plate, L-T

important to recognize that the L-S and T-S most closely
approximate the situation in which a surface flaw is present,
since the highest driving force is through the thickness of
the material.

One of the most confusing features of plane-strain
fracture toughness testing, and one which can introduce considerable scatter into the data, is the specimen size effect.
Although K_{Ic} is considered to be a rather fundamental property, the range of specimen sizes which one can normally encounter within the present framework of E399 can result in
almost 20 per cent spread in K_{Ic} values. Data illustrating
this effect were presented for some steel and titanium alloys
by Brown and Jones in STP 463 (16) and for some aluminum
alloys by Nelson, Schilling, and Kaufman at the 1970 National
Symposium on Fracture Mechanics. (17) In the latter case,
the situation for aluminum alloys was unknowingly over-simpli-
fied, because the data available at the time seemed to indicate
that relative constancy of values was achieved as crack length
and thickness increased.

As additional data have become available for larger
specimens, it is apparent that even when well above the minimum size requirements in ASTM Method E399 rather large variations can be expected, particularly for relatively tough
alloys. This is illustrated by data for 2124-T851 in Fig.
4, which suggest that so long as the crack length is increased,
the value obtained for K_{Ic} will increase; this is independent
of specimen thickness so long as the value is greater than
the existing.thickness criteria. Similar studies show that
using specimens of the standard proportions in E399 and simply
scaling them up as necessary as material increases, one can
obtain a range of L-T values from 25 to 30 ksi$\sqrt{inch}$ for 7075-
T76 and 30 to 36 ksi$\sqrt{inch}$ for 2219-T851. From plots such as
Fig. 4, it is indicated that if the study were expanded to
even larger crack sizes, even higher values would be obtained.

This type of variation is under study by ASTM Committee E24 and it is hoped that some type of width correction can be developed that will eliminate this variability and provide a realistic definition of plane strain toughness.

In the meantime, the recommendation has been that for all material thicknesses up to at least 2 inches, full thickness specimens of the standard geometry always be taken from aluminum alloy products; in this fashion all testing organizations should get the same values of K_{Ic} for each material independent of any geometry effects, and the selection of values for quality control of toughness will then be completely free of geometrical considerations. For material over 2 inches in thickness where the capability for full thickness testing may not be present, it is recommended that standard 2-inch thick specimens be taken from the quarter-thickness location if the products are thick enough, and if not, from the center of the thickness.

Some have recommended, with some justification, that specimens of the same overall plan size be used in testing all thicknesses of a given alloy and temper. This has the basic advantage that for each alloy and temper the values may be fairly constant, but they may not be directly comparable to other alloys and tempers for which different specimen sizes were selected. If such a procedure were to receive wider support, it would be our further recommendation that a single relatively large specimen be selected for all alloys, tempers, and products.

FRACTURE TOUGHNESS MINIMA AND QUALITY CONTROL TESTING

For the design of fracture-critical structures, it is obvious that materials engineers need either estimated or absolute minimum values of K_{Ic} (or perhaps the range from minimum to maximum) to enable them to determine the degree

to which their structure will be safe from the possibility
of unstable crack growth. For this purpose, the K_{Ic} minima
developed should be statistically meaningful values developed
from tests of many lots of the alloy, temper, and product
involved, and the test should be conducted in such a way that
it will provide the best possible value of plane-strain fracture toughness for the material as it will appear in the
structure. In light of the previous discussion on specimen
size effects, it would not be an unreasonable requirement
of a designer to demand values that represent the final thickness and reasonable size relationships to the prototype.

Quality control testing, on the other hand, has an entirely different purpose: i.e., ascertaining to the satis-
faction of the material producer and the customer that the
lot of material has been manufactured to the standards representative of the particular alloy, temper, and product. For
this purpose it is most important that the test that is conducted be one that (a) can be reproducibly carried out by
testing organizations of both the customer and producer and
any other laboratories which need to get involved, and (b)
the results are meaningful to all potential users and producers. In other words, it is imperative that quality control
tests be conducted by procedures that are well documented in
standards, accepted by everyone, and do not involve aspects
that have special interest to one group, but not to others.
For this reason we have strongly urged that tests for quality
control and procurement of all aluminum alloy products always
be made with the standard specimen specified in Method E399,
and by procedures which are consistent with E399. We have
discouraged any deviations from these procedures, even though
they appear to satisfy the problems of a specific group. If
and when technical knowledge indicates that ASTM Method E399
should be revised to improve the quality, meaning or reproducibility of data obtained from its use, then changes in

procedures used for quality control testing should and will
be instituted promptly. Until that time, however, the present
standard test method and the standard size of specimen should
be employed throughout.

Regardless of agreed upon test procedures, it is another
fundamental precept that all minimum values should represent
a statistically meaningful analysis of data from a large number of lots of material. The population should represent a
reasonable range of sizes for the particular alloy, temper,
and product involved. There has been an unfortunate tendency,
no doubt because relatively few data were available, to arbitrarily establish K_{Ic} minima at levels where designers might
like to see them rather than where the available data suggest
they should be. For example, guaranteed minimum values of
K_{Ic} have been sought for conventional alloys and tempers at
levels near the average of what few test results are available.
This was done under the guise that the customer wished to have
only the best lots of that given alloy and temper, and that
lots failing to come up to the artificial minima could be
scrapped or sold to other customers. This is an unacceptable
procedure both to the producer and to the consumer; it results
in increased costs to cover any scrapped material, or in the
sale of these lower-toughness lots to other customers who may
be equally interested in high toughness and will likely assume
(even if they do not specify) that toughness levels are about
average for the stated alloy and temper, whereas they would
actually be obtaining something consistently on the low side.

It has been Alcoa's emphatically expressed stand on this
point that if a level of toughness higher than that which a
conventional product will consistently supply is necessary
to satisfy design problems, then another alloy, temper, and
product (perhaps a premium product) should be selected that
will consistently provide that level of toughness. Then, both
the producer and the consumer can be assured that each lot of

material meeting normal quality control standards for that
alloy, temper, and product will have the stated relatively
high fracture toughness.

SCREENING TESTS FOR QUALITY CONTROL

All who have worked with the methods developed by Committee E24 and specifically with the ASTM Method E399 for
plane strain fracture-toughness testing recognize that it is
a complex test and quite expensive compared to quality control tests normally performed in plant laboratories. The
equipment for performing fracture-toughness tests is generally not available in the plants, notably the equipment for
fatigue cracking the specimens and the special recording
instrumentation necessary to obtain the load-displacement
curves, nor are there many people there who can make adequate judgments in the analysis of the data. As a result
there are few plant laboratories performing plane-strain
fracture-toughness tests, and there is interest in relatively
simple screening tests that provide assurance that plane-
strain fracture toughness levels are being achieved.

In the aluminum industry, tensile tests have been
routinely used for many years for quality control; tests are
made of every lot of material that is produced. The plant
laboratories are, therefore, well equipped to perform tensile
tests on a variety of sizes and types of specimens. As a
result, procedures for sharp-notch tensile testing have been
looked at closely for their possible value in screening for
plane-strain fracture toughness. (18) As shown in Fig. 5,
there is a good relationship between the notch-yield ratio
(notch-tensile strength/tensile yield strength) from the notch
tensile test and the plane-strain fracture-toughness, K_{Ic}.
This relationship can be used to provide assurance that required toughness levels are being achieved providing meaningful

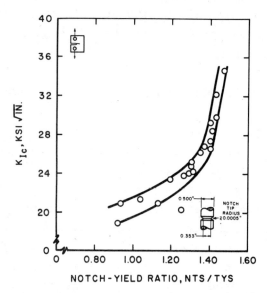

Fig. 5. K_{Ic} vs notch-yield ratio for 2124-T851 type plate

minimum values of K_{Ic} are involved. For example, considering the data in Fig. 5, if a producer is to provide a product with a minimum level of K_{Ic} of 22 ksi$\sqrt{inch}$, he does so by conducting notch-tensile tests and accepts all lots for which the notch-yield ratio is equal to or greater than 1.3. For those lots with ratios less than 1.3, the K_{Ic} value may be less than 22 ksi$\sqrt{inch}$, and in these cases it will be necessary to reject the lot and/or conduct a plane-strain fracture-toughness test to be certain of the value of K_{Ic}. Hopefully, however, this would represent only 5 per cent or less of the total population, and such tests could be handled satisfactorily by sending this material to a research laboratory or a nearby test laboratory. The thousands of dollars to equip that particular plant laboratory to conduct plane-strain fracture-toughness tests and the repeated cost of conducting these tests of every lot of material would be eliminated.

For relatively thin aluminum alloy products, ASTM Method E338 (19) provides an excellent opportunity for the same type of control. There is a good relationship between notch-yield ratio from the edge-notched sheet-type specimen and K_c obtained with a particular size of panel. (14) While K_c testing involves features that are far from being resolved, everyone is agreed that a tensile test of a relatively large center-cracked panel provides some useful information about the toughness level of the material.

There has been some consideration of the Charpy test (20) as a screening test for plane-strain fracture toughness. Since aluminum alloys do not exhibit a ductile to brittle fracture transition, for which the Charpy test was originally developed, the nonferrous industry has never utilized Charpy testing on a regular basis. However, it has been a standard test for the steel industry and little extra capital investment would be required to make use of it for additional tests. Therefore, if satisfactory correlations exist there is a good chance that the Charpy test may be a practical screening test for the fracture toughness of ferrous materials. If so, the basic concept would be similar to that as described above in which a selected value of foot-pounds of energy would be established as providing near 100 per cent assurance that K_{Ic} values above the prescribed level had been achieved. For lots with energies less than that value, it would be necessary to make a K_{Ic} test or reject the material outright.

SUMMARY

The status of fracture-toughness testing in the aluminum industry has been reviewed, first listing the variety of alloys available and their general toughness levels, and providing some specific values of plane-strain fracture toughness for the commercial aerospace alloys. Premium-toughness products that answer the needs of critical applications have been cited, with X7475 noted as the outstanding example. The distinction between the needs for fracture-toughness minima for design and for quality control has been explored, with recommendations about how these may be handled. Finally, the need for screening tests has been recognized, and the potential answer to the need in the form of notch-tensile tests for the aluminum industry has been noted.

References

1. Tentative Method of Test for Plane-Strain Fracture
    Toughness of Metallic Materials (Designation: E399-70T),
    1971 Annual Book of ASTM Standards, Part 31, pp. 919-
    935, American Society for Testing and Materials, Phila-
    delphia

2. J. G. Kaufman, "Fracture Toughness Testing," ASTM STP
    476 (Advanced Testing Techniques), 1970, pp. 96-111,
    American Society for Testing and Materials, Philadelphia

3. "Aluminum Standards and Data," Aluminum Association,
    1970-1971

4. ASME Boiler and Pressure Vessel Code, Section II, Section
    VIII, Div. 1, "Pressure Vessels" and Section IX, "Welding
    Qualifications," 1968

5. F. G. Nelson, J. G. Kaufman and E. T. Wanderer, "Tear
    Tests of 5083 Plate and of 5183 Welds in 5083 Plate and
    Extrusions," Advances in Cryogenic Engineering, Vol 15,
    1970, pp. 91-101, Plenum Press, New York

6. J. G. Kaufman, F. G. Nelson and E. T. Wanderer, "Mechan-
    ical Properties and Fracture Characteristics of 5083-0
    Products and 5183 Welds in 5083 Products," presented at
    1971 Cryogenic Engineering Conference, to be published
    in Advances in Cryogenic Engineering

7. R. L. Lake, F. W. DeMoney and R. J. Eiber, "Burst Tests
    of Pre-Flawed Welded Aluminum Alloy Pressure Vessels
    at -220°F," Advances in Cryogenic Engineering, Vol 13,
    1967, pp. 278-293, Plenum Press, New York

8. F. G. Nelson and J. G. Kaufman, "Fracture Toughness Tests
    of Plain and Welded 3-in. Thick Aluminum Alloy Plate Based
    on Fracture Mechanics Methods," The Metal Properties
    Council Contract No. 769-2. Final Report to be published

9. R. W. Judy, Jr., R. J. Goode and C. N. Freed, "Fracture
    Toughness Characterization Procedures and Interpretations
    to Fracture-Safe Design for Structural Aluminum Alloys,"
    Naval Research Laboratory Report 6871, March 31, 1969,
    Washington, D. C.

10. J. G. Kaufman, P. E. Schilling and F. G. Nelson, "Fracture
    Toughness of Aluminum Alloys," Metals Engineering Quarter-
    ly, August 1969, pp. 39-47

11. J. G. Kaufman, R. L. Moore and P. E. Schilling, "Fracture Toughness of Structural Aluminum Alloys," Engineering Fracture Mechanics, Vol 2, 1971, pp. 197-210, Pergamon Press, Great Britain

12. J. A. Dickson, "Aluminum Alloy 2124," Alcoa Green Letter 217, September 1970. Aluminum Company of America, New Kensington, Pa.

13. J. T. Staley, H. Y. Hunsicker, and R. Schmidt, "New Aluminum Alloy X7050," Alcoa Research Laboratories and U. S. Naval Air Systems Command, Joint Report Prepared for ASM Metal Congress and Fall Meeting of TMS, AIME, Detroit, Michigan, October 18-21, 1971

14. J. A. Dickson, "Alcoa 467 Process X7475 Alloy," Alcoa Green Letter 216, Revised October 1971, Aluminum Company of America, New Kensington, Pa.

15. J. A. Nock and H. Y. Hunsicker, "High Strength Aluminum Alloys," Journal of Metals, Vol 15, No. 3, March 1963, pp. 216-224

16. M. H. Jones and W. F. Brown, Jr., "The Influence of Crack Length and Thickness in Plane Strain Fracture Toughness Tests," ASTM STP 463 (Review of Developments in Plane Strain Fracture Toughness Testing), 1970, pp. 63-101, American Society for Testing and Materials, Philadelphia

17. F. G. Nelson, P. E. Schilling and J. G. Kaufman, "The Effect of Specimen Size on the Results of Plane-Strain Fracture-Toughness Tests," to be published in Engineering Fracture Mechanics in 1972

18. J. G. Kaufman, "Sharp-Notch Tension Testing of Thick Aluminum Alloy Plate With Cylindrical Specimens," presented at Fifth National Symposium on Fracture Mechanics, Urbana, Illinois, August 31-September 2, 1971, to be published in an ASTM Special Technical Publication

19. Standard Method of Sharp-Notch Tension Testing of High-Strength Sheet Materials (Designation: E338-68), 1971 Annual Book of ASTM Standards, Part 31, pp. 855-862, American Society for Testing and Materials, Philadelphia

20. Standard Methods for Notched Bar Impact Testing of Metallic Materials (Designation: E23-66), 1971 Annual Book of ASTM Standards, Part 31, pp. 275-289, American Society for Testing and Materials, Philadelphia

CORRELATIONS OF FRACTURE TOUGHNESS TO
OTHER MECHANICAL PROPERTIES OF Ti-6Al-4V

J. M. Partridge
Manager, Toronto Technical Laboratory
Titanium Metals Corporation of America
Toronto, Ohio

ABSTRACT

Plane strain fracture toughness values on Ti-6Al-4V mill products are shown to be inversely related to ultimate and yield strengths. Specific processes have given direct 1:1 relationships. Analyzing the data on a Ti-6Al-4V product mix produced by several different processes, however, results in only general trends useful to a mill producer but of no value for design. Also shown as general trends are the inverse relationships of fracture values with tensile ductility, notched tensile strength, and fatigue.

INTRODUCTION

Titanium Metals Corporation of America has been performing fracture toughness tests for a number of years. Since the early 1960's recommendations made by the ASTM E24 committee have been followed in order to generate useful data for designing improved processes on commercial alloys and developing new alloys for use in fracture toughness limited applications.

143

More Ti-6Al-4V has been tested by TIMET than any other
alloy because it is the most widely used alloy and therefore
serves as an excellent baseline for comparison to new processes or other alloys. Plus, of course, in the last two to
three years more and more customer specifications require
reporting a valid plane strain value on heavy section Ti-6Al-
4V products. This paper covers the data generated on heavy
section Ti-6Al-4V only.

During the many programs on Ti-6Al-4V, attempts have been
made to correlate fracture toughness with chemistry, processing, macro and micro structure, and other mechanical
properties. Specifically sought were correlations with standard mill data so one could predict the fracture toughness of
a given product of Ti-6Al-4V. For this paper, only the data
generated with recommended ASTM specimens and procedures are
presented. The two specimens used were the fatigue-cracked
notch-bend specimen and the compact tension specimen. Recently, most of the testing done by TIMET has been with the
CT (compact tension) specimen because it is the one normally
stipulated in customer specifications. However, both specimens give the same results if all validity requirements are
met.

The programs to be discussed cover a wide range of processing including working entirely in the beta field down to
working very low in the alpha-beta field. Chemistries were
also varied. Therefore, the microstructures vary markedly
and the yield strengths range from below 105 ksi to as high
as 145 ksi without the use of a solution treatment plus aging
cycle.

DISCUSSION

The first program to be discussed was a study done in
conjunction with the Naval Research Laboratory on the effects
of oxygen content and processing on plane strain fracture

toughness. Four commercial heats of Ti-6Al-4V were melted
with nominal oxygen contents of 0.06, 0.08, 0.12, and 0.16%,
respectively. The heats then were processed using beta and
alpha-beta forging followed by rolling to plate entirely in
the beta field, or at three successively lower temperatures
in the alpha-beta field. Therefore, strengths were affected
by both oxygen content and processing as shown in Fig. 1.
Corresponding to this range of strengths was a range of microstructures. The two microstructural extremes, shown in Fig.
2, are the completely transformed structure resulting from
working entirely in the beta field to the heavily worked
alpha-beta structure obtained by rolling at 1400°F.

Fracture toughness tests using the notch-bend specimen
were conducted on each plate in both the as-rolled condition
and after a 1350°F - 4 hr AC anneal. Figure 3 shows the results
of this study on the Ti-6Al-4V rolled low (1400°F) in the
alpha-beta field. Notice the range of strengths obtained by
varying both oxygen content and processing. In this plot the
actual fracture toughness values range from 65.3 ksi√inch for
the low strength material to 38.3 ksi√inch for the high
strength material. From the linearity of these plots the
fracture toughness of Ti-6Al-4V plate processed similarly
can be predicted. The key words of the above sentence are
"processed similarly," because another group of plates processed differently also will show linearity but the slope
of the curve will be different. For example, the other
processing extreme of this program was the beta field working,
with the results shown in Fig. 4. Here the actual fracture
values range from 64 ksi√inch to 55.9 ksi√inch. In this case,
the linear relationship is not as apparent, since the slope
is significantly different from the low temperature alpha-
beta rolled plates. The other two processes used in this
program, though not shown here, also gave linear plots with
slopes between the two shown in Fig. 4. The four different

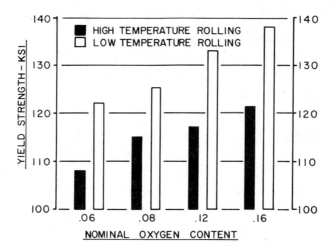

Fig. 1.   Strengthening variation in Ti-6Al-4V by varying both
          oxygen content and processing

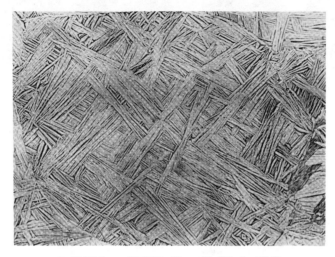

BETA FIELD ROLLED

1400 F ROLLED

Fig. 2. Structure of Ti-6Al-4V by beta and alpha-beta working

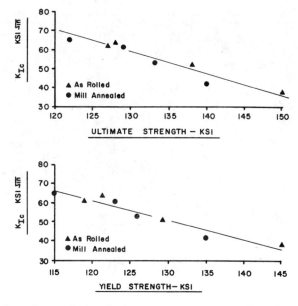

Fig. 3.   Low alpha-beta processed Ti-6Al-4V plate

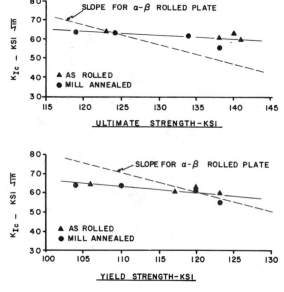

Fig. 4.   Beta processed Ti-6Al-4V plate

slopes are due to the four different microstructures obtained.
The effect of microstructures is quite pronounced and will
be discussed in more detail in the final section.

The next program to be discussed was a study to determine
the effects of Fe content on both fracture toughness and other
mechanical properties of Ti-6Al-4V. Although the purpose of
this paper is not to discuss chemical effects, the data obtained do fit the subject. The material used was Ti-6Al-4V
billet cut in half and then both halves were remelted -- one
half as is and the other half with additional Fe. The new
ingots then were conventionally forged and alpha-beta field
rolled to plate. Mill anneals were adjusted to give a range
in strength. The two extremes in microstructure are shown
in Fig. 5. Figure 5A shows the structure on air cooling from
1750°F and Fig. 5B shows the structure on furnace cooling
from 1750°F.

Figure 6 shows plots of the test data obtained. Here
the strength data plot linearly and separately for each Fe
level. Fracture values varied from 63 ksi$\sqrt{inch}$ to 53 ksi$\sqrt{inch}$.
In addition, the slopes shown match previous slopes obtained
on Ti-6Al-4V production plates conventionally alpha-beta
field processed. Note that the higher level Fe material does
give slightly higher strength and fracture toughness values.

Also shown in Fig. 6 is a plot of ductility with fracture
toughness. Frequently, a given program will result in reductions of area that appear related to fracture toughness,
even though there is considerable scattering of the data as
shown; yet, just as often there is no correlation at all.
Part of the reason is certainly due to microstructure and
part of it may be due to the inaccuracies of %RA measurements.
A subject for further study is why -- when there appears to
be a correlation -- the higher fracture toughness values correspond to the lowest ductilities?

250 X

A.   AIR COOLED FROM 1750F

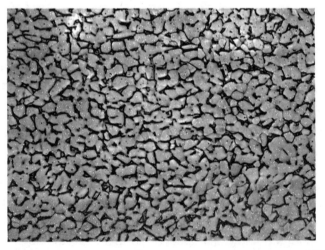

250 X

B.   FURNACE COOLED FROM 1750 F

Fig. 5.   Structure dependence on cooling rate in Ti-6Al-4V

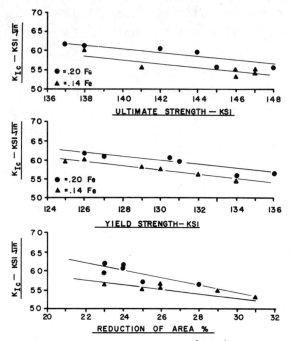

Fig. 6.   Fracture toughness of Ti-6Al-4V at two Fe levels

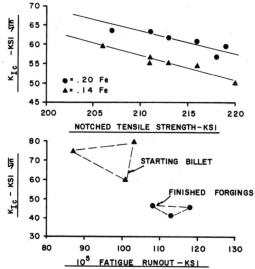

Fig. 7.   Fracture toughness of Ti-6Al-4V compared to notch
tensile and fatigue runout

So far the discussion has been limited to conventional
tensile data. Is fracture toughness related to second tier
mechanical properties such as notched tensile strength or
fatigue? Figure 7 shows some trends observed that are being
presented here because the same trends have been observed
more than once. The top graph shows fracture toughness
versus the notched strength for the Ti-6Al-4V plates with
the two Fe levels. It again appears that the higher Fe is
of some benefit. The trend shown is typical of conventionally
alpha-beta processed Ti-6Al-4V plate; i.e., high notched
tensile strengths do not correspond to high fracture toughness values.

The bottom curve shows general trends of fatigue versus
fracture toughness. In this program, Ti-6Al-4V billet produced in the mill using three different forging procedures
was tested both in fatigue and with compact-tension fracture
toughness specimens. The billet then was closed die forged
to a finished hub. The dashed lines are not significant,
but are only used to group the data points. The starting
billet in general had high fracture toughness values and
poorer fatigue performance. After closed die forging that
considerably refined the microstructure, the fatigue strength
improved significantly; but the fracture toughness dropped
to almost the same low level regardless of the original
billet forging process. Yield strengths in all cases averaged 125 ksi. The plot shown should be viewed in the light
of a general trend and not as a fixed correlation.

In fact, though one-to-one correlations of strength to
fracture toughness have been documented for controlled programs, if one considers all of the valid fracture toughness
values obtained on Ti-6Al-4V regardless of processing history,
it is obvious that the fracture toughness cannot be predicted
accurately by just examining other mechanical properties.
General trends are certainly noted but there is no substitute

for an actual plane strain fracture toughness test. For
example, Fig. 8 shows a toughness versus strength plot for
all of the programs discussed previously plus several additional values obtained from production mill orders. Obviously,
a specific strength will not give a specific fracture toughness value. The strength-fracture toughness trend, however,
is just as obvious.

The reason, of course, for not being able to establish
fixed, definite correlations is that microstructure plays a
major role during fracture. A very good example is shown in
Fig. 9. The top photomicrograph shows the center structure
of a 1.5 inch thick plate of Ti-6Al-4V that was alpha-beta
processed and then annealed to obtain recrystallization of
the alpha. Complete recrystallization did not occur, resulting in an almost continuous path of alpha for unimpeded crack
propagation. The fracture value of 55.2 ksi√inch is low for
heavy plate product processed in this manner. The bottom
microstructure shows the center of the very same plate after
it was re-annealed to obtain complete recrystallization. Now
nearly all recrystallized alpha grains are surrounded by beta
and transformed beta, which effectively blocks straight crack
growth. The fracture toughness value, therefore, was increased to 76.1 ksi√inch -- a 40% jump. Yet comparing the
tensile data would not give any indication that one structure
was so much tougher than the other.

In summary, what started out as a search for one-to-one
correlations between fracture toughness values and other
mechanical properties has really resulted in just the development of general trends. These trends are useful guidelines
to TIMET as a mill producer. From them, predictions for
different processes or new alloys can be made with reasonable
assurance that the predictions will be valid. For the designer, however, general trends are of no value. A valid test
must be made. Fracture toughness testing, then, is not only
going to stay, but it is going to increase in importance.

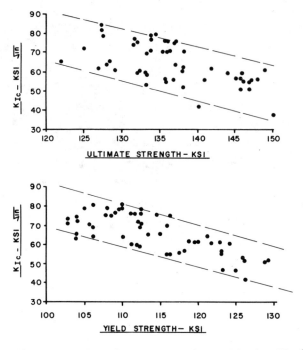

Fig. 8.   Fracture toughness vs strength in Ti-6Al-4V

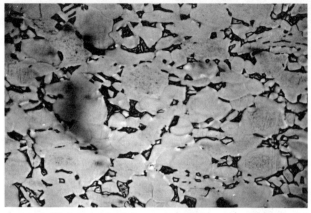

UNRECRYSTALLIZED   750 X

Ftu = 133.5 KSI

Fty = 122.4 KSI

% El = 16.0

% RA = 34.2

K_{Ic} = 55.2 KSI $\sqrt{in}$

RECRYSTALLIZED   750 X

Ftu = 136.5 KSI

Fty = 121.8 KSI

% El = 17.0

% RA = 36.0

K_{Ic} = 76.1 KSI $\sqrt{in}$

Fig. 9.   Effect of recrystallization on structure and toughness
in Ti-6Al-4V

SPECIFICATION REQUIREMENTS FOR FRACTURE TOUGHNESS

OF ENGINEERING MATERIALS

FRACTURE MECHANICS DESIGN REQUIREMENTS --
REVIEW AND REFLECTION

Nathan G. Tupper
Air Force Materials Laboratory

ABSTRACT

The fracture mechanics design requirements imposed by the USAF on new aircraft have occasioned
much discussion, controversy and misunderstanding
in their two years of existence. Despite the widespread resistance to the ideas and criteria embodied
by the requirements, it is clear at this point that
the fundamental objectives embraced are being realized, that much has been learned in the implementation of the existing requirements, and that similar
design criteria will be imposed on future aircraft.
This opportunity is taken to review the degree to
which those fundamental objectives have been attained
and to identify areas which may have not been ad-
dressed or in which weakness has become apparent.
The thrust of this discussion will be directed toward
the impact of fracture mechanics on the materials-
related activities, although some limited reference
will be made of necessity toward the attendant
structures-oriented function.

INTRODUCTION

Over the past twenty years, the increasing emphasis on
performance requirements for military aircraft has resulted
in strong pressure to maximize the structural efficiency,
customarily defined as minimum weight structure. Unfortunately, the approach most often taken to meet this goal has
been to use higher and higher strength materials at steadily
increasing design allowables coupled with extensive testing
to assure oneself of resulting structure possessing acceptable strength. As this cycle began to emerge, the problem
of fatigue and occasional early static fractures appeared
as the first major result. The so-called solution to the
problem of fatigue was the panacea of more structural testing, including first one, then two complete airframes, and
a catch phrase of better detail design. Although this approach has not solved the fatigue problem, it has provided
a mechanism whereby the structural design deficiencies can
be identified, i.e., by subjecting full scale airframes to
several times the anticipated number and type of flight and
ground loads, one can identify areas where the local stresses
are excessive. The high stresses can result from any number
of causes ranging from mistakes in design and stress analysis
to improper manufacturing operations. While design and analysis deficiencies can generally be corrected as a result of
fatigue test findings, manufacturing errors may very well
persist. The next step in the operation is to design new
structure, always heavier, which does not contain the deficiencies, test it, and install it on aircraft already built.
The unfortunate aspect of all this is that aircraft structures
have become almost unacceptably expensive, and the expense
of retrofitting aircraft with new structure has become almost prohibitive. For example, the process of redesign and
retrofit on the two most recent USAF aircraft has apparently

been accomplished by using the funds which would have been used to purchase additional flying articles.

Although the fatigue problems have steadily increased in number and severity, their occurrence has not seemed to slow the cycle of higher strength materials, higher design allowables, and reduced margins due to higher design stresses. The problem with uncovering structural deficiencies in fatigue testing now became steadily more acute in that fatigue cracks were beginning to cause complete failure of the test sections, and indeed aircraft in service, before they could be detected and repaired. These kinds of problems can be typified by two examples, i.e., an F-105 accident that was caused by a 1/8-inch fatigue crack emanating from a fuselage frame cutout, and an early F-111 fatigue failure that resulted from a fatigue crack slightly less than 3/4 inch long, originating in a fastener hole. As time progressed, this situation became a source of increasing concern to the top levels of the USAF. As is apparent, a series of directives from the Office of the Secretary of Defense caused a resurgence of interest in the concept of prototypes as a means of reducing to acceptable levels the cost of redesigning, retesting and retrofitting new structures. The situation peaked with the F-111 failure of December 1969 that was caused by a roughly elliptical defect approximately 1/4 inch deep and 7/8 inch long, a photomacrograph of which is shown in Fig. 1. Within two months of that accident, the Air Force activities charged with the responsibility for the development of new systems were directed by the Secretary of the Air Force to immediately implement procedures which would ensure a drastic reduction in the incidence of these kinds of problems. It was becoming clear that for future systems the approval of a production run of aircraft would be strongly dependent upon the completion of a highly successful structural test program. Obviously, then, some additional

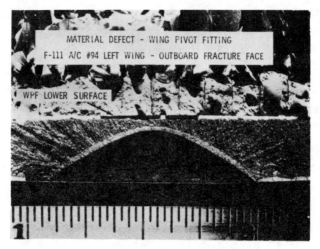

Fig. 1.   Defect causing failure of F-111

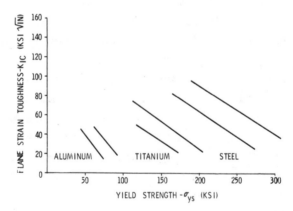

Fig. 2.   Trends in toughness variation

requirements were necessary in the structural design criteria, and fracture mechanics concepts were selected as the framework around which to build those requirements.

OBJECTIVES

In surveying the problem prior to actually preparing a requirement, the facts discussed above were analyzed carefully in order to distill some reasonably concrete conclusions concerning the nature of the problems that the objectives of a fracture mechanics requirement ought to address. Those conclusions can be quite quickly reached. The structural problems have been due to: (1) the use of high strength materials with little tolerance to damage of any kind; (2) the use of design stress levels that are too high in relation to the yield strength of the alloys used; and (3) manufacturing processes and the inspection function increasingly have been producing and passing into service parts with high stress concentrations of all kinds, parts which are located so that the resultant growing cracks are often not found in service until they have caused failure. It was apparent that the fracture mechanics requirement should be developed to avoid these deficiencies. It was necessary that the one overriding principle behind the new fracture mechanics requirements was that they be strong, comprehensive and as tightly contractual as possible. With regard to this point, guidance was available from the "lessons learned in the USAF" application of the Aircraft Structural Integrity Program.

Upon looking at the three basic conclusions outlined and considering what tools were offered by fracture mechanics and where the weakness in the fracture mechanics method appeared to be, a list of six objectives can be prepared which any fracture mechanics requirement must meet. The first objective is simply stated: the requirement as a whole must

result in the selection of higher toughness materials than
have been used in the recent past. In Fig. 2, showing the
well-known relation between yield strength and fracture
toughness, this objective is translated into moving upward
and probably to the left within each alloy classification.
The effect of this objective, then, is to increase the critical
crack length for a given design stress, thereby perhaps improving the possibility of finding cracks in service before
they become critical, and also possibly providing some increased life.

The second objective is also quite simply stated: any
set of fracture requirements should ensure the selection of
safe design stress levels. This objective speaks for itself,
but there are two basically different ways of accomplishing
this objective, and the choice made between them will be discussed below. The third objective is to provide incentives
for the use of multiple load path damage tolerant designs.
This objective could greatly improve the safety of a structure, i. e., greatly reduce the probability of a structure
completely losing its load carrying capability, but might
accomplish little to reduce the quantity of cracks and failures occurring in service, i.e., the in-service maintenance
problem.

The fourth objective, a complex item difficult to quantify, is to force all appropriate organizations involved in
design and construction of an airplane to work together in
the common goal of ensuring sound primary structure. While
this objective often sounds like "motherhood" it is nonetheless extremely important, and forms the heart of a proper
fracture mechanics requirement, as will become apparent below.
The fifth objective is to ensure the realization and acceptance of rational, quantified limits on the capability of nondestructive testing (NDT). The sixth objective is simply
stated: to provide incentives for the design of inspectable

structure. In order to write the best possible set of requirements, all of these objectives must be satisfied, but from
a materials and processes standpoint, the four objectives of
high toughness materials selection, integrating the organiza-
tional approach to fracture control, quantifying the NDT
capability, and designing for inspectability command the most
interest. With all these objectives in mind, the elements
of the existing USAF fracture mechanics requirement will be
dissected in order to ascertain how that requirement was
organized to satisfy the above stated objectives.

ELEMENTS OF THE EXISTING FRACTURE MECHANICS REQUIREMENT

There are some fundamental elements of the fracture
mechanics requirement that work together or independently to
approach the above objectives. The requirement is organized
into areas covering design, analysis, and test, and those
elements are spread throughout. The first element is that
the requirement forms one part of the structural design requirement contained in the second level contractual document,
and therefore can only be changed by formal contract change
procedures or by approved deviations. This element has caused
considerable controversy because of the uncertainties in some
of the analysis procedures and the data gaps for some of the
alloys and heat treatments. A particularly thorny problem
in this regard comes from the reluctance of the metal producers to guarantee minimum fracture toughness properties on
their products. Although much more will be said about this
later, it does seem, at first glance, a bit unreasonable to
levy contractual requirements on prime contractors when their
vendors and subcontractors are unwilling to support them,
but in view of the serious nature of the problem there is
really little choice. It must also be realized that fracture
mechanics procedures present a very tightly interdependent

group of individual aspects and that failure to properly
accomplish any one of them will greatly reduce the utility
of the whole.

The second element in the requirement is that of the
fracture mechanics analysis. In order to genuinely apply
fracture mechanics, the procedure is to start with an
initial crack and ensure that it does not grow to critical
size in a specified time period. The growth must take into
account the cyclic stress and chemical and thermal environments to which the particular component will be subjected.
Furthermore, in order to take proper advantage of the fracture mechanics procedure, the location and orientation of
the initial crack must be specified, that is, the life analysis must presume that the initial defect is most unfavorably
positioned with respect to the applied stresses and the
material properties. If this is not done, there is danger
that under the pressure of performance degradation the
structures engineer will assume an initial defect located
so as to result in the minimum weight impact, thereby completely negating the objective of obtaining safe design
stresses. There are major impacts for the materials engineer
in specifying an analysis procedure this thoroughly because
a new set of design allowable information is required for
materials selection. Data are needed on the cyclic crack
growth rates and static fracture properties of materials,
as well as on the effects of chemical and thermal environments on those properties. The data must be developed for
all applicable product forms (plate, forgings, extrusions
and sheet) as well as for weldments. Furthermore, the effects
of fabrication practices must be considered in the design
phase. While some of the ramifications of this objective may
seem difficult to satisfy because of the lack of existing
data, the data can be obtained in test programs, and the
importance of getting this data will be discussed below.

There are also some very important implications of all this in the structures side of the job, as in the case of how to treat load interaction effects in cyclic loading, and how to provide incentives for multiple load path design and/or inspectable designs, but these will not be treated in this paper.

The third element is concerned with the concept of initial crack size. It is clear from the above that the size of the initial crack presumed in the analysis plays fully as important a role as the more publicized da/dn and K_{Ic}, and must also be considered as a design allowable. Therefore, a_i must be put on a quantitative statistical basis in the same fashion as any design allowables. This is a highly significant element because it presents an entirely new philosophy to the Quality and Reliability Assurance (Q&RA) function and requires active cooperation between Q&RA, Design, and Materials and Processes.

The fourth major element, alluded to in the brief discussion of the second element above, is the one which holds the entire requirement together and puts in the necessary degree of control. This element requires that material procurement, fabrication processes, joining, inspection, etc., are all properly controlled so that every part which is finally installed in a structure in fact possesses the material properties assumed in the design phase. This element is essential for the simple reasons that fracture mechanics requirements are new, the conventional "A" and "B" allowables are not available in most cases, and very little is known about the possible effects of processing on the assumed fracture properties. This element has proven to be controversial and will be discussed below.

ASSESSMENT

The implementation of the fracture mechanics requirement has provided insight into strong and weak areas of the
requirement as originally prepared. Some of the weak areas
can be viewed as serious, and will be strengthened in the
requirements for future aircraft; other areas have seemed
to function reasonably well. In order to fully satisfy all
the elements discussed above, the requirement was made to
include provisions touching on the major functions: design,
analysis, and test.

The first element, i.e., to make the other three elements
of the requirements fully and tightly contractual, has proved
to be absolutely correct. Each step in a fracture mechanics
analysis is strongly dependent upon another step, and the result is only as good as its weakest portion. From a practical standpoint, this was the only unambiguous method of
telling our prime contractors, subcontractors and vendors
that the USAF was completely serious. The ramifications of
this firm commitment for design, analysis and test to the
manufacturing, material and Q&RA functions have been many.
The recognition of the need for this level of commitment is
readily seen in the decision to update the applicable Mil=
itary Standards and Specifications to reflect this approach.

The second element encompasses the analysis portion directly, as presented above, and of the four elements it has
proven to be most in need of improvement. Several aspects,
however, were properly written and will be continued. These
have to do with how the analysis is required to be performed.
An initial crack of specified size is presumed present initially in the structure, located in the most unfavorable
location with respect to the stress fields and the material
properties. The discussion concerning initial crack length
is deferred to the next paragraph. The analysis must then

predict the growth of that defect to the critical length
within a specified time in the appropriate chemical, thermal,
and stress environment to which that portion of the component
in which the defect is located will be subjected. This is
clearly a case of applying fracture mechanics to its full
extent, and has pointed out some glaring gaps in our knowledge.

One of the very first things pointed out was that the
chemical and thermal environments to which parts are subjected are not well known, so some rough approximations had
to be made. This information gap desperately needs filling,
particularly in the case of chemical environment, but it is
difficult when all the possible locations are considered in
the various kinds of aircraft, and the actual chemical and
thermal environments to which components in aircraft in
service are subjected are not known. However, because of
the sometimes drastic effect certain real environments have
on crack growth rate (see Fig. 3), this portion of the analysis is required and will remain. It is recognized, however,
that the materials selection task during preliminary design
can be made quite difficult when the necessary environmental data is meager. One desirable result is that this
requirement has forced the selection of higher toughness
materials, but it is somewhat ironic that the basic materials
property data, particularly where environments are involved,
are very scarce. To illustrate, the basic airframe structural steel in a late developmental aircraft is 9Ni-4Co-.20C,
selected for its high toughness. At the time of its selection, extensive literature searches were able to uncover less
than six crack growth rate tests. The success of this requirement in driving the selection of higher toughness materials is shown in Fig. 4, which is a replot of Fig. 1 on which
have been placed circles indicating the lower wing skin aluminum and structural steel alloys selected for a late develop-

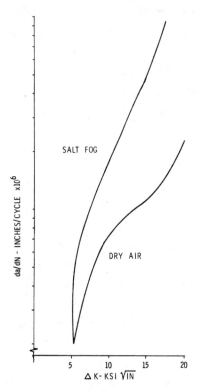

Fig. 3. Effect of environment on crack growth rate

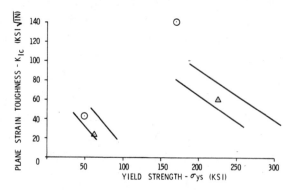

Fig. 4. Application of higher toughness materials

mental aircraft as well as triangles representing similar
selections made for the F-111. One other decision which
seems to have been correct was that of applying this analysis
to the entire structure. All structures subjected to substantial tensile loads must be analyzed for longevity under
these requirements.

The weaknesses in this analysis element have been in its
design aspects, which are covered thoroughly in the paper by
Wood. (1) Insufficient incentives were provided for inspectable designs and multiple load path designs with adequate residual strengths. Future fracture mechanics requirements should provide incentives in terms of specifying
longer critical crack lengths for monolithic structure and
reducing the life requirements for structures that are inspectable. The term inspectable structures when applied to
in-service aircraft refers to structures where the damage
is easily visible, preferably in the sense of a walk-around
inspection. Most frequently, this inspectable structure will
be multiple load path where inspections will be performed in
an attempt to locate failed members, although there may be
designs where the critical crack lengths are sufficiently
long to be detectable, analogous to the leak before break
criterion. In addition, initial flaw shapes and locations
need greater specification.

The third element, having to do with initial crack
length, has proved to be an interesting one. As the starting
point for the fracture mechanics analysis, its importance
cannot be overestimated. In defining the original initial
crack length requirements, thorough investigation of available information revealed many grandiose claims by NDT
specialists, but little hard data to support or negate
these claims other than the excellent work of Packman, et al
(2), some of which is summarized in Fig. 5. From those data,
it is clear that for his program crack lengths below about

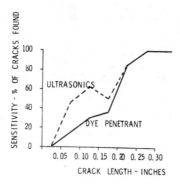

Fig. 5. Flaw detection capability (Ref 2)

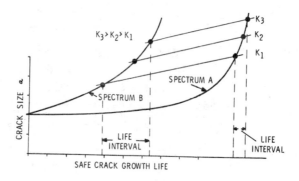

Fig. 6. Effect of fracture toughness on life

0.15 inch will not be found more than about half the time.
The basic capability of NDT was therefore presumed to be
approximately 0.15 inch. Although the desired detection
capability is much greater than 50%, it was felt that the
result of the fourth element, discussed below, would tend
to boost the detection capability up slightly, and that the
starting flaw size could then be set at 0.150 inch, which
has been done for the analysis of components where customary
manufacturing inspection will be accomplished. NDT en-
thusiasts can be heard to claim detection capabilities an
order of magnitude less than this, although such capabilities have never been demonstrated anywhere in a statistical
fashion, and recognizing this, provision has been made for
allowing the use of smaller initial defects in analysis
provided the capability to detect those defects has been
demonstrated. As finally settled upon, this demonstration
program must use production equipment, condition and personnel to demonstrate that a defect larger than that selected
will be detected with at least 90% probability with 95%
confidence, which puts the initial flaw size on the same
basis as a "B" allowable. Experience has taught us that the
demonstration must use tight defects, such as fatigue cracks,
which must be located in smooth plates as well as emanating
from fastener holes. It should be noted that such a demonstration program to be performed to the necessary statistics
will require on the order of 250 observations per material
per inspection procedure, which can be a lengthy and expensive process. In addition to satisfying the objective
toward which it is aimed, continued application of this idea
is proving to be a strong motivation for upgrading the capability of NDT in a quantitative way.

The fourth element, which involves the development and
implementation of those activities necessary to properly control material and manufacturing, is deserving of attention

both as to what activities it has caused and as to why those
many activities are necessary. The crux of the matter is
that this element pushes itself into many relatively unex-
plored areas, which is caused by the seemingly straightforward requirement that material in the actual hardware
possesses properties equal to or better than those assumed
in the analysis. Making this element tightly contractual,
rather than a general hand-waving statement, is what has
caused it to be both the most controversial, especially
among materials people, and probably the most important of
the three technical elements. That has happened because it
has largely accomplished the fourth objective above by attack-
ing the interfaces and forcing all related organizations and
functions to communicate with each other and, at least part
of the time, to work together. Some of these interfaces will
now be examined in some detail.

The interface between structural analysis and Q&RA starts
with the determination of initial crack length, continues
with determinations as to which structures are inspectable
and which are not, and how to change the latter into the
former and thereby gain weight reduction. It will also surface during the inevitable discrepant material review activities. The latter activity should be influential toward re-
jecting parts that are discrepant because of fracture mechanics
considerations, although it will be a few years before that
information is available. The structural analysis interface
with materials and processes has been strongly influenced by
this element which enforces frequent communication. Because
of the limited data on the materials of interest, extensive
data generation has been required. Furthermore, the material
and processing selection function has provided increased
visibility to the materials engineer because of his opinions
and data concerning the relative attractiveness among many
competing alloys, heat treatments, product forms, joining

processes and fabrication details. For example, small differences in K_{Ic} values can now have a strong influence on weld
process selection, and the choice between extrusions and plate
for wing skins may be made on the basis of crack growth rate
in salt water. These kinds of decisions are largely foreign
to the designer or stress analyst, and the opinion and data
of the materials engineer may be eagerly solicited. In order
to satisfy this element, the materials engineer must get
from structures what the design details are so that he can
carry out his other interface functions and provide the necessary feedback to design.

Once the design details begin to emerge, this element
produces an expanding network of interfaces, essentially all
of which depend on the materials and processes (M&P) group
for support. For the sake of clarity some of these interfaces will be described from the M&P group standpoint. The
starting point is the definition of which parts are fracture
critical or would become fracture critical if the fracture
properties of the material involved were not controlled. The
basics of the definition of which parts are fracture critical evolve down to whether or not part failure would cause
loss of control of the aircraft, whether or not the part is
actually sized by the fracture mechanics analysis, and what
the spread in fracture properties is around the given allowable. The first two decisions are structures decisions,
but the third is the responsibility of M&P. The M&P function
on this point really starts with the definition of design
allowables. One of the most frustrating aspects to implementation of these requirements has been lack of data on the
higher toughness materials. One is overwhelmed by the data
on 7075-T6 products, D6aC at the 220-240 ksi level, and Ti-
6Al-4V of uncontrolled microstructure, but is hard pressed
to uncover da/dn data on 2219-T8 products, any data on PH 13-
8Mo at the H1100 temper, and data on Ti-6Al-4V where the

microstructure has been controlled to the necessary extent.
So, the M&P function has been to select in advance preliminary design allowables which can be verified in test programs, since the fourth element is enforcing the requirement to make sure the proper allowables are used in the
design function. At this point the M&P specialist turns to
the material function for answers in terms of what the metal
producers will guarantee, but those answers have been, until
recently, of no help at all. Metal producers have simply
not stepped up to the problem of what controls can be im-
plemented to attain and maintain consistently reasonable
levels of appropriate fracture properties. The job of the
prime contractor would be greatly eased if the metal producers could provide products with improved guaranteed
properties. Most of the involved process to be described
subsequently is a direct result of the huge disparity between what K_{Ic} is guaranteed and what K_{Ic} seems to be reasonably attainable in rough "B" allowable terms. To be sure,
this is asking a great deal of the metal producers in such
a short period of time, but as it becomes apparent to even
the most recalcitrant that these requirements are here to
stay it is expected that this situation will improve.

The problem now facing the M&P function is compounded
by the realization that the design function is using a K_{Ic}
value of, for example, 25 ksi$\sqrt{\text{inch}}$ for an aluminum alloy,
which is on the low side of the scatter in available data
for that alloy, but the metal producer will only guarantee
19 ksi$\sqrt{\text{inch}}$. Of course, if the alloy could be purchased
guaranteed to 25 ksi$\sqrt{\text{inch}}$, the M&P function would be to
simply check out the processing, ensure preparation of a
respectable group of processing specifications, and prepare
to do some sampling along the way to make sure nothing is
going wrong. However, knowing that they have supplied an
allowable that seemed reasonably attainable, the M&P function

must now do everything possible to ensure that number is attained, and they must do it with starting material of unknown toughness. The only technically sound solution to the problem is to know the properties of the starting product (plate, extrusion, forging, etc.), which means actually testing the starting product at a high rate, as frequently as every piece. The objective is to build up a bank of fracture toughness data to correlate with microstructure and other mechanical properties at some future time; the sooner the better.

Assistance from the metal producers in this task is urgently needed. While this is a most desirable task, the problem, from the system development viewpoint, is to find the fine line between what is necessary and what amounts to research. Nevertheless, M&P must now interface with manufacturing to ascertain anticipated fabrication practices in order to develop any necessary test programs for determining the effect of each fabrication practice on fracture toughness properties. In the long run it would be most desirable to know the effects on da/dn in air and environments, on K_{Iscc}, as well as on K_{Ic} and K_c which could be expected from cold forming as a function of deformation, from various warm temperature heat treatments, from elevated temperature forming, as well as from all the candidate joining practices. However, in the short run there is simply too much to learn to control on all three properties, so the decision was made to just control on the so-called "static" properties, K_{Ic} and K_c. The most desirable situation for the long run is to control by microstructure after sufficient correlation has been done, and beginnings of this are already appearing. The control on K_{Ic} is not inappropriate, however, since that property describes the end point in the cracking process. As shown by Wood, Ref 3, the time to failure from an initial flaw can be significantly dependent upon K_{Ic}, although there may be

differences in effort, as shown in Fig. 6, depending upon the
shape and severity of the spectrum.

Again, because of the strong contractual nature of all
this it was envisioned that this fourth element would result
in the implementation of a documentation scheme where fracture
critical parts would be closely monitored every step of the
process from billet stage or earlier up through recording of
aircraft tail number the part was installed in. This was
expected because the requirement calls for proof of con-
formance testing on the design verification test articles,
and in the event such testing is unsuccessful, full trace-
ability would seem mandatory.

The fourth element, then, has definitely proven its
worth. It has forced communication among the various functions involved in design and manufacturing. It has served
notice to the metal producers and metalworkers that these
kinds of requirements are seriously levied. It has drawn
strong attention to the general lack of correlation between
the microstructural features of metals and the appropriate
fracture toughness properties. Finally, it has forced close
scrutiny of each manufacturing process every fracture critical part will be subjected to, and should therefore provide
some spin-off improvement in the care with which fracture
critical parts will be handled.

SUMMARY

In this paper an attempt has been made to state and
justify the objectives of a proper set of design, analysis
and test requirements based on fracture mechanics principles,
to present those elements included in the current set of
requirements which are felt necessary to satisfy those objectives, and to provide a discussion of the ramifications
of those elements as well as an assessment of how well those

elements have functioned. The six stated objectives and the author's assessment follow:

1. Selection of higher toughness materials. This objective has been satisfied.

2. Obtain safe design stress levels. It is perhaps somewhat early as yet to assess this objective, but an initial opinion is that it has only partially been achieved.

3. Provide incentives for multiple load path structure having the required level of residual strength. Additional incentives are needed.

4. Enforce integration of applicable functions - fracture control program. This objective is being satisfied.

5. Ensure realization and acceptance of rational and quantified NDT limits. At this point, it appears that this objective will be reached.

6. Provide incentives for the design of inspectable structure. Additional incentives seem to be necessary.

References

1. Wood, H. A., "Fracture Control Considerations in Air-craft Structural Design", in this book

2. Packman, P. F., et al, AFML-TR-68-32, "The Applicability of a Fracture Mechanics-Nondestructive Testing Design Criterion", May 1968

3. Wood, H. A., AFFDL-TR-71-89, "Fracture Control Procedures for Aircraft Structural Integrity", July 1971

EVALUATION OF Ti-6Al-4V FOR
SPECIFICATION REQUIREMENTS

George H. Hilton
Grumman Aerospace Corporation
Bethpage, New York

ABSTRACT

Fracture testing anomalies were encountered
when first applying ASTM methods of determining
fracture toughness to Ti-6Al-4V annealed material.
Due to the importance of the parameter to the design of critical airframe members, this and other
fracture-related characteristics were further investigated. These included plane strain fracture
toughness and crack growth as functions of plate
thickness, tensile strength and environment. The
relationship between toughness and crack growth
rates and their effect on stress level and service
life were shown to be of prime importance in establishing NDI levels. While a connection between
toughness and other physical, chemical and metallurgical properties was sought, a background of
toughness values was collected as a quality check
on incoming material. Although a specific cause-
and-effect relationship between fracture toughness
and other parameters has not been found, sufficient
knowledge and confidence were gained by the user
and by the producer to permit purchase of material
with guaranteed toughness properties.

The goal of the military aircraft designer is a strong, light-weight structure with maximum resistance to the growth of unavoidable inherent flaws. He cannot achieve this goal when forced to use materials of unknown damage and flaw tolerance characteristics. He must, therefore, work with the materials suppliers to insure that his requirements are realistic, fully understood, and within the suppliers' capabilities. One instance of such collaboration, the development and specification of fracture toughness of Ti-6Al-4V for the F-14 wing center section, is described in this paper.

The F-14 wing center section (Fig. 1) is the main attachment point for the wings and contains the pivots about which the wings rotate to achieve a variable sweep geometry. It consists of a titanium box structure approximately 3 feet wide by 1½ feet high and 21 feet long containing three major dihedral junctions, front and aft beams, top and bottom covers and a number of internal bulkheads. The outboard ends are terminated by four semi-circular platters which act as bearing retainers. The section is fabricated from Ti-6Al-4V annealed plate or forged stock procured by proprietary material specifications similar to military specifications. The box-like structure is built-up by a series of electron beam welds into major subassemblies and finally into the completed structure. During build-up it undergoes a number of thermal stress relief cycles, etching procedures to remove the resulting surface contamination, and nondestructive inspections by dye penetrant, ultrasonic and radiographic methods.

Preliminary design requirements for a new aircraft include such items as mission, performance, configuration, weight, life, structural geometry and loading spectra. From these inputs evolve requirements for various elements of construction, stress levels and detail construction configuration. Finally, the materials selection is based on

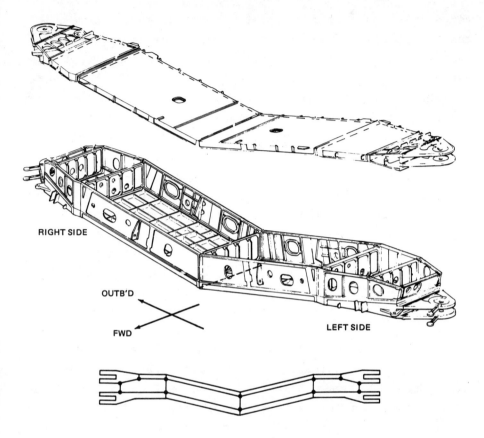

RIGHT SIDE

OUTB'D

FWD

LEFT SIDE

Fig. 1.   F-14 wing center section

compatible properties, inspection procedures and procurement limitations. After completion of the above, detail
evaluation of Ti-6Al-4V, the tentatively chosen material,
began.

Due to a great lack of information, one area chosen for
initial testing was fracture toughness. Since the then-exist-
ing plane strain toughness testing procedures were developed
for steel and aluminum alloys, early investigators found
some anomalies during the K_{Ic} testing of annealed Ti-6Al-4V.
Specimen configuration selected for standardization was the
compact coupon due to its more efficient use of material.
Initial testing of small fatigue-cracked bend coupons (Table
1) indicated low toughness (K_Q) with considerable indications
of shear failure. The use of larger compact coupons with
a thickness of 1¼ inches appeard to yield valid results
(Table 2) while sub-sized compact coupons machined from
broken halves of the larger coupons gave numerically similar
results but considerable shear lip on the fracture surface.
Further testing indicated (Fig. 2) that sub-sized coupons
may indicate values both above and below K_{Ic}. The selection
of a 1¼ inch base compact coupon assured us of valid results
within the anticipated range of toughness.

Incoming plate material was then tested with assurance
of reasonable test techniques. Variations of finished plate
thickness (Fig. 3) and other mechanical properties were noted.
An inverse relationship of fracture toughness and yield
strength (Fig. 4) became apparent but the width of the scatter band would indicate that other factors are also involved.

Microstructural changes (Fig. 5) were noted with changes
in mechanical properties. Toughness variations were noted
with such factors as mill rolling procedures and interstitial content. The most obvious is oxygen content, which
in small amounts is beneficial to toughness but causes a loss
in tensile properties.

Table 1 Annealed Ti-6Al-4V: 5/8 Inch Thick Plate, Precracked Notched Bend Specimens, 1/2 Inch Base, F_{ty} – 148.5 KSI

Specimen Direction	K_{IC}	Percent Shear In Fracture
RW-1	47.7 KSI$\sqrt{\text{In.}}$	~ 75%
RW-2	50.7	~ 75%
RW-3	47.9	~ 75%
RW-4	47.9	~ 75%
RW-5	48.2	~ 75%
	Avg.: 48.5	
WR-1	59.9 KSI$\sqrt{\text{In}}$	15 to 20
WR-2	62.1	15 to 20
WR-3	60.1	10 to 15
WR-4	63.8	15
WR-5	61.1	15
	Avg.: 61.4	

All Tests Valid by $B > 2.5 \left(\dfrac{K_{IC}}{F_{ty}}\right)^2$ Criterion

Table 2 Annealed Ti-6Al-4V: 3 1/2 Inch Thick Plate, F_{ty} = 126.3(L) and 132.2(T)

Compact Tension 1 1/4 Inch Base		Compact Tension 1/2 Inch Base (1)	Four Point Bend 1/2 Inch Base (1)	
RW-1	78.5 KSI√In	63.7 KSI√In	RW-1S	63.2 KSI√In.
RW-2	70.4		RW-2S	72.6
RW-3	81.9	72.0	RW-3S	65.6
RT-1	72.3 KSI√In	80.1 KSI√In	RT-1S	78.6 KSI√In.
RT-2	87.0		RT-2S	70.6
RT-3	84.2	71.3	RT-3S	75.3
WT-1	75.9 KSI√In	68.2 KSI√In	WT-1S	70.3 KSI√In.
WT-2	81.3		WT-2S	56.9
WT-3	73.5	65.6	WT-3S	69.7

(Compact Tension 1/2 Inch Base column: the RW, RT, and WT groups are each bracketed and labeled "Machined From" with an arrow pointing to the corresponding 1 1/4 Inch Base specimens.)

(1) All 1/2 Inch Base Specimens Invalid.

$$B < 2.5 \left(\frac{K_{IC}}{F_{ty}}\right)^2$$

All specimens had shear in less than 10% of the fracture.

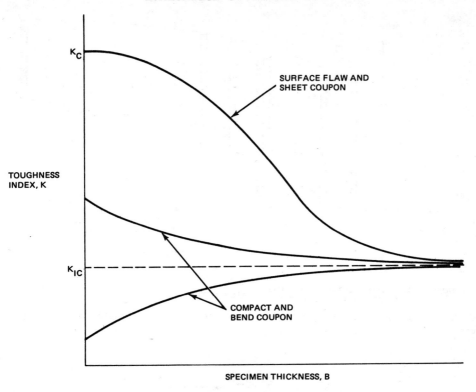

Fig. 2. Specimen size effects

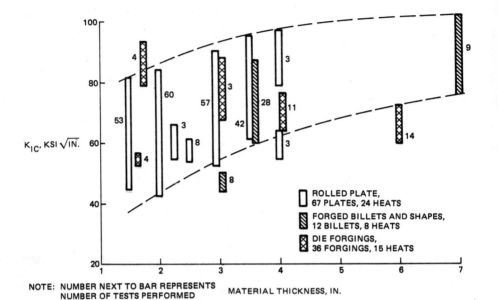

NOTE: NUMBER NEXT TO BAR REPRESENTS   MATERIAL THICKNESS, IN.
      NUMBER OF TESTS PERFORMED

Fig. 3.   Annealed Ti-6A1-4V: plane strain fracture toughness
          (K_{Ic}) vs material thickness

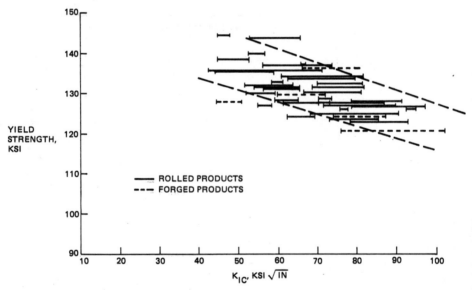

Fig. 4.   Annealed Ti-6A1-4V: plane strain fracture toughness
          (K_{Ic}) vs tensile yield strength

ROLLED 3½" X 16" X 35"
(α - β TO 3½)
HEAT K 1964
PO 9-87457
O_2 = .18%

K_{IC} = 76.9 KSI $\sqrt{IN.}$ (RW)
         81.2 KSI $\sqrt{IN.}$ (RT)
         76.9 KSI $\sqrt{IN.}$ (WT)

	L	I
F_{TU}	134.3	142.6
F_{TY}	126.3	132.2
e	11.5	10.5
RA	22.5	23.1

A

ROLLED 2" X 36" X 96"
(α - β 5" TO 2")
HEAT K 1811
PO 9-82774
O_2 = .19%

K_{IC} = 47.8 KSI $\sqrt{IN.}$ (WR)

	L	I
F_{TU}	143.5	152.5
F_{TY}	132.5	139.1
e	17.5	15.5
RA	33.0	24.4

B

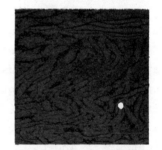

ROLLED 2½" X 40" X 96"
(α - β 5" TO 2½)
HEAT K 1683
PO 9-82774
O_2 = .17%

K_{IC} = 60 KSI $\sqrt{IN.}$ (WR)

	L	T
F_{TU}	140.6	143.5
F_{TY}	130.9	135.0
e	15.5	15.0
RA	29.7	24.5

C

ROLLED 3" X 40" X 65"
(α - β 6" TO 3")
HEAT K 1950
PO 9-87455
O_2 = .16%

K_{IC} = 77.3 KSI $\sqrt{IN.}$ (WR)

	L	T
F_{TU}	135.2	134.3
F_{TY}	124.3	125.7
e	17.0	10.0
RA	30.5	32.5

D

MAG: 250X

Fig. 5. Properties of four Ti-6Al-4V heats

K_{Ic} testing was carried out (Table 3) on material used for construction of the first four wing center sections. These would be used in the first two flight vehicles and for component structural test articles. Material for further toughness testing was processed along with the first four units and tested after all operations had been performed. While variations in K_{Ic} can be noted between the "A" and the "B" groups, no significant trend was evident. Material from various forging procedures (various amounts of work done in β and in the $\alpha - \beta$ fields) was tested and the results relayed to forging vendors for proprietary process improvement. Fracture testing also was performed on representative electron beam (EB) welded material during wing center section fabrication (Table 4). The results were similar to data generated during evaluation of the joining process and show a normal statistical distribution.

A knowledge of both flaw growth rates and K_{Ic} are required to define structure life. Flaw growth rate studies of Ti-6Al-4V were performed on both base and EB welded material under various conditions of loading spectra, limit stress and environment. Variations in spectra had minor effects on lifetime (Fig. 6) even though spectrum B contained an interdispersal of compressive loads not found in spectrums A and C. Variations in limit stress and location of the flaw with respect to welds had considerable effects on the shape of the growth rate curves (Fig. 7). As a result of lower toughness in EB weld as compared to base material, stresses in the welded areas were depressed to equate critical crack size in both welded and nonwelded areas. A jet fuel environment may tend to inhibit growth rate whereas salt water greatly accelerates growth.

Growth rate data and typical K_{Ic} values were combined to yield information (Fig. 8) on the maximum initial flaw size that would not cause premature failure. With such

Table 3 Material Toughness Investigations: Results Of Tests Run On Material Used On First Four Wing Center Sections

P/N	Name	Plate Thick. (In)	K_{IC}, KSI $\sqrt{in.}$ Avg "A" (Raw Material)				Avg "B" (In Process)			
			TB2	A/C 1	S1	A/C 2	TB2	A/C 1	S1	A/C 2
A51B21550-11	Inner Top	2-3	70	86	79	70	76	81	74	69
A51B21550-12	Lug	2-3	71	70	79	86	69	80	73	-
A51B21551-13	Inner Bottom	2-3	85	70	71	72	76	76	62	-
A51B21551-14	Lug	2-3	85	71	74	72	83	71	74	-
A51B21516-13	Outer Bottom	1 1/2-3	66	82	71	71	72	75	63	-
A51B21516-14	Lug	1 1/2-3	66	72	86	73	67	68	66	63
A51B21540-11	Outer Top	1 1/2-2	72	69	69	69	78	71	70	77
A51B21540-12	Lug	1 1/2-2	66	72	69	84	70	76	78	84
A51B21522-11	L/H Lower Inb'd Cover	3 1/2	77	85	94	66	67	87	67	67
A51B21600-11	R/H Lower Inb'd Cover	3 1/2	78	77	80	70	69	75	-	-

Table 4 W.C.S. – Weld Fracture Toughness Data: First Four Production Units

P/N	Name	Weld No.	Avg K_{IC} KSI$\sqrt{In.}$			
			TB2	A/C 1	S1	A/C 2
A51B21600-11 A51B21515-14	Lower Inb'd Cover Lower Outb'd Cover	30	37.4	44.1	37.9	30.8
A51B21600-11 A51B21522-11	R/H Lwr Inb'd Cover L/H Lwr Inb'd Cover	33	35.9	45.3	44.2	32.0
A51B21515-14 A51B21551-14	Lwr Outb'd Cover Inner Btm Lug	58	38.6	34.2	30.3	37.9
A51B21515-13 A51B21551-13	Lwr Outb'd Cover Inner Btm Lug	59	40.7	37.1	33.1	---
A51B21515-14 A51B21516-14	Lwr Outb'd Cover Outer Btm Lug	60	40.2	32.4	32.2	41.6
A51B21515-13 A51B21516-13	Lwr Outb'd Cover Outer Btm Lug	61	42.9	33.1	35.9	41.8
A51B21515-13 A51B21522-11	Lwr Outb'd Cover Lwr Inb'd Cover	90	37.8	43.9	33.4	38.9
A51B21550-11 A51B21542-11	Inner Top Lug Outb'd Top Cover	53	35.4	34.2	35.3	34.7
A51B21550-12 A51B21542-12	Inner Top Lug Outb'd Top Cover	54	37.0	33.9	---	---
A51B21540-11 A51B21542-11	Outer Top Lug Outb'd Top Cover	55	38.1	40.7	38.0	39.9
A51B21540-12 A51B21542-12	Outer Top Lug Outb'd Top Cover	56	40.1	36.3	---	---

P_{MIN} (% P_{LIN})	P_{MAX} (% P_{LIM})	CYCLES/95.5 HR
A 0	41.6	1240
0	62.4	497
0	88.2	141
0	104	30
0	124.8	1
C 0	20.8	2860
0	41.6	1240
0	62.4	497
0	83.2	141
0	104	30
0	124.8	1

P_{MIN} (% P_{LIN})	P_{MAX} (% P_{LIM})	CYCLES/200 HR (CYCLES/2000 HR)
B −51.2	20.8	3
−73.0	20.8	0 (1)
10.4	41.6	2238
−10.4	41.6	161
−31.3	41.6	1 (2)
−52.1	41.6	0 (2)
10.4	62.4	1138
−10.4	62.4	82
−31.3	62.4	0 (6)
−52.1	62.4	0 (1)
10.4	83.2	306
−10.4	83.2	22
−31.3	83.2	0 (2)
10.4	104	47
10.4	104	3 (4)
10.4	124.8	2
−10.4	124.8	0 (2)

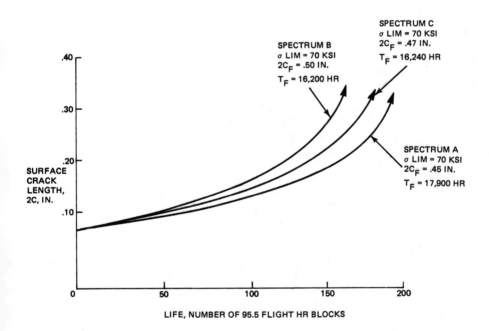

SPECTRUM B
σ LIM = 70 KSI
2C_F = .50 IN.
T_F = 16,200 HR

SPECTRUM C
σ LIM = 70 KSI
2C_F = .47 IN.
T_F = 16,240 HR

SPECTRUM A
σ LIM = 70 KSI
2C_F = .45 IN.
T_F = 17,900 HR

SURFACE CRACK LENGTH, 2C, IN.

LIFE, NUMBER OF 95.5 FLIGHT HR BLOCKS

Fig. 6.   Variations of F-14 wing fatigue spectra

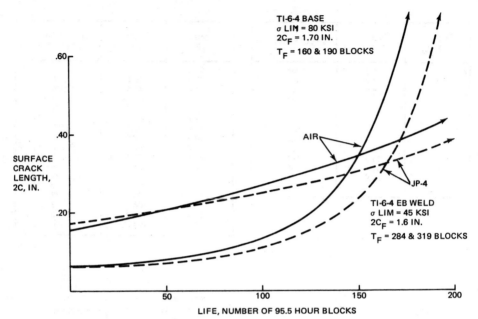

Fig. 7.   Environmental flaw growth rate

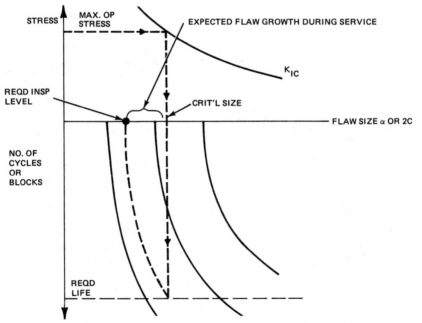

Fig. 8.   Fracture-flaw propagation relation

information the margin between the smallest flaw to be
detected by nondestructive inspection (NDI) and the largest
initial flaw size that will not grow to catastrophic dimensions within aircraft flight life may be determined. K_{Ic}
values calculated from the residual strength of flaw growth
coupons (Table 5) also are of interest, since the large coupon
containing a surface flaw is geometrically similar to service
conditions. Compact coupons indicated a lower K_{Ic} value than
residual strength derived K_{Ic} data.

Environmentally affected toughness data also was derived
from the compact coupons under both dynamic and static loading (Fig. 9). Limited testing indicates that susceptibility
to certain corrosive environments is closely related to plate
fabrication directions. In many cases crack propagation
directions did not remain normal to loading directions.

With additional background in forging parameters and
their effect on fracture toughness, the quality of Ti-6Al-4V
forgings has risen to the point where the forging producer
is willing to accept procurement specifications containing
fracture toughness requirements. With the knowledge of
fracture testing results and the fixing of forgings temperatures and reductions, the producer was confident of meeting
the fracture property requirements. A recent survey taken
of wing center section forgings (Table 6) indicates that
toughness values compatible with design requirements are
being met by suppliers.

Table 5 Fracture Properties from Large Surface Flaw Coupons
Correlate Well with Results from Compact Tension
Coupons Used for In-House Material Evaluation. Compact
Tension Tests Appear to be Conservative

Material	Surface Flaw Coupon, w = 4.5", t = 1.00"	Compact Tension Coupon B = 1.00"
Ti-6-4 Base Metal	80.2 KSI$\sqrt{\text{In}}$.	73.2 KSI$\sqrt{\text{In}}$.
Ti-6-4 EB Weld	44.5 KSI$\sqrt{\text{In}}$.	38.5 KSI$\sqrt{\text{In}}$.

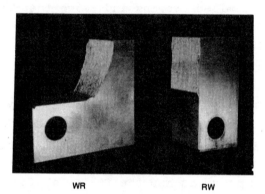

WR   RW

SUSTAINED LOAD IN SEA WATER

ENVIRONMENT	WR	RW
AIR KSI $\sqrt{\text{IN}}$. (K$_{IC}$)	55.8	52.3
SEA WATER KSI $\sqrt{\text{IN}}$.	62.4	53.2
SUST LOAD AIR KSI $\sqrt{\text{IN}}$.	54.6	34.7
SUST LOAD N$_2$ (DRY)	58.9	34.3
SUST LOAD SEA WATER	48.0	24.9

Fig. 9. Fracture testing in aggressive environments

Table 6 Results of Tests Performed on Prolongations From
Ti-6Al-4V Forgings Used for Later Wing Center
Section Fabrication

Part	Supplier	No. of Forgings Tested	Avg K_{IC}	Range of K_{IC}
A51B21533 Lower Outboard Cover	A	26	69 KSI$\sqrt{\text{in.}}$	60-84
A51B21537 Lower Inboard Cover	B	16	72 KSI $\sqrt{\text{in.}}$	65-83
A51B21557 Top Outboard Cover	A	5	64 KSI $\sqrt{\text{in.}}$	64-67
A51B45514 Lower Wing Pivot	C	9	90 KSI $\sqrt{\text{in.}}$	86-97
A51B21677 Ring Rolled Forging	C	6	92 KSI $\sqrt{\text{in.}}$	88-105
A51B21678 Ring Rolled Forging Top Lugs	C	5	91 KSI $\sqrt{\text{in.}}$	86-94

EFFECT OF CLEANLINESS AND PROCESS VARIABLES ON THE FRACTURE TOUGHNESS OF 4340 AND 300M BILLETS

M. G. H. Wells and J. J. Hauser
Colt Industries, Crucible Inc.,
Materials Research Center
I. Perlmutter
Air Force Materials Laboratory

ABSTRACT

Plane strain fracture toughness data for billets of the high strength steels 4340 and 300M produced by different melt practices are presented. While fracture toughness does improve somewhat in cleaner steels, the property most sensitive to non-metallic inclusion content is transverse reduction of area obtained in a tensile test.

The effect of billet hot reduction ratios on plane strain fracture toughness has also been studied. Reduction ratios from the ingot to billet of 2:1 to 10:1 do not affect toughness. In addition the longitudinal and transverse fracture toughness is substantially the same in all the products investigated. This finding is in direct contrast to other "ductility" parameters which show markedly different values in the two directions.

The nonmetallic inclusion contents were studied by optical and electron microscopy and analyzed quantitatively with the QTM. The results are discussed in terms of the very small plastic zone size at a crack tip in low alloy steels quenched and tempered to very high strength levels.

INTRODUCTION

The aircraft and aerospace industries are working toward the more efficient use of high strength structural materials to save weight for greater pay loads and more economical operations. In order to achieve this bold goal, the attainment of optimum properties is necessary. However, the presence of nonmetallic inclusions in steels is detrimental to this goal attainment and to substantially eliminate them would be extremely expensive. A more economical approach is to reduce the number and size of nonmetallic particles to a level compatible with performance requirements. Therefore, this study was undertaken to obtain quantitative inclusion data so that the effects produced by various steelmaking practices and processing variables can be related to the resulting mechanical properties, particularly tensile test properties and fracture toughness.

In this study, billets of AISI 4340 and 300M high strength steels were selected, for the most part, from commercially prepared and processed heats and possessed characteristics of large scale production methods. These included electric-furnace air-melted, vacuum degassed (DH processed), and vacuum-air-remelted (VAR) steels. The various meltings and hot working processes resulted in differences in inclusion types, sizes and distributions.

The approach used was to study the nonmetallic inclusions by means of optical and electron microscopy and to analyze them quantitatively with the Quantimet or Quantitative Television Microscope (QTM). The information gathered then was applied to the evaluation of reduction of area, fracture toughness, impact strength and fatigue properties. The latter two properties are discussed elsewhere. (1)

The general goal of the program was the development of a more precise understanding of the effect of inclusions on critical properties in order that specifications for better quality and more reliable high strength steels can be established, particularly for the aircraft industry.

MATERIALS AND EXPERIMENTAL PROCEDURES

Materials and Processing. The steels used in this study are listed in Table 1 with their chemical compositions. All of the materials originally were melted as heats weighing approximately 100 tons each. The air-melted and Dortmund-Horder (DH) vacuum degassed steels were poured as 20 to 27-inch rectangular ingots. All the VAR materials except VAR II 300M came from 32-inch diameter ingots weighing about 10 tons. The steels were hot worked to 4 to 4½-inch round corner square (RCS) billets. Most of the billets studied came from the central region of the ingots, and there was no upsetting of either ingots or intermediate products. Hot reductions from ingots to these billet sizes were over 96%.

The VAR II 300M ingot weighing about 1000 lbs. was melted in a smaller furnace into a 12-inch diameter mold. This ingot was stepforged by hammering to obtain hot reductions in the range 2:1 to 10:1.

Table 1.
CHEMICAL COMPOSITIONS OF STEELS

Process and Designation	C	Mn	P	S	Si	Ni	Cr	Mo	V	PPM N	PPM O
4340											
Air	0.42	0.70	0.018	0.014	0.22	1.72	0.82	0.28	–	88	44
DH I	0.38	0.75	0.010	0.014	0.25	1.64	0.85	0.27	–	42	21
DH II	0.38	0.66	0.006	0.011	0.23	1.72	0.78	0.25	–	54	16
VAR I	0.42	0.84	0.008	0.005	0.25	1.71	0.82	0.24	–	29	<10
VAR II	0.42	0.81	0.008	0.004	0.36	1.63	0.84	0.22	–	22	<10
300M											
Air	0.40	0.90	0.006	0.007	1.70	1.82	0.77	0.38	0.06	35	14
VAR I	0.42	0.80	0.006	0.006	1.59	1.81	0.79	0.37	0.08	–	<10
VAR II	0.41	0.79	0.004	0.006	1.76	1.75	0.87	0.37	0.08	27	<10

Analysis (Weight Percent)

Heat Treatment. The following heat treatments were
standardized for the mechanical property test specimens:

	4340	300M
(a) Normalized for 1 hr., air cooled	1650F	1700F
(b) Austenitized for 1 hr., oil quenched	1550F	1600F
(c) Refrigerated in liquid nitrogen ½ hr.		
(d) Tempered	400F	600F
	(2 hours)	(2+2 hours)

Heat treatments were done in neutral salt baths. Specimens
were refrigerated immediately after quenching. ASTM prior
austenite grain sizes varied from 5.5 to 9.0.

Mechanical Properties. Specimen blanks were taken from
the center and mid-radius positions of the billets in both
the transverse and longitudinal directions. The blanks were
rough-machined into the appropriate specimen configuration,
fully heat-treated and finish machined.

Tensile data were compiled on at least two each of the
longitudinal and transverse specimens measuring 0.252-inch
in diameter in the gage section. Specimen locations and
notch positions were systematically varied.

Plane strain fracture toughness behavior was determined
by using both three-point slow bend and compact tension test
specimens of the type recommended by ASTM Committee E-24 in
the proposed test method E-399-70T. (2) Both longitudinal
and transverse specimens were tested. Transverse specimens
were made by welding arms to the specimen blank ends to
obtain the necessary size for our three-point bend testing
fixture. Welding was done prior to heat treatment.   The
transverse blanks were sectioned from the billets so that
the direction of crack propagation was either parallel with
(WR) or normal to (WW´) the rolling direction. To test the
reproducibility of the results by both test methods compact
tension specimens were machined directly from tested bend
specimens on either side of the fracture surface by grinding

and spark machining methods. The compact specimens then were tested with the results shown in Table 2. The two sets of values are in excellent agreement and provide additional confirmation that both test specimens yield the same results.

Inclusion Evaluation. Polished samples from the center and mid-radius billet positions were examined under the optical microscope using petrographic techniques, and certain inclusions were quantitatively analyzed on an electron microprobe analyzer. In addition, samples were rated with the Quantimet (QTM) to determine the average volume percent of inclusions, the number per unit area, the aspect or length-width ratio, and other inclusion statistics. Description and use of this instrument can be found in several published articles. (3,4,5) Two hundred fields per sample at a magnification of 665X were used. This arrangement corresponded to a nominal area examined per sample in excess of 30 mm^2. The resolution at this magnification was nearly 2 microns.

RESULTS AND DISCUSSION

Mechanical Properties. The tensile properties of the steels as a function of the melt practice are given in Table 3 together with plane strain fracture toughness values. Tensile and yield strengths did not vary appreciably from heat to heat for each of the steel types. The average tensile strength for all 4340 steels was about 290 ksi, while the average yield strength was about 240 ksi; tensile strength values for 300M averaged about 300 ksi, yield strength values were about 260 ksi.

Reduction of area values for longitudinal specimens were uniform from heat to heat; however, transverse values varied considerably and were lower than longitudinal values for all heats of each steel. In fact, the most interesting feature of the tensile data was the improvement in transverse

Table 2.

FRACTURE TOUGHNESS, K_{Ic} OF VAR 300M AT A 0.2%
YIELD STRENGTH OF 239,000 psi

Bend Specimens W = 2a = 2B = 1.70 inches	Compact Tension Specimens W = 2a = 2B = 1.30 inches
58.3 ksi√in.	59.2, 60.6 ksi√in.
56.8	58.5, 58.0
57.7	57.1, 56.1
58.4	59.9, 58.9
Average 57.8	58.5

Table 3.

TENSILE AND PLANE STRAIN FRACTURE TOUGHNESS DATA FOR 4340 AND 300M STEELS

Grade, Practice and Designation	σ_t (ksi) Long.	σ_t (ksi) Trans.	0.2% σ_y (ksi) Long.	0.2% σ_y (ksi) Trans.	% RA Long.	% RA Trans.	Specimen Number	Plane Strain Fracture Toughness (ksi√in.) Longitudinal (RW)	Transverse (WR)	Transverse (WW')
Air 4340	291	290	241	240	47.5	8.9	1	40.0	40.3	43.8
							2	40.6	40.3	45.0
							3	41.0	42.6	
							Average	40.5	41.7	44.4
DH II 4340	285	286	231	233	47.9	21.0	1	46.9	46.1	52.5
							2	48.4a	47.8	52.5
							3	49.7	48.4	52.5
							Average	48.3	47.4	52.5
VAR I 4340	294	294	241	240	49.8	37.6	1	48.6	55.0	52.9
							2	51.1	56.2	53.9
							3	54.6	56.8	56.1
							4	58.6		
							Average	53.2	56.0	54.3
VAR II 4340	295	290	240	237	48.5	42.8	1	51.8	52.4	54.9
							2	55.0	52.9	55.5
							3	59.2	54.9	57.2
							4	61.3		
							Average	56.8	53.4	55.9
Air 300M	304	295	262	254	44.8	23.6	1	42.4a	58.0	55.3
							2	42.5a	58.2	55.3
							3	43.6	58.8	56.5
							4	45.1	58.8	56.5
							5	50.8		
							Average	44.9	58.3	55.9
VAR I 300M	302	292	259	255	47.8	33.6	1	51.1		
							2	51.2		
							3	53.0		
							4	53.6		
							Average	52.2		

a Longitudinal specimens with welded arms.

reduction of area with the more sophisticated melting methods. Air-melted 4340 had the poorest value, 8.9%; this was improved to 21 to 22.9% for two degassed heats, raised to 37.6 to 42.8% for the VAR heats. Vacuum arc remelting appreciably improved transverse reduction of area over that of the air-melted 300M.

Plane strain fracture toughness results of the individual specimens and average values for the 4340 and 300M steels are given in Table 3. For the 4340 longitudinal specimens, the air-melted material had the lowest average value of 40.5 ksi$\sqrt{\text{inch}}$, while VAR II had the highest value of 56.8 ksi$\sqrt{\text{inch}}$. The other 4340 steels fell between these two values. Likewise, for the 300M steels, the air-melted material had a lower average longitudinal value than the VAR product. The values of the transverse specimens were somewhat unexpected for their averages are slightly higher than the longitudinal values. The welded longitudinal control specimens (Table 3) did not show a significant discrepancy from the average.

The individual values reported in the table reflect the degree of scatter of plane strain fracture toughness expected for these variously melted high strength steels, heat-treated to high yield strengths. The largest deviation for all the steels is within 6 ksi$\sqrt{\text{inch}}$ of the average.

The 300M steels are superior to the 4340 steels because they have comparable toughness values at higher yield strength.

Inclusions statistics derived with the QTM showing the effect of melting practice are given in Table 4. For most correlations with mechanical properties the average inclusion content has been employed, although other parameters such as the number of inclusions per unit area may also be used. The considerable improvement in cleanliness resulting from steelmaking refining methods (particular VAR) can readily be seen.

Table 4.

INCLUSION STATISTICS DERIVED FROM QTM MEASUREMENTS ON 4340 AND 300M STEELS

Steel Grade	Melt Practice	Average Inclusion Cont. (%)	Avg. of 10 Worst Fields (%)	Worst Field (%)	Inclusions per mm²
4340	Air Melt	0.115	0.56	1.48	29.4
4340	DH	0.09	0.51	1.00	23.0
4340	VAR I	0.02	0.10	0.30	4.0
4340	VAR II	0.01	0.08	0.17	4.1
300M	Air Melt	0.075	0.37	0.89	24.8
300M	VAR I	0.03	0.16	0.30	8.5

Examination of the inclusions in the steels showed most of them to be of the manganese sulfide and calcium aluminate types. Occasionally titanium carbonitrides were observed. Continuous sulfides and discontinuous aluminate stringers were characteristic of the air-melted and DH processed steels. Inclusion stringers in VAR material were considerably shorter, as illustrated in Fig. 1 for 300M.

The relationship between certain mechanical properties and inclusion content is given in Fig. 2 and 3 for 4340 and 300M, respectively. In general, the longitudinal reduction of area was virtually insensitive to inclusions in the range investigated. These figures also show that transverse reduction of area for both grades of steels decreases uniformly with inclusion content. Similar curves were obtained using the average of the ten worst field readings or the number of inclusions per unit area.

Some variation of plane strain fracture toughness was noted especially for the higher inclusion content steels. However, it is interesting to note that there are only minor variations in toughness between longitudinal and both types of transverse specimens, in direct contrast to similar comparison of reduction of area.

The effect of forging reduction on tensile and K_{Ic} fracture toughness is shown graphically in Fig. 4. Average tensile and yield strengths did not change with reduction ratio and were isotropic for reduction ratios of 2:1 and greater. The yield strength results for the ingot (255 ksi) were higher than for the forged product (239 ksi). Plane strain fracture toughness was also constant over the range investigated and was independent of notch location. Reduction of area increased to some extent with forging ratio and this increase was greater for the longitudinal specimens. All of the reduction of area values for the forged products were greater than 27.5%; the ingot showed poor ductility

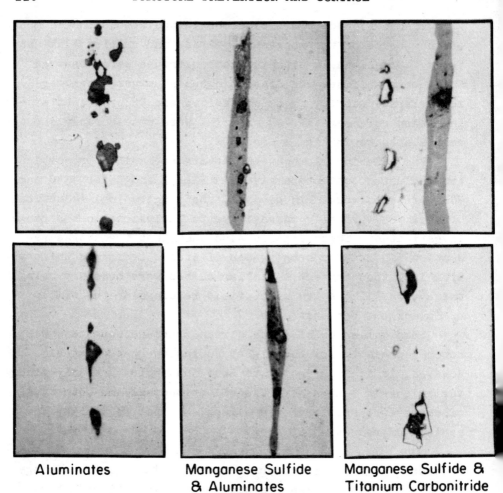

| Aluminates | Manganese Sulfide & Aluminates | Manganese Sulfide & Titanium Carbonitride |

1000X

Top Row – Air Melted 300M   Bottom Row – VAR 300M

Fig. 1. Typical inclusions in air-melted and VAR 300M billets

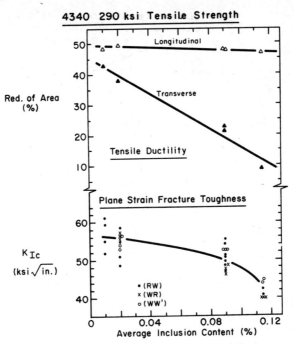

Fig. 2. Relationship between mechanical property and inclusion
content determined by QTM for 4340; 290 ksi tensile
strength

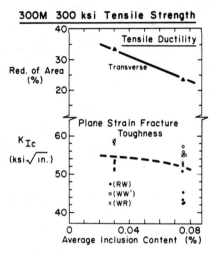

Fig. 3.   Relationship between mechanical property and inclusion
          content determined by QTM for 300M; 300 ksi tensile
          strength

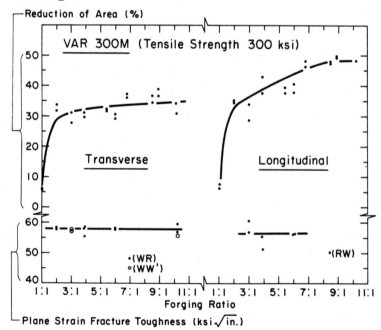

Fig. 4.   Effect of forging reduction on tensile and fracture
          toughness properties of VAR 300M

values of from 5.2 to 7.6% for both directions. Average
transverse reduction of area values for the worked products
ranged from 29.5 to 37.9% while average longitudinal values
ranged from 31.2 to 49.9%.

The inclusions found in this ingot consisted of complex
aluminates, some alumina, sulfides and titanium carbonitrides.
Upon hot working the inclusions tend to elongate, and the
length-to-width ratios of certain inclusion types are given
in Table 5 as a function of forging reduction. The length
measurements were for the overall length of discontinuous
stringers while the widths were based on the maximum width
of a stringer.

In Fig. 5 we have plotted the ratio of transverse to
longitudinal reduction of area and fracture toughness as a
function of the amount of hot reduction. The way in which
inclusions elongate with hot working also is shown. A
marked effect on reduction of area is observed, while plane
strain fracture toughness was found to be virtually insensitive to the amount of hot reduction and the inclusion
configuration.

DISCUSSION

Most work on plane strain fracture toughness to date
has been on the meaning of the test, specimen configurations,
testing procedures, validity requirements, etc., and on
steels, in particular, has been concerned with gathering
typical values for different compositions and heat treatments.
There have, however, been a few studies concerned with process variables and inclusions. Notably, Birkle, Wei and
Pellissier (6,7) have reported a considerable variation of
plane strain fracture toughness with sulfur content (and
thus manganese sulfide inclusions) in high strength steels.
However, the effect noted was quite small at the strength
level and sulfur content normally encountered in high quality

Table 5

INCLUSION LENGTH TO WIDTH RATIOS AT VARIOUS FORGING REDUCTIONS
FOR 300M

VAR 300M Forging Reduction Ratio	Inclusion L/W Ratio		
	Sulfide	Titanium Carbonitride	Aluminate
2 : 1	2.8	3.5	1.5
6 : 1	7.0	5.5	2.0
10 : 1	10.6	8.0	14.2

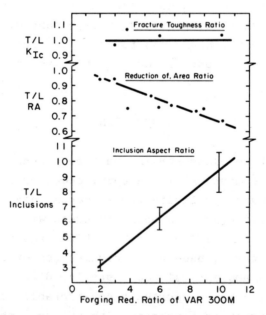

Fig. 5. Relationship of transverse to longitudinal ratios of
mechanical properties and inclusions with the forging
ratios for 300M; 300 ksi tensile strength

aircraft structural steels. Their results are plotted in
Fig. 6. For example, in the Ni-Cr-Mo steels studies, at a
tensile strength of 300 ksi, K_{Ic} varied from 37.1 ksi$\sqrt{\text{inch}}$
at 0.016% sulfur to 41.2 ksi$\sqrt{\text{inch}}$ at 0.008% sulfur. In
addition, the variation with sulfur content was smaller at
the higher strength levels where the plastic zone size at
the crack tip is smaller.

The K_{Ic} data obtained in this investigation thus con-
firm the results of Birkle et al and show that fracture toughness is not affected greatly by inclusions in typical aircraft quality high strength structural steels in which tensile
strengths are often in the range 275-300 ksi and sulfur is
usually well below 0.010%.

One particularly interesting observation in this study
is that there are only minor variations in fracture toughness
between longitudinal and both types of transverse specimens
for 4340 and 300M. This is in direct contrast to reduction
of area values and other parameters such as impact and fatigue
resistance. (1) In fact, the data show that the average
transverse values are slightly higher than the average longitudinal values. Also, there was no influence of notch location on K_{Ic} that could be related to the "tree-ring" patterns sometimes observed in VAR steels. The results of a
larger number of tests would be required to establish a
statistical significance. Some recently reported data on
high strength steels showed average longitudinal K_{Ic} values
only slightly greater than average transverse values, but
with overlapping standard deviations. (8,9)

In a previous study (10), correlation was made between
mechanical properties, particularly K_c fracture toughness
(11) and inclusion parameters rated by the ASTM-JK system
of several 4340 steels melted by different methods. These
steels (0.067-inch thick sheets) were re-examined with the
QTM and the relation between K_c fracture toughness and steel

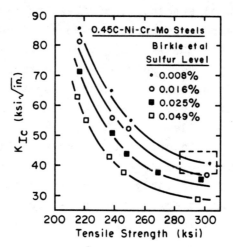

Fig. 6.   Influence of sulfur level on plane-strain fracture
toughness of 0.45C-Ni-Cr-Mo steel.   (Taken from Ref 6)

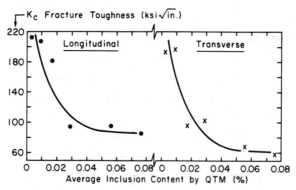

Fig. 7.   Relation between fracture toughness, K_c, and steel
cleanliness in 4340

cleanliness obtained as shown in Fig. 7. Fracture toughness
improved slowly with steel cleanliness from about 0.075 to
0.022% inclusion content, and there is very rapid improvement in toughness for the lower inclusion content steels.
The data show that K_c fracture toughness values are more
sensitive to inclusion content than the K_{Ic} values.

The QTM data given in Table 4 are for the total inclusion content without regard to type. Actually, the types
encountered in this study were generally limited to sulfides
and alumina-aluminates except for lesser amounts of titanium
carbonitride in some of the steels. The majority of the inclusions in all these highly worked materials were in the
form of stringers; either continuous as in the case of many
of the sulfides, or discontinuous as often observed for the
hard alumina-aluminate particles. In the stringer form, the
increased length to width ratio and notch acuity are re-
sponsible for the anisotropy in the steels considered here.
In order to show this anisotropy of these billet materials,
transverse to longitudinal ratios of the critical mechanical
properties were plotted against the average inclusion content; the data for both 4340 and 300M steels are given in
Fig. 8. A similar relationship with the mechanical properties was established when the number of inclusions per unit
area was plotted. The data show a decrease for reduction
of area ratios with increasing inclusion content; K_{Ic} fracture toughness was relatively insensitive over the inclusion
range investigated. The data established that the critical
properties of 300M were affected in the same manner as those
of 4340.

We have now shown that various ductility and toughness
parameters are affected in different ways by the nonmetallic
inclusion content of high strength steels. Many of these
differences can be rationalized by taking into account the
state of stress operating and the fracture mode. In the

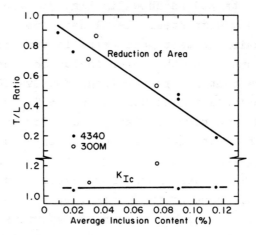

Fig. 8. Relationship between transverse to longitudinal
mechanical property ratio and inclusion content

tensile tests all fractures occurred by dimpled rupture.
Tipper (12) first suggested that ductile fractures start at
inclusions, and several examples have been photographed.
Puttick (13) has shown that voids at oxide particles in the
necked region of copper tensile specimens sometimes formed
by fracture of the inclusion and sometimes by separation
of the metal from the inclusion. This same observation has
been noted in several other alloy-inclusion systems. Also,
the results of calculations of the stress fields in the
vicinity of inclusions have shown fair agreement with the
experimental data of Edelson and Baldwin. (14) They showed
that all second phase particles as well as voids embrittled
copper-base alloys, and that decohesion of the matrix from
the particle frequently occurred. There is now little doubt
that inclusions provide nucleation sites for cracks, and
that on further straining the cracks become microvoids which
finally combine or coalesce leading to complete rupture.
All the steels in this study were in the wrought condition
and the inclusions, therefore, were elongated as stringers
in the rolling direction. The transverse reduction of area
was thus principally affected by the inclusion content as
shown in Fig. 3 and 4.

In explaining the effect of inclusions on the various
toughness parameters we must consider whether plane strain
or plane stress conditions are operating, and also whether
the test measures crack nucleation and growth or only propagation.

In plane strain fracture toughness testing we are concerned only with what is happening at the crack tip and in
the small plastic zone ahead of the crack. K_{Ic} is calculated
from the load required to produce an appreciable though very
small crack growth, and thus K_{Ic} is relatively insensitive
to the inclusion contents encountered in these steels heat-
treated to high strength levels. It is very unlikely that

inclusion material will occur for any great length along the
crack tip unless the inclusion content is unduly high. Also,
very large inclusion stringers that appeared in plane strain
fracture toughness specimens just beyond the point where the
crack propagated during testing did not at all, or at least
significantly, influence the toughness values. Plane strain
fracture toughness seems to be substantially independent of
the testing direction in high strength wrought steels because
the plastic zone size is sufficiently small to mask the effect
of inclusions and, in one instance, even banding. (15) Of
course, at lower strength levels than studied here, the plastic zone size would be larger and there would be a greater
probability for inclusion involvement, also the presence of
large amounts of inclusions would increase the chance for
inclusion interactions. (6,7)

It is interesting to reflect that the quantity K_{Ic} measures resistance to crack propagation under static loads.
As a parameter of toughness it does not take into account
crack initiation whereas transverse ductility does. Also
catastrophic failure of a component occurs at a flaw size
which can depend upon the rate of subcritical crack growth.
Since resistance to cyclic stresses is related to inclusions,
it follows that crack growth is an important parameter.
Fracture toughness measured under the plane stress conditions
described above shows a large dependence on inclusions. (10)
In this case, however, toughness is measured on a specimen
that has completely failed after slow crack growth over a
considerable volume of material, whereby the crack path may
follow inclusions present.

It, therefore, appears that K_{Ic} is more a measure of
the matrix toughness, that is, it provides a measure of the
inherent capacity of the material for unstable crack propagation, and is not as sensitive to other variables of quality
such as the usually encountered inclusion content or banding

or segregation. A test involving the plane stress state
seems better suited to detect effects of these anomalies.

Over the past several years there has been considerable
work in the development of specimens and testing procedures
for determining valid K_{Ic} values and although fracture toughness is useful in design considerations, it is now becoming
apparent that plane strain fracture toughness used as a
measure of quality control can be misleading for high strength
steels.

What then can the steel supplier or specifications engineer do to assure reliability in the selection of high
strength steel billets? This study has shown that the quality of steel is best judged through simple, inexpensive transverse reduction of area measurements of tensile specimens.
This ductility parameter was the one most significantly affected by inclusion content in these high strength steels.
Of course, for aircraft forgings the use of transverse reduction of area as a parameter of steel quality is only a
necessary single step in the early stages of the quality
control process and far from sufficient to assure component reliability. Of high importance to overall reliability
is a subsequent series of nondestructive tests at various
stages of component fabrication.

SUMMARY AND CONCLUSIONS

The way in which certain mechanical properties varied
with cleanliness in high strength structural steels has been
demonstrated. The properties for both 300M and 4340 improved
in a similar manner with cleanliness. In forging billets
transverse reduction of area varied widely over the inclusion
range evaluated. Plane strain fracture toughness, however,
was quite insensitive to inclusions and, in fact, only very
small variations in K_{Ic} were noted between longitudinal and
transverse specimens.

Properties were also measured as a function of the amount of hot reduction. Reduction of area increased to some extent with forging ratio, with a greater increase noted for longitudinal specimens. Plane strain fracture toughness was essentially constant over the forging range investigated and was isotropic.

From this study and analysis, we feel that K_{Ic}, plane strain fracture toughness should be an important factor in selecting a high strength steel for a particular application. It is not, however, a meaningful parameter for quality control measurement in these steels since it is relatively little affected by inclusions. The most important property that reflects the quality of aircraft structural steels is transverse reduction of area. While we realize that other factors, such as microsegregation, affect properties, we believe that for steels processed according to specified practices, the inclusion content is the most important variable influencing critical mechanical properties.

References

1. J. J. Hauser and M. G. H. Wells, "Inclusions in High-Strength and Bearing Steels," Wright-Patterson Air Force Base, AFML-TR-69-339, Feb 1970

2. ASTM "Proposed Method for Plane-Strain Fracture Toughness of Metallic Materials," ASTM Standards, Part 31, p 1099, May 1969

3. "Automatic Cleanness Assessment of Steel," Iron and Steel Inst. Special Report No. 112, London, 1968

4. "The Microscope," 1968, vol 16, entire April issue

5. E. Grethen and L. Philipps, "Use of the Quantimet for the Cleanliness Assessment of Steels," CNRM, vol 17, p 53-62, Dec 1968

6. A. J. Birkle, R. P. Wei and G. Pellissier, "Analysis of Plane-Strain Fracture in a Series of 0.45C-Ni-Cr-Mo Steels with Different Sulfur Contents," Trans. ASM, vol 59, p 981-990, 1966

7. G. E. Pellissier, "Effects of Microstructure on the Fracture Toughness of Ultrahigh-Strength Steels," Eng. Fract. Mechanics, vol 1, No. 1, p 55-75, June 1968

8. P. F. Packman, H. S. Pearson, J. S. Owens and G. B. Marchese, "The Applicability of a Fracture Mechanics - Nondestructive Testing Design Criterion," Wright-Patterson Air Force Base, Technical Report AFML-TR-68-332, May 1968

9. R. A. Celletti and C. J. Carter, "Ultrasonic Measurement and Influence of Nonmetallic Inclusions on Fatigue and Engineering Behaviour of Medium and High-Strength Steels," SAE Paper No. 690049, Jan 1969

10. B. R. Banerjee and J. J. Hauser, "Fracture Micromechanics in High-Strength Steel and Titanium," Wright-Patterson Air Force Base, Technical Report ML-TDR-64-182, July 1964

11. ASTM "Fracture Testing of High-Strength Sheet Materials," ASTM Bulletin No. 243, Jan 1960

12. C. F. Tipper, "The Fracture of Metals," Metallurgia, vol 39, p 133-137, Jan 1949

13. K. E. Puttick, "Ductile Fracture in Metals," Phil Mag vol 4, p 964-969, Aug 1959

14. B. I. Edelson and W. M. Baldwin, Jr., "The Effect of Second Phases on the Mechanical Properties of Alloys," Trans. ASM, vol 55, p 230-250, 1962

15. C. S. Carter, "The Effect of Heat Treatment on the Fracture Toughness and Subcritical Crack Growth Characteristics of a 350-Grade Maraging Steel," Met. Trans. ASM-AIME, vol 1, No. 6, p 1551-1559, 1970

EFFECT OF CHEMISTRY AND HEAT TREATMENT ON THE
FRACTURE PROPERTIES OF Ti-6Al-4V ALLOY

M. J. Harrigan
Ford Aeroneutronic
Newport Beach, California

M. P. Kaplan
United States Air Force
Dayton, Ohio

A. W. Sommer
North American Rockwell
Los Angeles Division

ABSTRACT

An investigation was conducted to determine
the processing parameters for the production of Ti-
6Al-4V alloy with optimum toughness for use in structural components of modern aircraft designed to fracture mechanics criteria. A study was made of the
effect of chemical composition and heat treatment
on the strength, fracture toughness, and fatigue-
crack growth rate characteristics of this alloy.
The effect of chemistry was determined by testing
several heats of Ti-6Al-4V plate in a fully annealed condition with wide compositional differences
in oxygen content and aluminum content. A comparison of these heats showed that modest reductions
in oxygen and aluminum contents of the metal significantly increased the fracture toughness and
caused an even larger decrease in the fatigue-crack

growth rate. The effect of heat treatment was investigated within a single heat of material and included studying the mill anneal (the low-temperature
stress relief cycle described in MIL-H-81200), recrystallization anneal, solution treat and overage,
and beta anneal conditions. Results indicated that
the recrystallization anneal and the beta anneal
produced important increases in fracture toughness
over that of the mill annealed or solution treated
and overaged heat treatments. The fatigue-crack
growth rate as a function of cyclic stress intensity
of the material decreased correspondingly with the
increase in fracture toughness. The influence of
chemistry and microstructure on the fracture properties of this alloy are explained with the aid of
optical and electron metallography.

INTRODUCTION

Since aircraft were first produced on an assembly line
basis, man has strived to improve the flight characteristics
of these vehicles. To obtain higher performance, it has been
necessary to increase the wing loading area, thereby neces-
sitating a more stress efficient structure. This increase
in structural efficiency, while imposing higher gross stresses
on fracture-critical parts, was relatively unimportant as
the development of medium-strength, high-toughness metals
surpassed the designer's ability to fully utilize the available properties. Starting in the late 1950's, the airframe
manufacturers began designing and producing aircraft that
required the use of very-high-strength materials. The high-
strength materials that were developed, however, possessed
poor fracture toughness. Furthermore, improved design efficiency lowered the residual strength characteristics of
the air vehicle structure.

The outcome of this use of high-strength materials possessing poor toughness and subcritical flaw growth characteristics became evident in structural integrity problems that occurred in the F-111, F-4, and C-5A aircraft. For these reasons, the Air Force has changed its emphasis in structural design criteria to include the requirement that the airframe manufacturers of newer air vehicles analyze and design their structure based upon fracture mechanics criteria, in addition to static strength and the more classical fatigue requirements.

In its complete form, the use of fracture mechanics concepts in designing aircraft may be designated as fracture control. This philosophy of structural design differs radically from the older or more conventional method of design, as fracture mechanics assumes that a flaw exists. Therefore, materials must be selected not only on the basis of strength, but also on the basis of their flaw growth and fracture toughness characteristics.

As most existing aircraft materials were developed almost exclusively on the basis of minimum guaranteed strength, the chemistry and production processing parameters often were not carefully controlled. This results in materials having high-strength characteristics, yet exhibiting a wide range of fracture toughness values. In order to change the mill philosophy on metal production, the airframe manufacturers have started incorporating fracture mechanics requirements into their material purchase specifications. Due to these minimum guaranteed fracture toughness requirements on existing materials, the metal producers now more carefully control both the chemistry and processing parameters. This tighter control results in the production of materials with consistently higher toughness without any loss in static strength. A further result has been in the development of new alloys that attempt to optimize both strength and fracture toughness.

One of the existing alloys that has undergone modification in the past to optimize fracture properties is Ti-6Al-4V. In order to optimize toughness, the extra-low interstitial grade (ELI) was developed. A further development was the use of Ti-6Al-4V products that were worked above the beta transus. During these development programs, it was found that Ti-6Al-4V, was highly sensitive to both the microstructure (i.e., grain size, shape, and morphology) and chemistry. To date, the most extensive metallurgical studies have centered on the effects of chemistry.

In Ti-6Al-4V, the alpha stabilizers have been found to exert the most significant effect on properties. Some investigations (1,2) have shown that increasing the aluminum content increases the strength and decreases the toughness. Variations in oxygen content cause the properties to behave similarly. (3,4) When aluminum is added to titanium, the alpha or low-temperature phase is stabilized. If large amounts of this element are added to titanium (<9 per cent), undesirable compounds such as Ti_3Al form. However, aluminum may cause detrimental effects when present in lesser quantities (6 to 7 per cent). This amount of aluminum may cause short-range order that subsequently causes planar slip to become the dominant mechanism of plastic deformation at 70°F. (5) Altering the slip mode from wavy to planar slip causes an increase in strength and decreases both the static and dynamic toughness and resistance to stress corrosion cracking. (1,6,7) Oxygen also is an alpha stabilizer. Unlike aluminum, which is substitutional, oxygen is an interstitial and has been shown to impede cross slip, although the mechanism is not known. (8) Thus, oxygen, when present in sufficient quantities (oxygen >3,000 ppm), also causes planar slip at 70°F, subsequently reducing the alloy's toughness.

From these studies, it has become clear that to produce alloys such as Ti-6Al-4V with optimum toughness, the aluminum

and oxygen content must be limited. On the other hand, re-
stricting chemistry without controlling rolling practice and
microstructure can result in reduced strength properties,
as is the case with Ti-6Al-4V ELI grade. The objective of
this work was to define the limits to which chemistry safely
can be used to strengthen Ti-6Al-4V and to further the development of thermal treatments and rolling practices which optimize toughness. This was accomplished by studying three
heats of Ti-6Al-4V with wide ranges of aluminum and oxygen
content. All three compositions were heat treated to the
same condition to remove microstructure as a significant
variable. Secondly, one heat was heat treated to produce
a wide range of microstructures independent of chemistry.

EXPERIMENTAL PROCEDURE

Materials and Heat Treatment. Three heats of Ti-6Al-4V
were used in this study, one rolled to a thickness of 0.625
inch and the other two to 1.5 inches thick. The composition
of the Ti-6Al-4V plates is shown in Table 1 with the allowable composition limits of the current military specification
for titanium alloy, sheet, and plate also noted. The 0.625-
inch-thick heat was received in the mill annealed condition
and heat treated in a controlled atmosphere vacuum furnace
to the solution treated and overaged condition, beta anneal
condition, or was recrystallization annealed. The heat treatment cycles are shown in Table 2, and the resulting microstructures are shown in Fig. 1. Heat 2 was received in the
mill annealed condition and was recrystallization annealed.
Heat 3 was purchased in the recrystallized annealed condition. The microstructures of both materials in the recrystallization annealed condition are shown in Fig. 2.

Mechanical Testing. The mechanical testing for each
condition consisted of determining the tensile properties,
plane strain fracture toughness, and fatigue-crack growth

Table 1.

ALLOY COMPOSITIONS

Product Size	Producer	Heat	Al	V	Fe	C	N	O	H	Heat Ident
0.625 x 72 x 120	TMCA	K6271	6.4	4.1	0.23	0.026	0.016	0.20	0.003	1
1.5 x 48 x 120	RMI	294773	6.2	4.2	.18	.020	.012	.16	.004	2
1.5 x 36 x 48	TMCA	K8294	6.0	4.0	.12	.022	.011	.12	.005	3
MIL-T-9046F			5.5 - 6.75	3.5 - 4.5	0.30 Max	0.08 Max	0.05 Max	0.20 Max	0.015 Max	

Table 2.

HEAT TREATMENT SCHEDULE

Mill anneal (MA)	1,350°F, 1 hour, air cool
Beta anneal (BA)	1,900°F, 0.5 hour, air cool
	1,350°F, 2 hours, air cool
Solution treat and overage	1,750°F, 2 hours, water quench
(STOA)	1,000°F, 2 hours, air cool
	1,300°F, 2 hours, air cool
Recrystallization anneal (RA)	1,700°F, 4 hours furnace cool to
	1,400°F, air cool

(a)   250 DIAMETERS

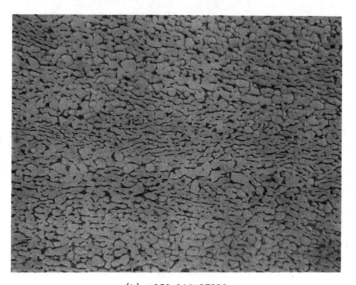

(b)   250 DIAMETERS

Fig. 1.   Microstructure of Ti-6Al-4V, heat 1, in (a) mill
annealed; (b) recrystallized annealed conditions

(c) 100 DIAMETERS

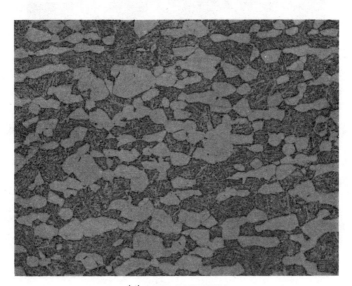

(d) 750 DIAMETERS

Fig. 1. Microstructure of Ti-6Al-4V, heat 1, in (c) beta
         annealed; and (d) solution treated and overaged
         conditions

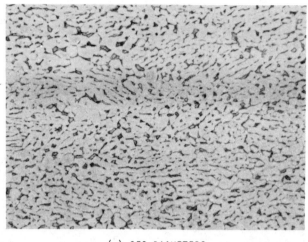

(a) 250 DIAMETERS

(b) 250 DIAMETERS

Fig. 2.   Microstructure of Ti-6Al-4V, (a) heat 2, (b) heat 3
in recrystallized annealed conditions

rate in low humidity air. Standard 0.250-inch-diameter, 1-inch-gage length specimens were used to determine the tensile properties, while the specimen design for the fracture toughness determination is shown in Fig. 3. The specimen configurations used for the fatigue-crack growth rate tests are shown in Fig. 4.

Precracking of all fracture mechanics type specimens was accomplished in an Amsler Vibrophore fatigue machine. The final precracking loads were selected to meet the ASTM requirements. Fatigue-crack growth rate specimens were final precracked at a load less than the intended cyclic test load. Sufficient precracking was performed in order to establish an equilibrium crack shape and to ensure that the starting crack was long enough to avoid stress effects due to pin loading.

All K_{Ic} testing follows the procedures specified in ASTM E399. Precracked specimens were monotonically loaded to failure in a 120,000-pound-capacity Riehle universal testing machine. Strain gage load cells and an MTS clip-on compliance gage were used to measure the load and crack opening displacement during testing. All tests were conducted at a constant crosshead velocity that produced a loading rate that was within the ASTM requirements.

Fatigue-crack growth rate testing was performed using one of the two compact tension specimens described previously. Actual testing was accomplished in a bank of specially constructed closed-loop electrohydraulic fatigue machines using waveform generators to program the desired load cycles (sine waves) and test frequencies. The cracks were followed on both sides of the specimen by use of transit sighting scopes, with the crack being illuminated by a tungsten light source. During testing, the crack length was determined by measuring it against the scales attached to both sides of the specimen. Crack length measurements were made at intervals of 0.050 inch

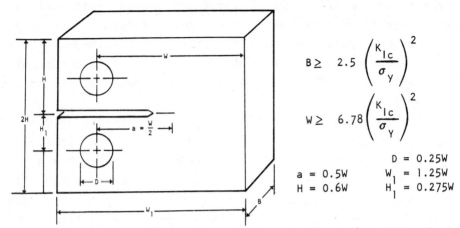

$$B \geq 2.5 \left(\frac{K_{Ic}}{\sigma_Y}\right)^2$$

$$W \geq 6.78 \left(\frac{K_{Ic}}{\sigma_Y}\right)^2$$

$$D = 0.25W$$

$$a = 0.5W \qquad W_1 = 1.25W$$

$$H = 0.6W \qquad H_1 = 0.275W$$

Fig. 3. General configuration and proportions for compact tension specimens for K_{Ic} fracture toughness measurement

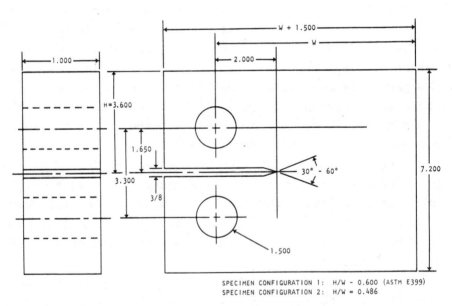

SPECIMEN CONFIGURATION 1: H/W – 0.600 (ASTM E399)
SPECIMEN CONFIGURATION 2: H/W = 0.486

Fig. 4. Compact tension crack growth specimen

and recorded along with the cumulative number of cycles that
have elapsed at each reading. The fatigue-crack growth rate
tests were performed in a low-humidity air environment, with
R = +0.08 or +0.030 and a test frequency of either 1 or 10
cps. The specimens were enclosed within a plastic bag filled
with freshly dried desiccant to obtain the dry-air environment.

RESULTS

The results of static testing are presented in Table 3.
Figure 5 summarizes the effect of oxygen and aluminum on
fracture toughness for the materials in the mill annealed
and recrystallization annealed conditions. The trend line
in this figure indicates that decreasing the aluminum and
oxygen content increases the fracture toughness. In addition,
this figure illustrates the improvement in fracture toughness
that results from recrystallization annealing the microstructure.

The fatigue-crack growth rate in the RW orientation for
these alloys when recrystallization annealed behaved similarly with decreasing oxygen and aluminum, as can be seen
in Fig. 6. Figure 6 shows the crack growth rate as a function of ΔK tested at an R factor of +0.30.

Examination of the tensile properties in Table 3 reveals
a strong anisotropy in material 1. X-ray diffraction pole
figures of this material (Fig. 7) indicate that the anistropy
was probably due to a strong basal plane (0002) texture that
was present in this material. The effect of texture on the
strength and fracture toughness is discussed in detail elsewhere. (10) It is clear from Fig. 7 and Table 3 that the
direction that contains the highest concentration of basal
poles (transverse or WR) also exhibits the highest strength.

Table 3.

EFFECT OF ORIENTATION, CHEMISTRY, AND HEAT TREATMENT
ON MECHANICAL AND FRACTURE MECHANICS PROPERTIES

Heat Identi-fication No.	Heat Treat.	Orientation	F_{ty} (ksi)	F_{tu} (ksi)	Elong (%)	RA (%)	K_{IC} (ksi$\sqrt{\text{In.}}$)
1	MA	RW	139	149	13	27	39
		WR	160	170	14	30	33
	STOA	RW	151	161	14	27	41
		WR	160	164	15	30	43
	BA	RW	136	145	14	22	89*
		WR	150	160	14	23	82*
	RA	RW	134	145	12	20	51
		WR	152	166	14	21	57
2	MA	RW	138	147	15	32	42
		WR	139	148	15	34	42
	RA	RW	129	141	15	34	59
		WR	128	141	15	34	65
3	RA	RW	121	135	13	33	87
		WR	122	134	13	28	99

*failed thickness criteria for validity

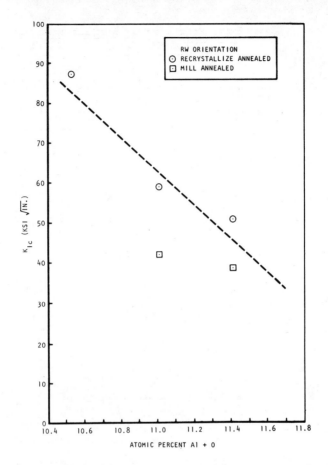

Fig. 5. Effect of alpha stabilizers (oxygen and aluminum) on fracture toughness

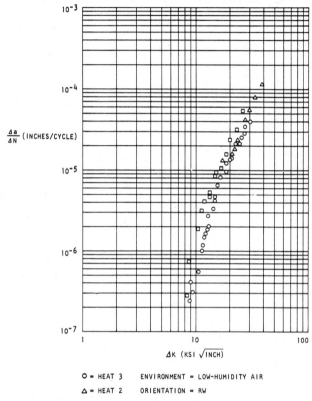

Fig. 6. Effect of chemistry on fatigue crack growth rate

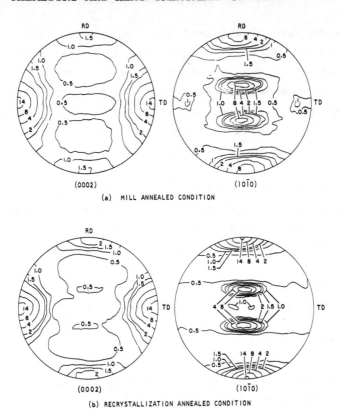

(a) MILL ANNEALED CONDITION

(b) RECRYSTALLIZATION ANNEALED CONDITION

Fig. 7. X-ray diffraction pole figures for heat 1

The results of the heat treatment study on the static properties of heat 1 also are shown in Table 3. The basis for the property changes are the microstructural changes produced by the heat treatments. The various microstructures are shown in Fig. 1. The tensile strength results indicate that the high aluminum and oxygen content of this material prevented any of the treatments from significantly altering the strength, with the exception of the STOA treatment, which appears to have leveled out the texture-induced anisotropy that persists in the other heat-treatment conditions.

One of the readily apparent effects of heat treating were the changes that occurred in the fracture toughness as summarized in Fig. 8. In this study, beta annealing produced the maximum improvement. The trends found in K_{Ic} also were apparent in the fatigue-crack growth rate test results, as shown in Fig. 9,10, and 11. In this case, the ranking of improvements in da/dN are identical to the ranking for K_{Ic} (see Fig. 8), with beta annealed Ti-6Al-4V showing the slowest cyclic growth rate characteristics at any ΔK level. For both K_{Ic} and da/dN, the recrystallization annealed product exhibited the best properties, second only to the beta annealed material.

DISCUSSION

The results of this study indicate that the strength and toughness properties of Ti-6Al-4V are dependent upon both the chemistry and heat-treatment history. These investigations (Table 3) show that a significant lowering of aluminum and oxygen content decreases the tensile ultimate and yield strength, and increases the fracture toughness. Table 3 also shows that changing the heat-treatment cycle while keeping the chemistry constant changes these same properties. Changing the chemistry and heat-treatment cycles simultaneously

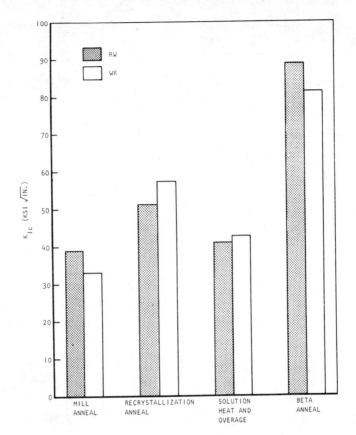

Fig. 8.   Effect of heat treatment on fracture toughness -
          heat 1

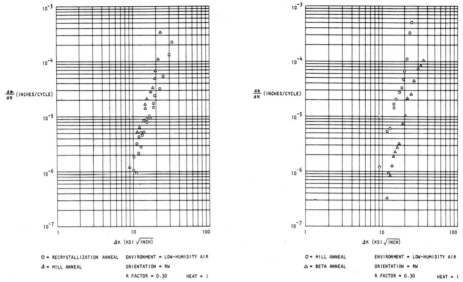

Fig. 9. Effect of heat treatment on crack growth
rate

Fig. 10. Effect of heat treatment on crack growth
rate

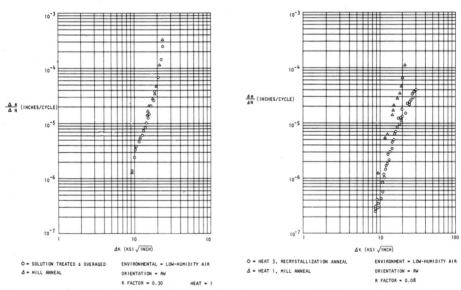

Fig. 11. Effect of heat treatment on crack growth
rate

Fig. 12. Effect of chemistry
and heat treatment
on fatigue crack
growth

results in a greater per cent increase in desirable properties (e.g., toughness) than that obtained from changing
either the chemistry or heat-treatment cycle separately.
The fatigue-crack growth rate characteristics behave in a
similar fashion to the toughness, as can be seen in Fig.
12. The mill annealed alloy with the high aluminum and oxygen content exhibits a fatigue-crack growth rate five times
faster than the growth rate observed for the low chemistry
heat in the recrystallized anneal condition.

The study of heat treatments has shown that several
approaches are available for controlling properties. As
will be discussed, it is important to consider many factors
in selecting the optimum thermal cycle.

It is apparent from the results that mill annealing
actually only represents a stress relief. This is shown in
Fig. 1 and 13. Figure 13(a) shows a transmission electron
micrograph of the 0.625-inch plate in the mill annealed condition, and Fig. 13(b) shows the RA condition. Figure 13(a)
shows extensive dislocation debris throughout the structure,
indicating the material is still in a heavily warm-worked
condition. Thus, this anneal cycle had little effect on the
material characteristics. The RA cycle does represent a true
anneal because the microstructure is fully recrystallized,
as can be seen in Fig. 13(b). The cleanness of the structure
brought about by complete recrystallization is obvious. Figure 1(a) shows the alloy's microstructure in the mill annealed
condition, while Fig. 1(b) shows the same alloy after a recrystallization anneal. Again, at this lower magnification,
the effect of the recrystallization heat treatment is obvious.

A summary of the change in properties affected by this
change in microstructure is shown in Table 2 and Fig. 11.
This change in properties is due to the fact that the recrystallized grains are capable of absorbing much more deformation prior to failure than the heavily cold worked mill

Fig. 13(a).   Transmission electron micrograph of mill annealed
              Ti-6Al-4V

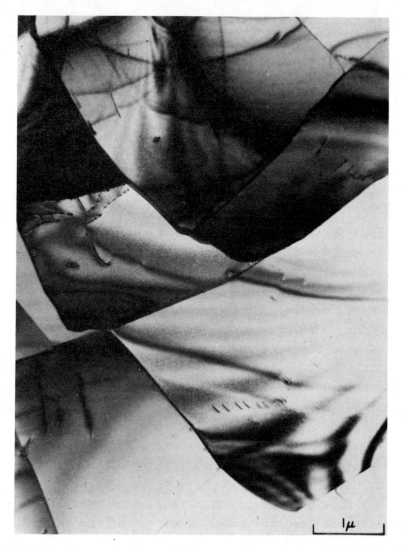

Fig. 13(b).   Transmission electron micrograph of Ti-6Al-4V in
recrystallized annealed condition

annealed grains. Furthermore, the residual dislocation
structure in the mill annealed material represents local
stress raisers that cooperate with the applied stress. Thus,
a lower contribution of the applied stress is required in
order to cause crack growth or catastrophic failure.

Beta annealing accomplishes much the same goal as recrystallization annealing in that the prior cold work structure is totally eliminated. It differs in that it creates
a large prior beta grain size (Fig. 1c) and the alpha phase
that forms on cooling is acicular rather than equiaxed.
Such acicular basketweave microstructures are known to exhibit high fracture toughness and high resistance to fatigue-
crack growth rates. (9,10,11) This improvement is due to
the alpha grain size and shape, although a detailed mechanism
never has been developed. It is likely, however, that a
significant portion of the improvement is due to the elimina-
tion of the cold work substructure.

Solution treating and overaging is an attempt to combine
the ductility of equiaxed material with the high toughness
and resistance to crack growth attributed to the massive
acicular basketweave microstructure obtained by beta processing. In theory, fast cooling from below the beta transus
will produce a fine acicular structure from very small beta
grains whose size is limited by primary alpha. In the case
at hand, however, the alpha phase interparticle spacing was
extremely fine and the resulting structure remained so fine
(Fig. 1d) that the strengthening effect of the small interparticle spacing of alpha in the transformed grains over-
shadowed the effect of having an acicular structure in the
transformed grains. The results of maintaining strength in
the microstructure by producing a fine interparticle spacing
in the transformed grains can be seen in Fig. 8 and 11. These
data show that no significant change occurred in the toughness
or fatigue-crack growth rate of the material when heat treated
to the solution treated and overaged condition.

It should be noted that iron content, in addition to aluminum and oxygen, represented a significant variable in the chemistry of the experimental materials. As is shown in Table 1, the iron content varied in the same fashion as the aluminum and oxygen. Iron, unlike aluminum and oxygen, is a beta stabilizer. However, like these elements, when present in sufficient quantities, it increases the strength and lowers the toughness. (12) The mechanism for this is not known. However, some observations may be made:

(a). Iron has an increasingly lower solubility in alpha titanium with decreasing temperatures; therefore, it may be partitioned and exist locally at high concentrations.

(b). Ti-Fe alloys form extremely brittle phases.

From the foregoing, one may conclude that the effect of excessive iron additions in titanium may be deleterious to the fracture properties. Iron may embrittle the beta phase or the alpha to beta grain boundaries. In this study, however, it was not possible to isolate or identify any deleterious effect of iron additions. Based upon the known effect (12) that excess amounts of this element can have, however, it is clear that the amount present should be limited.

It should also be noted that rolling practice was not controlled per se in this work, although it is known that this is a powerful tool for varying properties. (4) The microstructures (Fig. 1 and 2) and the results obtained here (Table 3) indicate, however, that the rolling practice used was at least similar for all of the material studied because it was possible to completely recrystallize each of the materials used in this work using the same annealing treatment (i.e., 1,700 F, 4 hours). Moreover, it is probable because of the final gage obtained and the texture present that material number 1 was rolled more extensively below that beta transus than materials 2 and 3. While rolling practice was

not deliberately controlled in these experiments, it is believed that the conclusions drawn from the results of testing are no less applicable.

The results of this study tend to indicate that the current material specifications for Ti-6Al-4V allow too wide a
range on the chemistry of Ti-6Al-4V and do not specify an
adequate thermal cycle to produce truly annealed material.
As a result, it is possible to purchase Ti-6Al-4V condition
A material with extremely high tensile strength, but with
rather poor fracture toughness and rapid fatigue-crack growth
rate characteristics. Based upon the test data, it is believed that an optimum blend of strength and fracture properties can be obtained by beta processing. Beta processing,
however, results in a material that exhibits (1) low ductility
(thus is difficult to form) and (2) improved creep strength
that limits its applicability to production processes that
rely on elevated temperature flow such as creep forming or
diffusion bonding. By contrast, an equiaxed α + β microstructure has no such drawbacks and an optimum situation can
be obtained by recrystallization annealing the final mill
product after working extensively at temperatures significantly below the beta transus and by limiting the maximum specification chemistry to less than approximately 6.3 per cent
aluminum and 0.13 per cent oxygen.

It is important to realize that limiting the chemistry
and fully annealing the microstructure still can lead to wide
variations in strength and toughness if, in addition, other
controlling factors are not brought into play. One such additional control is to place a lower limit on the chemistry.
It is within the normal operating limits of most titanium
mills to melt Ti-6Al-4V within an allowable range of 5.9 to
6.3 per cent aluminum and 0.09 to 0.13 per cent oxygen, for
example. Such a step would ensure that an adequate, but safe,
level of solid solution strengthening was available.

The most important remaining means for controlling strength and toughness, however, is through control of the ingot forge down-and-rolling practice. The thermal and mechanical sequences used during the primary breakdown of ingots into slab can influence the prior beta grain size and the alpha grain size of the material prior to rolling into plate. Beyond this stage, if it is desired to produce a final microstructure consisting of equiaxed alpha and beta, then the final rolling operations must impart controlled amounts of work below the beta transus. Controlling the reductions below the beta transus would serve two purposes. First, it would refine the final alpha grain size which should lead to increased strength and second, it should impart enough cold work to the microstructure to ensure that complete recrystallization occurs within practical limits on subsequent annealing time and temperature. It is not clear, at present, what grain size may be necessary to achieve minimum strength levels consistently. Furthermore, the relationships between rolling temperature and the amount of hot deformation and subsequent recrystallization temperature and time have not been characterized; thus, completely rational control of the rolling process will require further work. It is believed that control of the rolling practice must be achieved, however, in order to fully control the strength and toughness of equiaxed alpha plus beta Ti-6Al-4V.

Similar control would be required for the production of beta processed Ti-6Al-4V. In this case, the objective of controlled rolling would be to limit the prior beta grain size and to promote homogeneous nucleation of alpha needles during cooling. Because of its greater potential for improving toughness, the strength of beta processed Ti-6Al-4V might be controlled exclusively by chemistry and would allow the use of higher chemistry allowables than those suggested for recrystallized annealed equiaxed material.

Finally, it should be noted that all of the materials and processes studied here resulted in materials with strength in excess of the minimums required in MIL-T-9046. This gives strong indication that achieving high-toughness Ti-6Al-4V having adequate strength is well within the limits of current technology.

CONCLUSIONS

(a). It has been shown that the fracture properties of Ti-6Al-4V can be improved significantly with no penalty in guaranteed static strength by reducing the maximum allowed chemistry permitted in MIL-T-9046 for this alloy

(b). The results of this study also show that the currently accepted mill anneal cycle for Ti-6Al-4V only acts as a stress relief treatment. When a full anneal heat treatment is applied, which involves completely re-crystallizing the microstructure, a significant improvement in the fracture toughness and fatigue-crack growth rate characteristics is achieved.

(c). The data also point out that other factors such as primary and final metal working practice, grain size, and morphology and texture dictate, in part, the fracture properties of this alloy.

Acknowledgments. The authors would like to thank Dr. J. C. Williams for the transmission electron microscopy photomicrographs and for his careful guidance and thought-provoking discussions throughout this project. The authors also are deeply indebted to Mr. G. Keller for his suggestions and discussions on the practical aspects of manufacturing titanium alloy products and to Mr. N. Klimmek for his support of this work. Others who contributed to the experimental aspects include Messrs. I. Z. Gray, B. Cooper, K. Newland, R. Farwell, B. Olsen, and R. Sapp.

References

1. Rosenberg, H. W., "The Effect of Substitutional Alpha Stabilizers on the Properties of Alpha Titanium," Titanium Metallurgy Course, New York University, September 13-15, 1965

2. Blackburn, M. J., and Williams, J. D., "Strength, Deformation Modes and Fracture in Titanium-Aluminum Alloys," ASM Trans. Quart., June 1969, Vol 62, p 398

3. Wood, R. A., "The Effect of Interstitials on Mechanical Properties of Titanium and Its Alloys," Titanium Metals Course, New York University, September 13-15, 1965

4. Partridge, J. M., "The Influence of Oxygen Level and Processing Parameters on the Fracture Toughness of Ti-6Al-4V Plate," AIME Presentation, May 1969

5. Paton, N., and Williams, J. C., to be published in Proceedings of Second International Conference on Titanium, Massachusetts Institute of Technology, May 1972

6. Blackburn, M. J., and Williams, J. C., "Metallurgical Aspects of the Stress Corrosion Cracking of Titanium Alloys," Proceedings of Conference, Fundamental Aspects of Stress Corrosion Cracking, 1969, p 620

7. Kovacs, W. J., and Low, J. R., Jr., "Intergranular Fracture in a Al-15 Wt Pct Zn Alloy," Met Trans., December 1971, Vol 2, p 3335

8. Williams, J. C., Sommer, A. W., and Tung, P. P., "The Influence of Oxygen Concentration on the Internal Stress and Dislocation Arrangements in Alpha Titanium," to be published in Met. Trans.

9. Cook, O. H., and McClaren, S. W., "Beta Forging Titanium," presented at Westec, March 1968

10. Spurr, W. E., "Commercial Supersonic Transport Program Phase IIC," Contract FA-33-66-S, March 1966

11. Harrigan, M. J., Sommer, A. W., Riemers, P. G., and Alers, G. A., "Effect of Rolling Texture on the Fatigue and Fracture Behavior of 6Al-2Sn-42r-6M. Ti Alloy Sheet," presented at 2nd International Conference on Titanium, May 1972

12. Curtis, R. E., Boyer, R. R., and Williams, J. C., "Rela-
     tionship Between Composition, Microstructure, and Stress
     Corrosion Cracking - in Salt Solution - in Titanium Alloys
     Trans. ASM, Vol 62, 1969, p 452

USE OF THE PRECRACKED CHARPY SPECIMEN
IN FRACTURE TOUGHNESS TESTING

R. A. Wullaert and D. R. Ireland
Effects Technology, Inc.
Santa Barbara, California

A. S. Tetelman
University of California
Los Angeles, California

ABSTRACT

Before the era of fracture mechanics, the
relatively simple and inexpensive Charpy V-notch
impact test was used to determine whether a material
was sufficiently tough for service conditions. The
advantages and disadvantages of the Charpy impact
test and the newer fracture toughness tests are
critically reviewed. Efforts to preserve the advantages of the Charpy impact test through empirical
correlations with newer tests, such as the drop
weight, dynamic tear and standard fracture mechanics
tests are discussed. Finally, it is shown how modification of the Charpy test by fatigue precracking
of the specimen and instrumentation of the impact
machine results in a fracture toughness test with
distinct advantages for most applications.

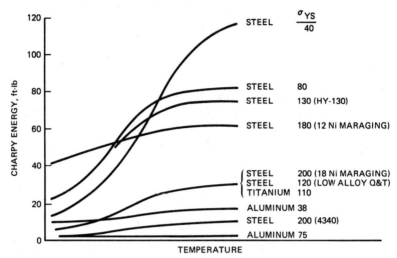

Fig. 1.   Typical Charpy V-notch energy vs temperature behavior of various materials

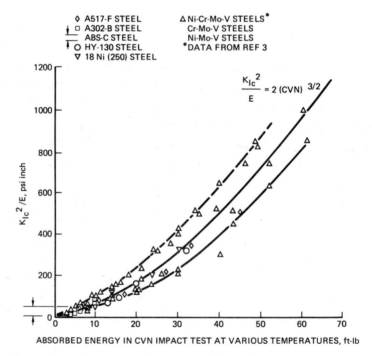

Fig. 2.   Relation between K_{Ic} and CVN values in the transition-temperature region. (2)

INTRODUCTION

Before the era of fracture mechanics, the Charpy V-notch impact test was essentially the only test used to determine whether a material was sufficiently tough for service conditions. It is still the most widely used test and has been standardized internationally. Toughness is measured in terms of energy absorbed or a ductile brittle transition temperature (DBTT). Typical Charpy V-notch curves for various materials are shown in Fig. 1. (1) The quantities measured in the Charpy impact test are total energy, lateral expansion (or notch contraction) and fracture surface appearance as a function of temperature at which the test was conducted. Adequate toughness is determined by a minimum energy requirement at a given temperature or a DBTT below anticipated service temperatures. Many definitions of the DBTT have been used, including the temperature corresponding to the nil ductility temperature (NDT) ft lb fix, 80% cleavage, 50% shear, 50% energy, and so on.

Although the Charpy V-notch test has been useful, it has some known deficiencies. Some of the criticisms of the Charpy test have been (a) it is inadequate for materials that do not show a sharp ductile to brittle transition, (b) it does not differentiate between crack initiation and propagation energies, (c) there is no direct relationship between energy absorbed or the DBTT and fracture parameters such as yield strength, fracture strength, and fracture toughness (K_{Ic}), (d) valid fracture toughness values (K_{Ic}) cannot be measured because of the blunt notch and small thickness of the Charpy specimen.

Even with these objections, many investigators still prefer the Charpy test because it is fast, relatively inexpensive and simple. It also has many years of correlation with service performance behind it. Because of the basic

attractiveness of the Charpy test, many empirical correlations
have been developed between Charpy data and parameters such
as the Nil Ductility Transition Temperature (NDTT) and fracture
toughness K_{Ic}.

Charpy Correlations. Probably the best known correlation
is the Navy correlation developed to relate the Nil Ductility
Transition Temperature determined from the drop weight test
to a Charpy energy value. The Liberty ship failures of the
second World War led to the Charpy 15 ft-lb NDT fix for ship
steels. The use of a correlation between energy absorbed
and the NDT temperature has been an integral part of the
Navy's approach to fracture safe design and has been incorporated into many codes. The use of this correlation is
limited to low and medium strength steels that exhibit a
ductile to brittle transition. The actual NDT ft-lb fix is
a function of yield strength and therefore must be empirically
determined for each class of steels.

In the past few years, correlations have been developed
between Charpy V-notch impact energies and static fracture
toughness K_{Ic}. The correlation established by the US Steel
group (2) for lower shelf and transition Charpy energies is
shown in Fig. 2. The steels ranged in yield strength from
39 ksi to 246 ksi. Almost all of the data above 30 ft-lb
were obtained from various rotor steels by Greenberg, et al.
(3) The scatter band for this correlation is substantial.
For example, at 30 ft-lb the spread in K_{Ic}^2/E values from 200
to 400 psi inch corresponds to a range in K_{Ic} values from
approximately 80 to 110 ksi$\sqrt{\text{inch}}$. This scatter is not surprising since there is no theoretical justification for a
correlation to exist. Thus a correlation is made between a
Charpy test that involves a relatively thin specimen, a blunt
crack (V-notch), a high strain rate, and a mixed mode fracture
(flat fracture plus shear lips); and a fracture mechanics test
that involves a sharp crack, a thick specimen, a slow strain
rate and a flat fracture mode.

The yield strength of low and medium strength steels increases with increasing strain rate and this produces a lower fracture toughness under dynamic conditions. Barsom and Rolfe (2) observed that fracture toughness (DBTT or K_{Ic}) was strain rate sensitive for steels with static yield strengths less than 120 ksi. Therefore a transition temperature region correlation between static K_{Ic} and dynamic C_V values would not be expected for steels with yield strengths less than 120 ksi. For steels with yield strengths greater than 120 ksi, it is still difficult to theoretically justify a correlation between C_V and K_{Ic} because of potentially large differences in fracture energies produced by root radius effects (initiation energy) or fracture mode differences (flat fracture and shear lip energies).

Barsom and Rolfe (2) also obtained an empirical correlation between C_V values in the upper shelf region and K_{Ic}. The correlation was based on steels with yield strengths between 100 and 246 ksi and all of the tests were performed at 80°F. The results shown in Fig. 3 indicate a rather good correlation for these conditions. The loading rate difference between the C_V and K_{Ic} tests may not be a factor in this correlation since the fracture toughness of most of the materials was strain rate insensitive (σ_y > 120 ksi). However, it should be noted that the upper shelf energy increased with strain rate for steels with σ_y < 180 ksi. The micro-fracture mechanism for a given steel was probably the same in the C_V and K_{Ic} tests since the tests were performed at the same temperature in the upper shelf region. Notch acuity may not be important in the upper shelf region because of the relatively large amount of local deformation that precedes fracture. In general, a good correlation between Charpy upper shelf values and K_{Ic} would be expected if $K_{Ic} = K_{Id}$ and the same micro-fracture mechanism occurs in both tests.

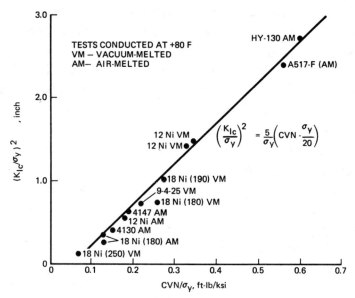

Fig. 3.   Relation between K_{Ic} and CVN values in the upper-shelf region. (2)

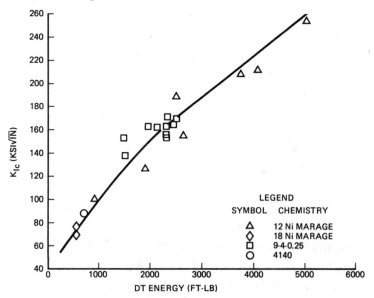

Fig. 4.   Relation between 1-in. dynamic tear energy and K_{Ic} values for various high-strength steels. (5)

Corten and Sailors (4) have reported a new empirical correlation between C_V and K_{Ic} for the Charpy transition region that is based on the US Steel correlation data plus recent results on pressure vessels steels such as A533B. Using materials with yield strengths less than approximately 120 ksi and using C_V values in the range of 5 to 50 ft-lb, they found a correlation of the form

$$\frac{K_{Ic}^2}{E} = 8C_V \tag{1}$$

This equation approximately describes the data in Fig. 2 in the range of 5 to 30 ft-lb. Above 30 ft-lb, Eq 1 is a linear extrapolation of the low C_V data in Fig. 2. Equation 1 was also reported in the form

$$K_{Ic} = 15.5(C_V)^{\frac{1}{2}} \tag{2}$$

and is listed in Table 1 along with a similar equation obtained for a correlation between C_V and K_{Id},

$$K_{Id} = 15.873(C_V)^{0.375} \tag{3}$$

Equation 3 has the merit that dynamic energy values are being compared with dynamic fracture toughness values, but there still exists a difference in notch acuity between the two tests.

Empirical correlations have also been obtained between K_{Ic} and energy values obtained from the dynamic tear test (DT). These correlations have been reported as graphs rather than equations of the type listed in Table 1. An example of the correlation for various high strength steels (5) is shown in Fig. 4. Similar graphs have been developed for aluminum alloys (6) and titanium alloys. (7) These empirical correlations are a fundamental part of the Ratio Analysis Diagram (RAD) approach to fracture-safe design proposed by Pellini and associates (8) at the Naval Research Laboratory. The RAD procedure can only be used in the upper shelf energy region and generally applies only to metals that are not rate sensitive. Since

TABLE 1

CHARPY ENERGY - FRACTURE MECHANICS CORRELATIONS FOR STEELS

1. Barsom, Rolfe and Novak (Eleven structural steels)[2]

$$\frac{K_{Ic}^2}{E} = 2(C_V)^{3/2} \qquad \text{Lower shelf and transition region}$$
$$\sigma_y = 39 \text{ to } 246 \text{ ksi}$$

$$(\frac{K_{Ic}}{\sigma_y})^2 = 5 \ [\frac{C_V}{\sigma_y} - 0.05] \qquad \text{Upper shelf, } \sigma_y = 100 \text{ to } 246 \text{ ksi}$$

2. Corten and Sailors (USS data plus HSST data)[4]

$$K_{Ic} = 15.5 \ (C_V)^{1/2} \qquad \text{Lower shelf, transition region}$$

$$K_{Id} = 15.873 \ (C_V)^{0.375} \qquad \text{Lower shelf, transition region}$$

3. Begley and Logsdon (Rotor steels)[10]

$$K_{Ic} = 0.45 \ \sigma_y \qquad \text{at } C_V \ 100\% \text{ brittle fracture temperature}$$

4. General Observation (Steels)[3,9,10]

$$\frac{K_{Ic}}{\sigma_y} \cong 1.0 \qquad \text{at NDT temperature}$$

the DT specimen has a sharp flaw, a reasonable correlation
between K_{Ic} and DT would be expected for a <u>specific</u> class of
strain rate insensitive materials, since notch acuity and
strain rate effects are not involved.

It is clear that no single empirical correlation between
K_{Ic} and C_V has been developed that fits all of the available
data. Another approach to establishing a correlation between
C_V and K_{Ic} has been to develop a relationship between K_{Ic} and
σ_y at a specific temperature. Some investigators (3,9,10)
have observed for specific steels that

$$\frac{K_{Ic}}{\sigma_y} \approx 1.0 \qquad (T = NDT) \tag{4}$$

at the NDT temperature. The NDT temperature is determined
from the Charpy energy curve by use of the NDT ft-lb fix.
If σ_y is known at this temperature, K_{Ic} can be calculated
using Eq 4. Begley and Logsdon (10) have calculated that

$$\frac{K_{Ic}}{\sigma_y} = 0.45 \quad T = 100\% \ C_V \text{ brittle fracture} \tag{5}$$

at the temperature corresponding to the appearance of 100%
brittle fracture in a Charpy V-notch specimen. K_{Ic} can be
calculated if σ_y is known at this temperature.

One obvious shortcoming of this approach is that it provides a correlation between K_{Ic} and Charpy data only at one
temperature and the yield strength must be independently
measured at this temperature. This approach depends on some
empirical correlation between a temperature determined by a
dynamic test and a ratio of static properties. There is no
guarantee that this relationship will be the same for different materials or material conditions, or even that Eq 4
and 5 will hold for different classes of material.

The many theoretical hurdles to the existence of a correlation between a slow, sharp notched fracture mechanics test
and a dynamic, blunt notched Charpy test would be expected

to discourage attempts at achieving a meaningful correlation. The mere fact that so many correlations have been attempted clearly illustrates the value placed on the Charpy test. However, as is the case for most empirical correlations, the relationship obtained for a given class of material may not be applicable to other materials or even to the same material in a different condition (i.e., welded, forged, irradiated).

One approach to minimizing the differences between the K_{Ic} test and the Charpy test has been to modify the Charpy specimen and the Charpy machine. Specimen modifications have included fatigue precracking to minimize initiation energy and side notching to increase constraint. Under appropriate conditions, slow bend tests on precracked Charpy specimens have been used to measure valid static fracture toughness K_{Ic}. (11) Fracture energy per unit fracture area (W/A) measurements on precracked Charpy specimens tested in slow bend or impact have been correlated with static fracture toughness K_{Ic}. (11,12) The impact machine has been instrumented so that load-deflection information is obtained during the impact test. This information is similar to that obtained in slow bend testing and can be analyzed in the same manner. (13) Instrumented impact tests on precracked Charpy specimens have been used to obtain dynamic fracture toughness K_{Id}. (14,15) The load-deflection data (obtained from slow bend or instrumented impact tests) on regular Charpy V-notch specimens has been analyzed to differentiate between the energies associated with the initiation and propagation of fracture. The load information also has been used to calculate yield strengths and fracture strengths. (13)

It seems appropriate after discussing the many limitations associated with obtaining a meaningful empirical correlation between different types of fracture toughness tests, to discuss the similarities and differences between the leading tests in more detail. An attempt will be made to categorize each test with respect to testing variables, data generated, and desirable qualities.

Comparison of Fracture Toughness Tests. Fracture toughness tests can be divided into two general groups; those that
measure energy absorbed and those that measure critical loads.
Variables within these two general groups are usually specimen size, type of artificial flaw used, and the strain rate
of the test. Table 2 identifies the particular testing variables associated with four different fracture toughness tests.
The Charpy V-notch and dynamic tear tests are representative
of the energy transition approach to fracture safe design;
whereas the K_{Ic} or fracture mechanics test is representative
of the critical load or design stress-critical flaw size approach. The instrumented precracked Charpy test can be used
for both the energy transition or design data (K_{Id}) approach
to fracture safe design.

The type of data generated by each type of test is cat-
egorized in Table 3. The Charpy V-notch (C_V) and dynamic
tear (DT) tests measure only the total energy absorbed during
impact, while the fracture mechanics and instrumented precracked Charpy (IPCC$_V$) tests record load-time information
that allows separation of the total energy into initiation,
propagation, and shear lip energies. Fracture appearance
and lateral expansion measurements are mainly used in the C_V
and DT tests to supplement the total energy absorbed data.

The various fracture toughness tests have been graded
according to a list of qualities that would be found in the
ideal fracture toughness test (Table 4). Technical, economic
and human factor parameters were considered in compiling the
list of desirable characteristics.

Charpy V-Notch Test. The Charpy V-notch test scores very
well in the economic category because of the low cost associated with both the testing equipment and the preparation and
testing of small Charpy specimens. It also does well in the
human factor category because the test is simple and very
familiar to the testing community. In the technical category,

TABLE 2
TESTING VARIABLES FOR FRACTURE TOUGHNESS TESTS

VARIABLES	CHARPY V-NOTCH, C_V	DYNAMIC TEAR, DT	FRACTURE MECHANICS, K_{Ic}	INSTRUMENTED PRECRACKED CHARPY, I PCC_V
DIMENSIONS				
SMALL	●			●
MEDIUM-LARGE		●	●	
ROOT RADIUS				
ρ = 0.01"	●			
PRECRACKED		●	●	●
TEMP. CAPABILITY				
EASY	●			●
MODERATE		●		
EXPENSIVE			●	
STRAIN RATE				
HIGH (200 sec^{-1})	●	●		●
LOW			●	

TABLE 3
DATA GENERATED BY FRACTURE TOUGHNESS TESTS

DATA OUTPUT	CHARPY V-NOTCH, C_V	DYNAMIC TEAR, DT	FRACTURE MECHANICS, K_{Ic}	INSTRUMENTED PRECRACKED CHARPY, I PCC_V
ABSORBED ENERGY				
TOTAL ENERGY ONLY	●	●		
INITIATION, PROPAGATION, SHEAR LIP			●	●
LOAD				
YES			●	●
NO	●	●		
FRACTURE APPEARANCE				
YES	●	●		●
NOT USED			●	
LATERAL EXPANSION				
YES	●	●		●
NOT USED			●	

TABLE 4
TECHNICAL, ECONOMIC AND HUMAN FACTOR ADVANTAGES
ASSOCIATED WITH FRACTURE TOUGHNESS TESTS

ADVANTAGES	CHARPY V-NOTCH, C_V	DYNAMIC TEAR, DT	FRACTURE MECHANICS, K_{Ic}	INSTRUMENTED PRECRACKED CHARPY, I PCC_V
LOW COST	●	○	○	●
SIMPLE TEST	●	●	○	●
SMALL SIZE	●	○	○	●
FAMILIARITY	●	●	○	○
LARGE SAMPLING	●	○	○	●
HIGH STRAIN RATE	●	●	○	●
SHARP ENERGY TRANSITION	○	●	●	●
LOW INITIATION ENERGY	○	●	●	●
SMALL SHEAR LIP ENERGY	○	○	●	●
ENERGY SEPARATION POSSIBLE	○	○	●	●
DESIGN DATA K_{Ic}, K_{Id}	○	○	●	●
FULL THICKNESS BEHAVIOR	○	●	●	○
ESTABLISHED CORRELATION WITH SERVICE PERFORMANCE	●	●	○	○

● YES
○ NO

the high strain rate of the Charpy test provides conservative
values of toughness (low absorbed energy, high ductile-
brittle transition temperature) for most strain rate sensitive materials. The extensive historical correlation between
a material's Charpy V-notch value and its eventual service
performance is a distinct advantage of the "incumbent"
Charpy test.

Probably the most serious technical disadvantage of the
Charpy V-notch test is the fact that the blunt notch results
in a high initiation energy for fracture. Other disadvantages
are that the test does not allow energy separation, it does
not measure loads which can be related to metallurgical or
design parameters, and it does not measure thick section
behavior.

Dynamic Tear Test. The dynamic tear test (or drop weight
tear test) has some of the same advantages as the Charpy V-
notch test. The test is basically simple, involves high strain
rates, and is reasonably familiar to most people. The DT
test was developed to overcome some of the disadvantages of
the C_V test. Specifically, the DT test has a sharp starter
crack, exhibits a sharp energy transition, and can be used
to measure full thickness behavior. The sharp starter crack
produces a sharp knee in the energy transition curve and ensures that the Nil Ductility Transition Temperature (NDTT)
occurs in this knee region. The longer crack propagation
path available in the DT specimens (approximately four times
the C_V specimen for a 5/8-inch DT specimen) results in a
large amount of absorbed energy in the ductile temperature
range and thus a well-defined upper shelf energy. Thus the
combination of the sharp root radius and long crack propagation path for ductile fracture results in a sharp energy
transition curve.

Although the DT test has a low initiation energy component because of the sharp starter crack, it still has some

of the inherent disadvantages common to the energy transition
approach to fracture toughness testing. Like the C_V test,
the DT test does not allow energy separation and it does not
measure loads that are of interest to metallurgists and designers. In addition, the larger specimens required for both
longer crack propagation lengths and full thickness behavior
means that DT test equipment and specimen preparation is more
expensive compared to the C_V test. Another disadvantage of
the standard DT test is that the large shear lip energy component of the total energy (once the crack propagation has
stabilized) prevents determination of the plane strain fracture toughness in the transition temperature region. This
disadvantage could be removed if the test were instrumented
to separate fracture energy into initiation (flat), propagation (flat) and propagation (shear lip) components.

   Fracture Mechanics Test. The fracture mechanics test
was developed so that designers would be able to determine
a material parameter, fracture toughness K_{Ic}, which was independent of thickness and related design stresses σ to allow-
able flaw sizes a in structures $K \propto \sigma \, (\underline{a})^{\frac{1}{2}}$. The fracture
mechanics specimens used for comparison are the standard ASTM
precracked notch bend specimen or compact tension specimen.
This, in the case of the former specimen, seems appropriate
since the other fracture toughness tests discussed have been
of the notch bend type. Also in this comparison, only plane
strain fracture toughness K_{Ic} will be considered. To ensure
that valid plane strain conditions are achieved in a test,
the fracture mechanics specimen must meet rigid geometric
requirements such as sufficient thickness compared to the
plastic zone size expected and sufficient crack depth to
specimen depth. When a material has high toughness and/or
a low strength, the thickness required to obtain a valid
static value of fracture toughness (K_{Ic}) is usually greater
than the thickness of a Charpy specimen (∼0.4 inches).

The most distinct advantage of the fracture mechanics
test is that it measures the load required to cause a well
characterized flaw to propagate under a well known stress
state. Since load-deflection information is obtained, the
various energies associated with the fracture process can be
distinguished if desired. The fatigue precracked flaw requirement ensures a low crack initiation energy, and the
requirement for plane strain conditions ensures thick section behavior.

Probably the greatest disadvantages of the fracture
mechanics test are in the economic and human factor categories. The stringent geometric requirements usually mean large
specimens (relative to Charpy specimens) and therefore expensive testing equipment and expensive specimen preparation.
Valid specimens may even be thicker and more expensive than
the eventual product. The testing requirements are relatively
complicated. The relatively large and expensive specimens
can make large sampling techniques for alloy development or
quality control purposes prohibitive.

Instrumented Precracked Charpy Test. The instrumented
precracked Charpy test (instrumented "mini" DT test) is
essentially a new concept, although impact tests on precracked Charpy specimens using uninstrumented impact machines
have been conducted by investigators such as Hartbower (16)
for many years. Also, in recent years slow bend tests on
precracked Charpy specimens have been used to obtain load-
time information. However, only in the last few years has
the instrumented Charpy impact machine been used to measure
fracture toughness from precracked Charpy specimens.

The primary advantage of the instrumented precracked
Charpy test is that it combines the best features of the
energy transition approach to fracture toughness with the
capability of measuring important loads. It has all of the
advantages of the standard Charpy V-notch test (small specimen,

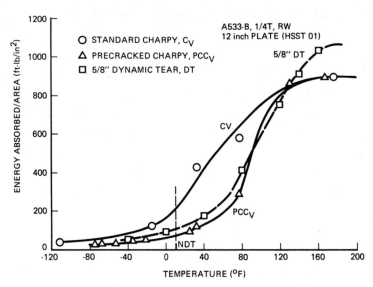

Fig. 5. Comparison of V-notch and precracked Charpy data with 5/8-in. dynamic tear data on A533-B steel

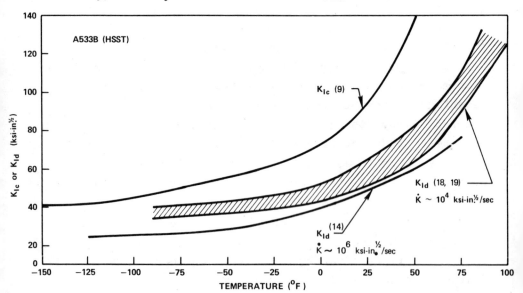

Fig. 6. Comparison of static, dynamic and instrumented precracked impact fracture toughness as a function of temperature

low cost, simple test, high strain rate, large sampling
capability) except for an established correlation with
service performance. It also has some of the advantages
of the dynamic tear test (sharp energy transition, low
initiation energy). Recording loads during the precracked
Charpy test means that energy separation is possible and that
fracture toughness K_{Id} can be measured under appropriate
conditions. The only serious disadvantage of the instrumented precracked Charpy test appears to be that it cannot
measure full thickness behavior.

INSTRUMENTED PRECRACKED CHARPY STUDIES

As pointed out previously, the technical differences
between the Charpy test and the dynamic tear or fracture
mechanics test can be minimized by precracking the Charpy
specimen or instrumenting the impact machine. The beneficial effects of fatigue precracking the Charpy V-notch
specimen and using only the total energy absorbed (W/A)
and the energy transition behavior as indications of fracture
toughness are illustrated in Fig. 5. Total energy absorbed
(W/A) values from V-notched and precracked Charpy specimens
of A533B steel are compared with 5/8-inch dynamic tear values
obtained by Loss (17) on identical material. The energy
transition curve for the precracked Charpy specimen is sharper
than the C_V curve and corresponds closely to the 5/8-inch
DT curve. Note that the NDT temperature occurs below the
knee of the precracked Charpy curve. Thus the small Charpy
specimen, when precracked, can be used to obtain the type of
data normally obtained from the dynamic tear test, at least
for 5/8-inch and 1-inch DT specimens.

The additional modification of instrumenting the Charpy
impact machine has been very useful for studies on low and
medium strength steels. The toughness of these steels is

such that large fracture mechanics specimens are required
to measure static fracture toughness K_{Ic} at ambient temperatures. As part of the AEC Heavy Section Steel Technology
(HSST) program on nuclear pressure vessel steels, the static
(9) and dynamic (18,19) fracture toughness of A533B steel
(σ_y ~70 ksi) has been measured as a function of temperature
(Fig. 6). The yield strength of this steel is strain rate
sensitive and $K_{Id} < K_{Ic}$. At the NDT temperature (+10°F),
6-inch thick specimens were required for valid K_{Ic} tests
and 2-inch thick specimens were required for valid K_{Id}
tests ($\dot{K}$ ~10^4ksi$\sqrt{in.}$/sec). Valid K_{Ic} values could not be
obtained above 50°F for 12-inch thick specimens and valid
K_{Id} values could not be obtained above 125°F for 8-inch thick
specimens. There are several points to be made concerning
these curves: (a) K_{Ic} and K_{Id} show the same type of transition temperature behavior as the Charpy and dynamic tear
curves for this steel (Fig. 5); (b) a change in the micro-
fracture mechanism from cleavage to fibrous tearing produces
a large increase in toughness, and increasing the specimen
thickness (constraint) has very little effect once this
metallurgical transition occurs; (c) dynamic testing allows
valid fracture toughness values to be obtained at higher
temperatures for a given thickness or allows use of a thinner
specimen at a given temperature; (d) the curves were very
costly to obtain (approximately 1.5 million dollars total).

The remaining curve in Fig. 6 represents the dynamic
fracture toughness of A533B steel determined from instrumented
precracked Charpy impact tests. (14) The impact velocity
of the Charpy hammer was approximately 200 inches/sec and
this corresponds to $\dot{K}$~10^6ksi$\sqrt{in.}$/sec. The higher strain rate
of the Charpy impact test causes a greater increase in the
yield strength of A533B steel and thus a lower K_{Id}. The
high strain rate allows valid K_{Id} measurements to be obtained
at the NDT temperature with Charpy thickness specimens

(0.394 inch). Server and Tetelman (14) found that

$$\frac{K_{Id}}{\sigma_{yd}} = 0.4 \qquad (T = NDT) \qquad (6)$$

at the NDT temperature. This equation can be used to estimate K_{Id} at the NDT temperature if σ_{yd} is known.

The Pressure Vessel Research Committee (PVRC) has proposed that a lower bound fracture toughness curve be used in the design of nuclear pressure vessels. Their recommended design curve essentially parallels the lower part of the scatter band for K_{Id} at $\dot{K}$ ~10^4~ksi$\sqrt{in.}$/sec. It is apparent from Fig. 6 that a slightly more conservative lower bound K_{Id} design curve can be obtained from instrumented precracked Charpy tests for temperatures up to 70°F. Most important of all, the K_{Id} curve from the instrumented precracked Charpy test can be determined very inexpensively (~$500) compared to the presently accepted techniques.

The most prevalent use to date of the precracked Charpy specimen has been by Hartbower and associates. (12,16,20,21) Their slow bend tests were instrumented, but unfortunately their impact tests were not. Total energy absorbed per unit of fracture area (W/A) was used to obtain semi-quantitative and sometimes quantitative measurements of fracture toughness (both K_c and K_{Ic}) for steel, titanium, and aluminum alloys. Hartbower has reviewed the effect of thickness, temperature, loading rate, composition and heat treatment on the (W/A) approach to fracture toughness measurements. (12) He has shown that W/A measurements on precracked Charpy specimens are highly sensitive to variations in toughness produced by the above parameters. For example, Hartbower's precracked Charpy results were probably the first indication of the phenomenon of increasing fracture toughness (W/A) with increasing rate of loading for many aerospace materials. (20)

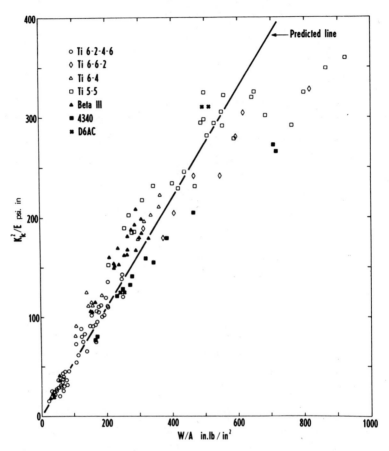

Fig. 7. K^2_{Ic}/E vs W/A for precracked specimens tested in slow bend

One material that many investigators have studied
using precracked Charpy specimens is Ti-6Al-4V. Hartbower
(12) found that slow bend W/A values $(W/A)_{SB}$ provided a good
estimate of K_{Ic} through the relationship

$$K_{Ic} = 0.17 \ (W/A)_{SB} + 16.2 \ psi\sqrt{in.} \qquad (7)$$

where $(W/A)_{SB}$ is the precracked Charpy slow bend value in
in.-lb/in.^{2} and valid K_{Ic} values were obtained from center
notched fracture mechanics specimens. Similarly, impact W/A
values $(W/A)_I$ were found to correlate with plane stress fracture toughness through the relationship

$$K_c = 0.10 \ (W/A)_I + 6.7 \ psi\sqrt{in.} \qquad (8)$$

Additional correlations between K_{Ic} and W/A from slow
bend and impact tests on precracked Charpy specimens of Ti-
6Al-4V have been reported by Newcomer and Garland (22) and
Ronald et al. (11) Figure 7 shows the correlation determined
by Ronald et al (11) between valid K_{Ic} values and slow bend
W/A measurements on precracked Charpy specimens of various
titanium and steel alloys. The predicted line corresponds
to the theoretical relationship expected between K_{Ic} and G_{Ic},

$$K_{Ic}^2 = \frac{E \ G_{Ic}}{(1-\nu^2)} \qquad (9)$$

where E is the elastic modulus and ν is Poisson's ratio.
Ronald assumed that

$$G_{Ic} = \alpha(W/A) \qquad (10)$$

where the factor $\alpha = \frac{1}{2}$ was used to account for the fact that
two fracture faces are formed. Combining Eq 9 and 10,

$$K_{Ic}^2 = \frac{E}{2(1-\nu^2)} \cdot (W/A) \qquad (11)$$

Ronald's predicted line was drawn by assuming Eq (11) and
using a value of 0.3 for ν and 16.5×10^6 psi for E. The
agreement between K_{Ic} and $(W/A)_{SB}$ is very good up to $\dfrac{K_{Ic}^2}{E}$
values of 300 psi in. When shear lip energies were subtracted
from the W/A values, the corrected W/A values fell closer to

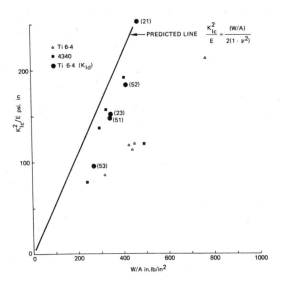

Fig. 8. K^2_{Ic} /E vs W/A for precracked specimens tested in impact

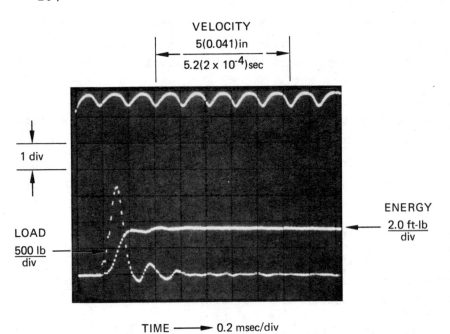

Fig. 9. Typical instrumented Charpy trace from impact test of
precracked Ti-6Al-4V Charpy specimen

the predicted line for the high toughness materials. Ronald's reason for using $\alpha = \frac{1}{2}$ appears incorrect, since the basic definition of G_{Ic} takes into account the formation of two fracture surfaces. However, the fact that $\alpha = \frac{1}{2}$ results in a good correlation between experimental results and theory indicates the need for knowing the initiation and propagation energy components of the total energy.

Ronald attempted a similar correlation between independently measured K_{Ic} data and W/A measured from impact test on precracked Charpy specimens. The results shown in Fig. 8 indicate that a slightly lower slope of the predicted line would fit the 4340 steel data, but that the Ti-6Al-4V data do not fit the assumptions of Eq.11 for $(W/A)_I$.

The fact that $(W/A)_I$ measurements do not correlate with K_{Ic} measurements according to theoretical predictions should not be surprising based on the previous comments about correlating static and dynamic results. The $(W/A)_I$ data for Ti-6Al-4V would fit a predicted line if only a quarter of the total energy absorbed was used to calculate fracture toughness, i.e., $\alpha = \frac{1}{4}$, $G_{Ic} = \frac{1}{4}(W/A)$. Implicit in this modification of Eq 10 is the assumption that $K_{Ic} = K_{Id}$ for Ti-6Al-4V.

A program is presently in progress to determine the validity of Eq 10 and 11 for strain rate sensitive and strain rate insensitive materials, (23) and to determine the reasons for the variation in α. Instrumented Charpy impact tests have been performed on precracked Charpy specimens of Ti-6Al-4V supplied by Ronald. A typical load-time trace obtained from an instrumented impact test is shown in Fig. 9. Fracture loads (maximum loads) were used to calculate dynamic fracture toughness K_{Id} and total energy measurements were used to calculate $(W/A)_I$. Energy measurements were obtained by electronic integration of the load-time trace and measured energy values were corrected to account for velocity changes in the Charpy hammer during the impact test. The $(W/A)_I$ values and corresponding K_{Id} values for Ti-6Al-4V in five different conditions

have been added to Ronald's data of Fig. 8. For a given
$(W/A)_I$ value, it is evident that $K_{Id} > K_{Ic}$.

The Ti-6Al-4V material used to obtain K_{Id} (closed
circles) was not identical to the original Ti-6Al-4V (open
triangles) used to obtain the K_{Ic} values shown in Fig. 8.
Slow bend precracked Charpy tests on the identical material
used to obtain K_{Id} were performed by Ronald (23) to obtain
$(W/A)_{SB}$ and K_{Ic} values. The $(W/A)_{SB}$ and $(W/A)_I$ values obtained from Ti-6Al-4V in various conditions are plotted in
Fig. 10 along with their corresponding K_{Ic} and K_{Id} values.
For a given strain rate, the correlation between K and W/A
is reasonably close to the predicted relationship. Material
with the same fabrication and thermal history is identified
by a given plate number. For a given condition of the Ti-
6Al-4V alloy, it was consistently found that $K_{Id} > K_{Ic}$ and
that $(W/A)_I > (W/A)_{SB}$. The strain rate sensitivity of the
fracture toughness K_{Id}/K_{Ic} ranged from 1.05 to 1.56 depending
upon the processing history of the titanium alloy. (23)

The conclusions to be drawn from this preliminary work
on titanium are:

(a). A good correlation exists between K_{Ic} measured by
standard ASTM techniques and $(W/A)_{SB}$ measured from precracked
Charpy specimens. A similar correlation exists between valid
K_{Id} values and $(W/A)_I$ obtained from an instrumented precracked Charpy test.

(b). The correlation between $K_{Ic,d}$ and $(W/A)_{SB,I}$ closely
fits the theoretical relationship between these quantities
assuming that $G_{Ic} = \alpha(W/A)$, where $\alpha = \frac{1}{2}$.

(c). A correlation between $(W/A)_I$ and K_{Ic} should not
be attempted for titanium alloys because the fracture toughness is strain rate sensitive and the strain rate sensitivity
is a function of the processing history.

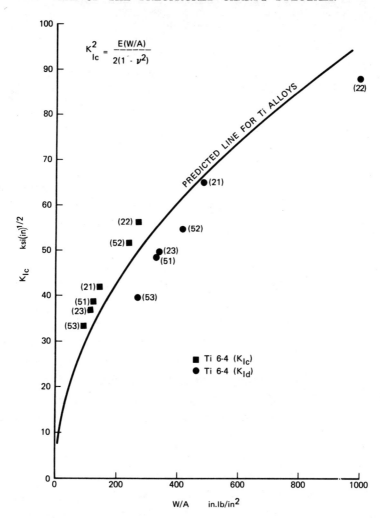

Fig. 10. K_{Ic} vs W/A for precracked specimens tested in slow bend and impact

SUMMARY

This paper has endeavored to review the past and present methods of fracture toughness testing and to establish the practical limitations of each type of test. The rapidly growing application of fracture toughness concepts in fracture-safe design and the general trend towards procurement to fracture toughness criteria requires that human and economic factors, in addition to technical factors, be considered in evaluating each type of fracture toughness test. The inherent economic and human factor advantages of the incumbent Charpy V-notch test have led to empirical correlations with technically superior fracture toughness tests. The practical and theoretical limitations of these empirical correlations have been discussed.

It is the conclusion of this paper that the instrumented precracked Charpy test is the most useful fracture toughness test when all factors are considered. It is the only test which successfully bridges the gap between the economically desirable Charpy test and the technically desirable fracture mechanics test. Because it does bridge this gap, it makes empirical correlations between K_{Ic} and C_V values an obsolete approach. A specific example of the value of directly measuring the relationship between fracture toughness (K_{Ic}, K_{Id}) and instrumented precracked Charpy data {$(W/A)_{SB}$, $(W/A)_I$} was presented for a Ti-6Al-4V alloy. Finally, the use of a lower bound K_{Id} curve for the design of thick-section nuclear pressure vessels represents a specific example of the use of the instrumented precracked Charpy test for fracture prevention and control.

References

1. Matthews, W. T., "The Role of Impact Testing in Characterizing the Toughness of Materials", _Impact Testing of Metals_, ASTM STP 466, American Society for Testing and Materials, 1970, pp 3-20

2. Barsom, J. M. and Rolfe, S. T., "Correlations Between K_{Ic} and Charpy V-Notch Test Results in the Transition-Temperature Range, _Ibid_, pp 281-302

3. Greenberg, M. D., Wessel, E. T., and Pryle, W. H., "Fracture Toughness of Turbine-Generator Rotor Forgings", _Journal Engineering Fracture Mechanics_, vol 1, No. 4, 1970, pp 653-674

4. Corten, J. T., and Sailors, R. H., "Relationship Between Material Fracture Toughness Using Fracture Mechanics and Transition Temperature Tests", T.&A.M. Report No. 346, University of Illinois, August, 1971

5. Lange, E. A., and Loss, J. J., "Dynamic Tear Energy-A Practical Performance Criterion for Fracture Resistance", _Impact Testing of Metals_, ASTM STP 466, American Society for Testing and Materials, 1970, pp 241-258

6. Judy, R. W., Jr., Goode, R. J., and Freed, C. N., "Fracture Toughness Characterization Procedures and Interpretations to Fracture Safe Design for Structural Aluminum Alloys", NRL Report 6879, Naval Research Laboratory, March, 1969

7. Goode, R. J., Judy, R. W.,Jr., and Huber, R. W., "Procedures for Fracture Toughness Characterization and Interpretations to Failure-Safe Design for Structural Titanium Alloys", NRL Report 6779, Naval Research Laboratory, Dec., 1968

8. Pellini, W. S., "Integration of Analytical Procedures for Fracture-Safe Design of Metal Structures", NRL Report 7251 Naval Research Laboratory, March, 1971

9. Shabbits, W. O., Pryle, W. H., and Wessel, E. T., "Heavy Section Fracture Toughness Properties of A533 Grade B Class 1 Steel Plate and Submerged Arc Weldment", WCAP-7414, Westinghouse Electric Corp., Dec., 1969

10. Begley, J. A., and Logsdon, W. A., "Correlation of Fracture Toughness and Charpy Properties for Rotor Steels", Scientific Paper 71-1E7-MSLRF-P1, Westinghouse Research Laboratories, July, 1971

11. Ronald, T. M. F., Hall, J. A., and Pierce, C. M., "Some Observations Pertaining to Simple Fracture Toughness Screening Tests for Titanium", AFML-TR-70-311, Air Force Materials Laboratory, March, 1971

12. Hartbower, C. E., Reuter, W. G., and Crimmins, P. P., "Tensile Properties and Fracture Toughness of 6Al-4V Titanium", AFML-TR-68-163, Air Force Materials Laboratory, Vol 1; Sept. 1968, Vol 2; March, 1969

13. Wullaert, R. A., "Applications of the Instrumented Charpy Impact Test", Impact Testing of Metals, ASTM STP 466, American Society for Testing and Materials, 1970, pp 148-164

14. Server, W. L. and Tetelman, A. S., "The Use of Pre-cracked Charpy Specimens to Determine Dynamic Fracture Toughness", UCLA Report Eng. - 7153, July 1971 (to be published in Engineering Fracture Mechanics)

15. Stelzman, W. J. and Berggren, R. G., "Preliminary Results from Static and Dynamic Fracture Toughness Tests on Precracked Charpy Specimens", Paper No. 25, Heavy Section Steel Technology Program 6th Annual Information Meeting, Oak Ridge National Laboratory, April 25, 1972

16. Hartbower, C. E., "Crack Initiation and Propagation in the V-Notch Charpy Impact Specimen", Welding Journal, Vol 36, No. 11, Nov., 1957, p 494-s

17. Loss, F. J., "Dynamic Tear Test Investigations of the Fracture Toughness of Thick-Section Steel", NRL Report 7056, Naval Research Laboratory, May, 1970

18. Crosley, P. B., and Ripling, E. J., "Crack Arrest Fracture Toughness of A-533 Class 1 Pressure Vessel Steel", HSSTP-TR-8, Materials Research Laboratory, March, 1970

19. Shabbits, W. O., "Dynamic Fracture Toughness Properties of Heavy Section A533 Grade B Class 1 Steel Plate", WCAP-6723, Westinghouse Electric Corporation, Dec., 1970

20. Orner, G. E., and Hartbower, C. E., "Sheet Fracture Toughness Evaluated by Charpy Impact and Slow Bend", Welding Journal, Vol 40, No. 9, Sept., 1961, p 405-s

21. Hartbower, C. E., "Materials Sensitive to Slow Rates of Straining", Impact Testing of Metals, ASTM STP 466, American Society for Testing and Materials, 1970, pp 113-147

APPLICATION OF FRACTURE TOUGHNESS CRITERIA TO DESIGN

FRACTURE CONTROL CONSIDERATIONS
IN AIRCRAFT STRUCTURAL DESIGN

Howard A. Wood
Aerospace Engineer
Air Force Flight Dynamics Laboratory
Wright-Patterson Air Force Base

ABSTRACT

This paper describes the relevant role of
fracture control criteria in the design, analysis
and qualification of aircraft structures.

A representative set of specifications for
fracture control is described in which such factors
as structural arrangement, accessibility and inspectability are of prime importance. The key seg-
ment of the program is the fracture analysis; a
corollary to current strength and fatigue analysis.
The successful accomplishment of the fracture analysis requires the development of sophisticated
analytical techniques to combine the complex loading
behavior with basic growth and fracture parameters.
Some examples of analysis and testing correlation
are presented in which the retardation of crack
growth due to intermittent overloads is taken into
consideration. The impact of sequence on the simulation of the flight loads is discussed. The manner
in which fracture mechanics and fracture control
procedures impact current design requirements is
described.

285

INTRODUCTION

The traditional Air Force approach to ensuring structural integrity through design analysis and demonstration of a "crack free" safe life is currently being augmented with specific requirements aimed at ensuring structural safety and thus reducing the probability of catastrophic failure or loss of aircraft due to the presence of undetected flaws throughout the service life of the air vehicle.

"Damage tolerant" or "damage resistant" are the terms most often used to describe the features of the design which prohibit the catastrophic loss of integrity. "Fail safe", for years a practice employed in commercial aircraft design, is one means of achieving damage resistance.

In current activities, in the Air Force and outside its activities, Fracture Control has become the more common term used to describe the general features of the plan to achieve structural safety. Fracture control for aircraft structures, as will be described in the paper, encompasses rather broad disciplines.

It is important to emphasize at this point that the essentials of the Air Force Structural Integrity Program (ASIP), as currently in effect, require the demonstration of static strength and crack-free fatigue quality. An extensive cyclic test program is the central feature of the fatigue certification program, wherein a full-scale article is tested using simulated flight load conditions to four times the design lifetime.

The achievement of "fatigue quality" or durability involves the careful attention to workmanship, surface finish and protection, detailed design, local stresses and ease of inspection. The absence of fatigue quality usually results in frequent and costly maintenance, and more important, system down time and loss of fleet readiness. Obviously, then, the

achievement and demonstration of crack-free fatigue life is
basic and essential. The implementation of fracture control
measures and the use of damage resistant design are not considered to be a substitute for basic fatigue consideration.
What is essential, however, is that consideration be given
to the probable existence of flaws within the basic primary
structure. This is the fundamental premise under which
fracture design and fracture analyses are conducted.

Naturally, there has been resistance among many to accept
the pre-existent flaw philosophy in aircraft design because
of weight penalties normally associated with supplemental
strength or life requirements. There are those who cite
systems performance degradation and the time and cost of
implementing fracture requirements as deterrents.

Answers to these and many more concerns are certain to
evolve with time since fracture programs have been initiated
and are currently underway on the B-1 and F-15 programs. In
addition, USAF regulations, standards, specifications and
guidelines for compliance are being formulated for use on
future systems.

In this paper, a general review of fracture control procedures will be presented, particularly as they impact analysis requirements in design.

THE NEED FOR FRACTURE CONTROL

The need for radically new regulations for structural
safety has arisen primarily because of the increasing usage
of high strength, highly efficient and limited ductility
materials necessary to achieve desired mission performance
with a minimum weight. Increasing initial systems and re-
placement costs have provided additional impetus to the need
for more reliable and safer aircraft. So-called conventional
design using materials such as aluminum have been produced

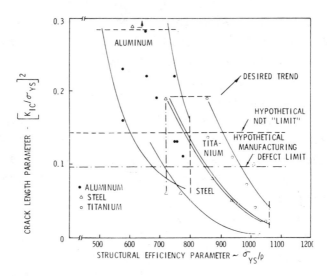

Fig. 1. Crack length parameter variation with structural efficiency parameter

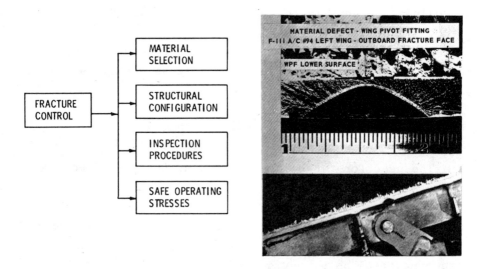

Fig. 2. Objectives of fracture control procedures

over the years with each new model being designed to higher
allowables, thus reducing the tolerance to both initial manufacturing defects and service produced cracks. In moderate
and heavy section applications critical flaw dimensions are
of the order of the part thickness and often much less, thus
making positive detection during normal service inspections
improbable.

In a previous summary (1), the author presented a review
of materials utilization wherein the variation of fracture
toughness with strength was shown for a wide cross section
of structural alloys. In general, trends indicate a decrease
in toughness with increasing strength level for most alloys.
In some instances, it has been shown that material processing
procedures can cause extremely wide differences in toughness
for otherwise equivalent strength levels (e.g., D6ac steel).
The most significant effect of general decreased toughness
with increased strength is noted when structural efficiency
or the strength to density ratio σ_{ys}/ρ is compared to the
parameter, $(K_{Ic}/\sigma_{ys})^2$. Data from Ref 1 is indicated in Fig.
1 for the range of aluminum, titanium and steel alloys common
to aircraft structure. Designs driven or controlled expressly
by minimum weight considerations require materials with maximum structural efficiency with titanium generally considered
to be superior from this point of view. The crack-length
parameter indicated may be quantitatively thought of as a
critical crack dimension for a through-the-thickness plane
strain situation where failure is assumed at a design limit
stress on the order of 0.6 σ_{ys}. In practice, it would be
mandatory that inspection procedures be developed to posi-
tively detect cracks prior to catastrophic failure, and unless detection is certain for these cases, the material usage
and/or design configuration should be reviewed. Hypothetical
defect limits are plotted in Fig. 1 to illustrate the fact
that some material applications may be unjustified. On the

other hand, large critical crack sizes are achievable with
some materials, i.e., those for which $(K_{Ic}/\sigma_{ys}) \rightarrow 1.0$.

Of the recent Air Force experiences with high strength
materials none is more dramatic or illustrative than that of
D6ac steel used in major structural locations of the F-111.
(2) An accident in December 1969, which has been attributed
to the presence of a critical defect in the steel wing pivot
fitting, was the singular event which caused widespread action
and reaction within the Air Force and the contractor and resulted in the formation of a fleet recovery program and
structural proof test effort.

The wing pivot flaw is an excellent example to illustrate
the need for fracture control considerations in design and
will be used here to assist in identifying major goals which
are to be achieved as the result of instituting fracture requirements.

In examining this failure, Fig. 2, one could conclude
that a higher toughness would have resulted in a larger critical crack size, possibly through-the-thickness and a much
improved probability of detection. For some cases, fuel
leakage might be expected. Thus, we can say that fracture
considerations should encourage the intelligent selection of
materials and control procurement and processing to ensure
consistent properties, and assist in establishing inspection
procedures including such requirements as positive detection
and leak before break situations. In addition to material
selection, growth of flaws can be lessened and critical crack
sizes increased considerably by limiting or controlling design stress. This can have additional benefit from the point
of view of fatigue resistance or durability and can significantly result in reduced maintenance cost and system down
time.

The wing pivot fitting used in this example is essentially
a single load path member. Failure of this element resulted

in loss of the aircraft. A more damage tolerant structural
arrangement, including possible multiple load paths or crack
arrest members, if properly designed, could have improved the
overall safety. These major goals are summarized in Fig. 2
and are, in essence, the key objectives of fracture control
in design.

ACHIEVEMENT OF GOALS - FRACTURE REQUIREMENTS

Aside from the selection, procurement and control of
processes for engineering materials, which are discussed by
Tupper (3), implementation of fracture considerations consists
of the formulation of safe crack life and strength goals that
must be satisfied by primary structure. Compliance with these
requirements is accomplished by analysis in all cases and
often requires substantiation by element, component or full-
scale testing. The fracture analysis is completed in connection with the conventional analysis (e.g., static and
fatigue) for which a flaw-free structure is assumed.

In the fulfillment of these analyses, basic materials
allowables, knowledge of operational environments and an
analysis capability to perform complex flaw growth and strength
analyses are among the items necessary. Supplemental tests
may be required to establish or substantiate stress intensity
relationships, verify real time and spectrum growth behavior,
and demonstrate crack arrest capability.

Within the USAF, initial attempts have been made to define fracture control programs for systems currently in the
design stages. Figure 3 includes a summary of the major
elements for the B-1 and F-15 programs. Plans to supplement
the Air Force Structural Integrity Program (ASIP) and Military Specifications Mil A8866 are currently being formulated
to provide general "across the board" requirements for all
future systems. The essential elements of this plan are shown

	B-1	F-15
• MATERIAL SELECTION	YES	YES
• MATERIAL CONTROL		
• AT SUPPLIER	YES (K_{IC})	INDIRECT (σ ys)
• IN PROCESS	EXTENSIVE	CRITICAL ITEMS
• FRACTURE TEST PROGRAM		
• BASIC ALLOWABLES DATA	EXTENSIVE	YES
(K_{IC}, da/dN, K_{ISCC} etc.)	(~ 2400 TESTS)	
• SPECTRUM LOADED TESTS	YES	
(SMALL ELEMENTS & CONPONENTS)	(~300 TESTS)	(~160 TESTS)
• FULL SCALE TESTS		
FAIL-SAFE	YES (1)	YES (1)
SAFE CRACK GROWTH	YES (2)	
• DESIGN & ANALYSIS		
• FAIL-SAFE DESIGN	YES (WCTS)	YES (WING ATTACH YES)
• SAFE "CRACK GROWTH" LIFE DESIGN	YES	YES
• QUALITY ASSURANCE		
• INDI CAPABILITY DEMONSTRATION	YES	YES
• SPECIAL N.D.I. PROCEDURES	YES	YES
(INCLUDING DWG. CONTROL)		

Fig. 3. Major elements of the B-1 and F-15 fracture control programs

Advisory Inputs		Responsible Organization	Approval Authority	Current Status
	USAF REG 80-13			
NONE	INSTRUCTS SPO's TO COMPLY WITH MIL-STD XXX	ASD	USAF HDQS	MINOR REVISIONS REQUIRED
	MIL-STD XXX			
I.A.G. AIA	DESCRIBES ASIP	ASD/EN	USAF HDQS	IN PREPARATION
	MIL-A-8866			
AIA	PROVIDES SPECIFIC DAMAGE TOLERANT REQ.	ASD/EN AFFDL	ASD	REQUIRES UPDATING
	FRACTURE MECHANICS HANDBOOK			
NONE		ASD/EN	ASD	BEING INITIATED
VOL I	GUIDELINES FOR COMPLIANCE	AFFDL	ASD/EN	
VOL II	BASIC DATA	AFML	ASD/EN	

Fig. 4. USAF specifications and control on damage tolerant design of military aircraft

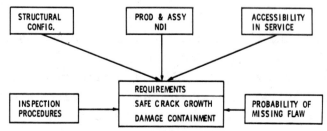

Fig. 5. Factors that affect requirements for fracture control

in Fig. 4. Note that in addition to the new specifications,
a Fracture Mechanics Handbook is being established to provide
potential contractors with material data and specific guidelines for compliance with the regulations.

To illustrate the type of requirements being considered
for general use a set of general design specifications has
been derived based on the assumption of pre-existing flaws
in new structure and the premise that (a), all primary structural members must be designed for a period of safe crack
growth and (b), the remaining or residual strength of all
structures should not be degraded below a specified strength
level throughout the service life of the aircraft.

In the derivation of the fracture specifications consideration has been given to the type of construction, to
the quality and confidence in the inspection procedures during manufacture, to the accessibility of the member in service
and to the type and frequency of in-service inspection.
These factors are summarized in Fig. 5.

Requirements have been assembled for three basic structural classes, Fig. 6. Class I includes all single load path
members, the failure of which would cause loss of the aircraft. Class II includes applications where critical damage
size is obvious. For this case, requirements stipulate that
crack arrest and containment will occur between stiffeners,
discontinuities, etc. Examples of Class II structures include pressure cabins, pressure vessels, or lightly stressed
structural regions. Gun fire or projectile damage is a typical consideration. Life and strength requirements for Class
II structures in general need not exceed those necessary for
one safe flight. Multiple load path structure is included
as Class III, where critical crack dimensions in any member
may be considerably less than the size of individual elements
and in fact, may be on the order of the part thickness. Major
emphasis in this discussion will be centered around requirements for Class I and Class III structure.

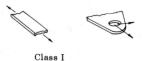

Class I
Single Load Path

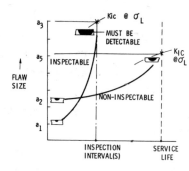

Safe Crack Growth Life Requirements
Class I Structure

Class II
Single Load Path
Damage Arrest Capability

Class I (monolithic, inspectable)-structure which is classified as single load path, the failure of which could cause loss of aircraft and which is accessible and easily inspectable in service shall be designed so that initial flaws of size a_1 will not grow to critical size (at limit design stress) during one inspection interval. To qualify as inspectable, however, it shall be demonstrated that the critical crack size at design limit stress shall be a through the thickness crack of dimension large enough to insure positive detection without major disassembly.

Class I (monolithic, non-inspectable)-structure which is classified as single load path, the failure of which would cause loss of aircraft, and which is neither accessible nor easily inspectable in service or which will not receive periodic inspection, shall be designed so that initial flaws of size a_2 will not grow to critical size (at limit design stress) in one lifetime.

Class II-shall have sufficient residual strength and life to complete mission following the incurrence of damage.

Fig. 6(a). Summary of requirements

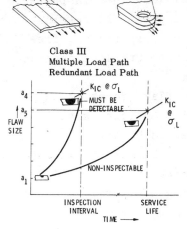

Safe Crack Growth Life Requirement
Class III Structure (Any Member)

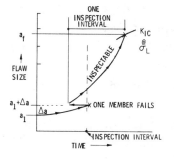

Safe Life Requirement For Remaining
Structure After Failure Of Single
Principal Element Requirement
Class III-Inspectable

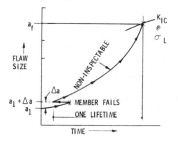

Safe Life Requirement For Remaining
Structure After Failure Of Single
Principal Element Requirement
Class III-Non-Inspectable

C. Class III (inspectable)-structure which consists of
multiple load paths,which is easily accessible for
inspection and for which periodic in service inspections are planned shall be designed so that
initial flaws of size a_1 in any member will not grow
to critical size (at design limit stress) in one inspection period and cause failure of the element.
In addition, one principal member shall be assumed
to fail at any time during the service life. The remaining structure (assumed to be flawed initially)
shall be capable of carrying design limit stress at
the end of one inspection interval. The safe crack
growth analysis for the remaining structure shall
be performed by assuming that each member is
flawed initially and that growth in each member
has continued at the assumed time of failure of the
principal element. The most critical time of member failure shall be determined and safe crack
growth allowable stress based on this criteria.

D. Class III (non-inspectable)-structure which consists of multiple load paths and fulfills the
residual strength requirements of C, but is neither
easily accessible or inspectable in service shall
be designed so that initial flaws in any member of
size a_1 shall not grow to critical size (at limit
design stress) in one lifetime. One principal element failure shall be assumed to occur at any point
in the design life. The remaining structure (assumed flawed initially) shall be capable of carrying
design limit stress at the end of one lifetime. The
safe crack growth analysis for the remaining structure shall be performed by assuming that each member is flawed initially and that growth on each member has continued at the assumed time of failure of
the principal element. The most critical time of
member failure shall be determined and the safe
crack growth allowable stress based on this
criteria.

Fig. 6(b).   Summary of requirements

The requirements are further subdivided into inspectable and noninspectable under each class. Inspectable refers to the probability of conducting in-service inspections, frequency of IRANS, etc. Each member or structure is classified accordingly.

Since the assumption is made that flaws do exist in new structures and can go undetected, full compliance with this philosophy necessitates that consideration be given to the probability of flaws existing in any or all members including each element of a multiple load path structure. This is easily rationalized since often the origin of cracking, e.g. stress corrosion, is common to all members.

In applying these requirements in a trade study, incentives should be logically assigned. For example, inspectable structure should have less stringent safe crack growth requirements than those that are noninspectable. In most cases, multiplicity of load path is more desirable than single design; however, highly inspectable, safe monolithic designs can be achieved. Certainly, they are preferred over noninspectable fail safe design.

In the requirements presented here, the incentives are achieved by assigning a smaller initial crack size to all inspectable Class I, monolithic and all Class III structures. Thus, these types of structures would feel a lesser impact from the fracture requirements and allowable safe crack growth stresses would be higher than those for the noninspectable Class I and Class III structures. These incentives could also be derived by assigning different factors to the required safe crack growth period, for example, multiple inspection periods based on different levels of confidence in the inspection techniques used in-service.

DISCUSSION OF INSPECTABLE DAMAGE LIMITS

Obviously, the key factors that control the allowable
safe crack growth stresses are the sizes of initial and final
cracks that are considered in the analysis. Initial cracks
reflect the production inspection capability of the contractor and should be substantiated. Under the B-1 program,
NDI capability is being demonstrated to qualify a detectable
range of crack size to 90% probability and a 95% confidence
limit. To give some insight into the relative capability of
the more common methods, Packman et al (4) published results
under Air Force sponsorship in which 100% assurance of detection was not achieved until a crack size of 0.25 inches was
reached for specimens in which the crack locations were unknown, Fig. 7. Flaw shape may be a factor in demonstrated
detection capability, and for this reason the flaw shape
parameter (a/Q) is perhaps a more correct way to describe the
severity of initial crack. Equivalent flaws based on depth,
a, and a/Q capability are illustrated in Fig. 8.

It should be important to qualify NDI capability for
flaws emanating from holes so as to measure any possible increase in detection sensitivity due to the presence of the
hole. Otherwise, it must be assumed that crack sizes demonstrated are acting in conjunction with the open hole. In
analysis, this is the more severe case.

If initial NDI capability is qualified on the basis of
a/Q rather than a fixed surface or depth value, the analyst
must assume the shallow crack condition and examine the possibility of this case becoming critical. Shallow cracks tend
to grow semicircular in a rather short period of time so long
as they remain subcritical. This phenomenon is illustrated
in Fig. 9 where growth in the depth direction only is assumed
for the shallow crack. The total life is the same regardless
of initial shape, so long as (a/Q) initial is the same and

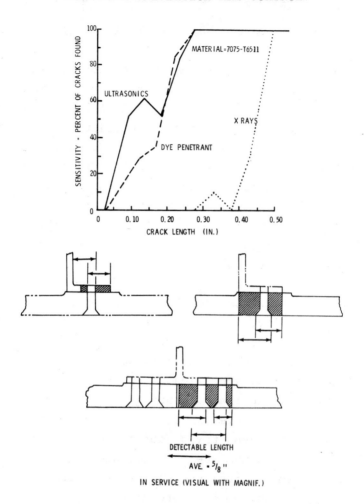

Fig. 7. Examples of demonstrated flaw detection capability

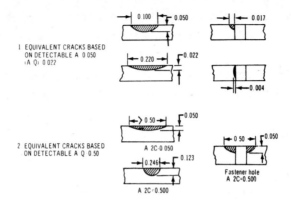

Fig. 8. Equivalent surface flaws for criteria based on demonstrated detection capability

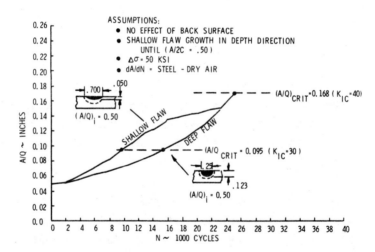

Fig. 9. Growth of equivalent surface flaws under sinusoidal loading from initial $(A/Q)_i = 0.050$

the flaw is allowed to grow to a semicircular shape, assuming no effects of free surfaces prior to achieving critical size.

The final crack size criteria based on fracture at critical K and maximum service load is supplemented by the requirement that critical size must be such that detection is certain. This is most important for the inspectable monolithic structure wherein safety and survival is based on the fact that the flaw must be found.

Obviously, geometry and thickness are primary in this case, although spectrum severity (stress level) may play an important role. To illustrate this fact, surface flaw growth tests in D6ac steel have been conducted under spectrum conditions for the F-111 to simulate the A/P #94 failure. (5) The results are shown in Fig. 10. For the 7.33g spectrum, growth was decelerated as the crack approached the back surface and critical fracture occurred prior to the transition to a through crack. When the level of maximum stress was reduced, growth proceeded without interruption with transition to a through-the-thickness crack. Thus, assurance must be given that final crack size is indeed a large through-the-thickness crack, otherwise, the condition should be reclassified as noninspectable. Bryan (6) has defined a detectable size for built-up aluminum structure for the B-52 using close visual examination with magnification, Fig. 7. It is interesting to note that a 2-inch crack remained undetected in this same test program and was 16 inches long when discovered. Similar cases of large undetected cracks have been reported for the C-130 during in-service examination. (7)

A "worst case" structure should be assumed for each analysis. Flaws are assumed to be orientated in the most unfavorable direction with respect to the stress field, materials properties, etc.

7.33g SPECTRUM
σ MAX 118 KSI
HI LO SEQUENCE

4.5g SPECTRUM
σ MAX 100 KSI
HI LO SEQUENCE

Fig. 10. Effect of spectrum of surface flaw growth transition -
          D6ac steel

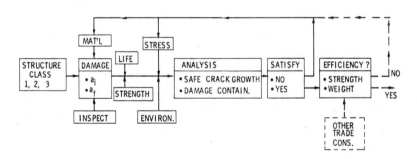

Fig. 11. Fracture control analyses for design trade studies

APPLICATION OF REQUIREMENTS

In practice, the analysis requirements would be exercised in the manner illustrated in Fig. 11 to perform design trade studies. Iterations of the analysis would be conducted until materials and stress levels consistent with flaw size and growth requirements are achieved.

To illustrate the application of the fracture analysis requirements, a representative tension structure for a fighter aircraft was considered and relative safe allowable stresses determined which would satisfy the requirements. (1) A blocked random maneuver stress spectrum was used in conjunction with the CRACKS computer routine to produce life versus maximum spectrum stress from two initial flaw sizes, a_1 = 0.050 and a_2 = 0.150. Only one material, 7075-T6, was investigated in this example as indicated in Fig. 12. The resultant design allowable stresses are summarized in Fig. 13. Note that the requirements for monolithic inspectable (A) could not be optimized using this material in this application. The allowable stress is based on achieving the a_3 dimension in the shortest time period. The maximum allowable safe crack growth stress for this limited example is achieved for the inspectable multiple load path, Class III structure. While this example cannot be used to completely judge the validity of the requirements, the relative allowables do, however, give indication to the desired trends and incentives. As mentioned previously, the safe crack growth, inspectable monolithic design must be considered as a desirable approach particularly if high toughness materials are employed with relatively low stresses in order that critical flaw dimensions are large. The most optimum approach to develop compatible requirements would therefore be to establish damage limits, safe crack growth periods and strength levels based on equal probability of failure for the various classes of structure.

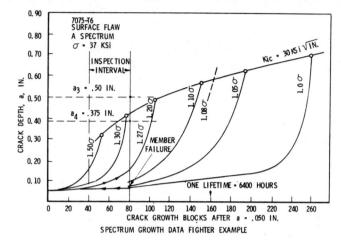

EXAMPLE TENSION COVER -

AIRCRAFT TYPE - FIGHTER

MATERIAL - 7075 - T6
K_{IC} = 30 KSI $\sqrt{IN}$
THICKNESS + 0.375"

SPECTRUM GROWTH DATA FIGHTER EXAMPLE

INITIAL FLAW ASSUMPTIONS (SURFACE FLAW) (a/2c) = 0.5)

a_1 = 0.050 IN (FOR ALL INSPECTABLE CASES)
a_2 = 0.150 IN (FOR ALL NON-INSPECTABLE CASES)

FINAL FLAW SIZE

a_4 = MINIMUM DETECTABLE SIZE = 0.375 IN
a_3 = MINIMUM ACCEPTABLE EQUIVALENT = 0.500 IN
FOR SINGLE LOAD PATH STRUCTURE

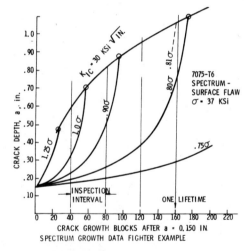

STRESS INFORMATION

- LIMIT DESIGN STRESS = 55.5 KSI
- SPECTRUM - 58 LAYER 40 HOUR BLOCK RANDOMIZED
- UNIT GROWTH DATA DERIVED FOR σ_{MAX} = 37.0 KSI

LIFE REQUIREMENTS

- SERVICE LIFE = 6400 HOURS
- INSPECTION INTERVAL = 1600 HOURS

Fig. 12.   Example of the application of fracture requirements

Requirement	Structure Class	Inspectability	Safe Crack Growth Period	Initial Crack Size	Equivalent Final Crack Size	Maximum Allowable Safe Crack Growth Stress	Remarks
A	Class I (monolithic)	Inspectable	one inspection period (¼ life)	$a_1=0.050$	$a_3=0.500$	$\sigma=42.5$	Allowable stress based on the achievement of a_3 (detectable size) in one inspection interval or greater. Optimum allowable stress cannt be achieved with this material application
A^1	Class I (monolithic)	Inspectable	two inspection periods (½ life)		$a_3=0.500$	$\sigma=35.0*$	Alternate approach based on larger initial flaw size and alternate inspection period requirement.
B	Class I (monolithic)	Non-inspectable	one lifetime	$a_2=0.150$	not req'd	$\sigma=31.0*$	
C	Class III	Inspectable	one inspection interval	$a_1=0.050$	$a_4=0.375$	$\sigma=47.0$	Any element – structures intact
			one inspection interval (¼ life) after failure of principal element	$a_1=0.050 +\Delta a$ prior to failure	not req'd	$\sigma=50.0$	Remaining structure – failure of element after first flight
						$\sigma=44.0$	Remaining structure – failure of element at ¼ lifetime
						$\sigma=41.0$	Remaining structure – failure of element at ½ lifetime
						$\sigma=40.0*$	Remaining structure – failure of element at 3/4 lifetime
D	Class III	Non-inspectable	one lifetime	$a_2=0.150$	not req'd	$\sigma=40$	Any element – structure intact
			portion of one life-time after failure of element	$a_2=0.150 +2\Delta a$ prior to failure	not req'd	$\sigma=33*$	Remaining structure – failure of element after first flight
						$\sigma=37$	Remaining structure – failure of element after ½ lifetime

* Design values

Fig. 13.   Summary – application of fracture requirements

This approach is currently being investigated by Lockheed
California Co. under sponsorship of the AFFDL. (7)   An
alternate version of the Class I inspection requirements is
indicated in Fig. 6 where a safe life of two inspection
intervals from a crack size a_2 is required. The same inspection requirements are levied, i.e., critical crack size
shall be large. Examining the spectrum growth data from Fig.
12, it is seen that a stress of $\sigma = 0.95\sigma$ will satisfy the
requirements. At the end of two inspection intervals, the
crack size would be greater than the $a_3 = 0.500$ requirements.

For the Class III case, it appears that safe life subsequent to failure of the principal member is dominant, as
might be expected.

ANALYSIS METHODOLOGY AND SUPPORTING DATA
REQUIRED TO IMPLEMENT FRACTURE PROCEDURES

The successful implementation of safe crack growth
analyses requires the capability to predict the growth behavior of flaws under complex spectrum loading and chemical
and thermal environments. An extensive amount of basic
material property data such as cyclic growth rate data (da/dn)
is required to support the analysis, particularly if there
are several materials being considered as possible candidates.

Computer routines have been developed to "integrate"
growth rate (da/dn) data and to account for the retardation
effects of overloads in variable amplitude spectra. The
CRACKS routine (8), developed at the AFFDL, includes a recently developed mathematical model for predicting the growth
delay effect. (9) This model, described in Fig. 14, is based
on the effect of the overload plastic zone on the subsequent
rate of growth. A hypothetical residual or reduction stress
is computed which suppresses the subsequent cyclic load. Retardation is accomplished in three modes, depending upon the

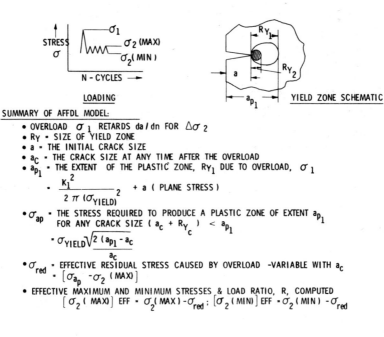

LOADING   YIELD ZONE SCHEMATIC

SUMMARY OF AFFDL MODEL:

- OVERLOAD σ_1 RETARDS da/dn FOR $\Delta\sigma_2$
- R_Y = SIZE OF YIELD ZONE
- a = THE INITIAL CRACK SIZE
- a_C = THE CRACK SIZE AT ANY TIME AFTER THE OVERLOAD
- a_{p_1} = THE EXTENT OF THE PLASTIC ZONE, R_{Y_1} DUE TO OVERLOAD, σ_1

$$= \frac{K_1^2}{2\pi(\sigma_{YIELD})^2} + a \quad (\text{PLANE STRESS})$$

- σ_{ap} = THE STRESS REQUIRED TO PRODUCE A PLASTIC ZONE OF EXTENT a_{p_1} FOR ANY CRACK SIZE $(a_C + R_{Y_C}) < a_{p_1}$

$$= \sigma_{YIELD}\sqrt{\frac{2(a_{p_1} - a_C)}{a_C}}$$

- σ_{red} = EFFECTIVE RESIDUAL STRESS CAUSED BY OVERLOAD — VARIABLE WITH a_C

$$= [\sigma_{a_p} - \sigma_2(\text{MAX})]$$

- EFFECTIVE MAXIMUM AND MINIMUM STRESSES & LOAD RATIO, R, COMPUTED

$$[\sigma_2(\text{MAX})]\text{ EFF} = \sigma_2(\text{MAX}) - \sigma_{red}; \quad [\sigma_2(\text{MIN})]\text{ EFF} = \sigma_2(\text{MIN}) - \sigma_{red}$$

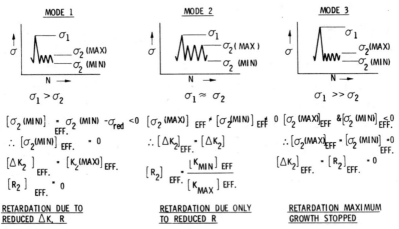

MODE 1	MODE 2	MODE 3

$\sigma_1 > \sigma_2$ $\sigma_1 \approx \sigma_2$ $\sigma_1 \gg \sigma_2$

$[\sigma_2(\text{MIN})]_{EFF.} = \sigma_2(\text{MIN}) - \sigma_{red} < 0$ $[\sigma_2(\text{MAX})]_{EFF} \neq [\sigma_2(\text{MIN})]_{EFF} \neq 0$ $[\sigma_2(\text{MAX})]_{EFF}$ & $[\sigma_2(\text{MIN})]_{EFF} \leq 0$

$\therefore [\sigma_2(\text{MIN})]_{EFF.} = 0$ $\therefore [\Delta K_2]_{EFF.} = [\Delta K_2]$ $\therefore [\sigma_2(\text{MAX})]_{EFF} = [\sigma_2(\text{MIN})]_{EFF} = 0$

$[\Delta K_2]_{EFF.} = [K_2(\text{MAX})]_{EFF.}$ $[R_2]_{EFF.} = \dfrac{[K_{MIN}]\text{ EFF}}{[K_{MAX}]\text{ EFF}}$ $[\Delta K_2]_{EFF.} = [R_2]_{EFF.} = 0$

$[R_2]_{EFF.} = 0$

RETARDATION DUE TO REDUCED ΔK, R   RETARDATION DUE ONLY TO REDUCED R   RETARDATION MAXIMUM GROWTH STOPPED

Fig. 14. Summary of AFFDL retardation model

relative size of the overload in relation to the subsequent cyclic level. Effective ΔK and R values are computed and reduced rates obtained from normal da/dn, ΔK relationships.

The model as currently being used requires no empirically derived parameters other than basic growth rate data for the material. Correlation between predicted growth and available test data has been moderately successful for the cases of simple constant amplitude loading with periodic single overloads and blocked randomized ordering of a maneuver spectrum. Examples of this correlation are shown in Fig. 15 and 16. In Fig. 16, several versions of the basic blocked spectra are indicated in which the effects of overall stress level and maximum stress truncation are compared. As might be expected, a faster growth is produced when the overall level of stress in spectrum A was increased. On the other hand, removal of the three maximum stress occurrences in each 200-hour block produced an acceleration of growth in the A3 spectrum, and the removal of the 13 highest levels produced a further growth acceleration in the A4 spectrum. Each block of growth consisted of approximately 17000 cycles of stress composed into 58 layers of constant amplitude.

Activity is currently underway to further validate this model for other materials and flight-by-flight spectra in which the occurrences of stress are distributed to simulate the aircraft mission including take-off and landing. In limited tests on D6ac steel, the flight-by-flight sequence indicates a lesser amount of retardation than the blocked random version. Additionally, little is known regarding the interaction effects of spectrum loading with chemical environment.

While moderate success in predicting spectrum growth has been demonstrated, a considerable amount of element testing is generally required under any systems program to verify predictions and stress intensity solution, particularly where

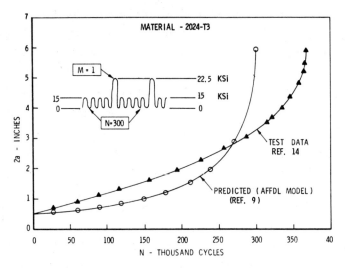

Fig. 15.   Comparison of test and predicted crack growth –
single overload

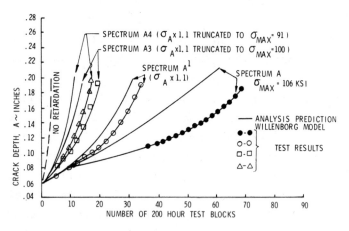

Fig. 16.   Comparison of predicted and actual growth – surface
flaws in D6ac steel

complex geometry and stress patterns exist. Basic growth
rate data can exhibit a spread of approximately two to one
even under carefully controlled conditions, as was demonstrated under the F-111 program. (10) Thus, spectrum results
which agree within a factor of two are not surprising, although most of our experience indicates that closer agreement
is most generally true.

Under spectrum conditions, considerable growth occurs
at low ΔK values. Growth rate data is generally lacking in
these ranges and until an adequate data base is derived, the
representation of the ΔK, da/dn relationship in this region
will be suspect and predicitions will continue to be in error.

SUMMARY

In this paper the author has attempted to present the
significant features of fracture control and fracture analysis
considerations in design. The true weight, cost, and performance trade-offs associated with the implementation of
requirements can best be judged by experience and application.
A fair assessment can only occur, however, if continued
materials and structures development efforts are directed
toward upgrading existing fracture mechanics and fracture
analysis technology.

References

1. Wood, H. A., "Fracture Control Procedures for Aircraft Structural Integrity," presented to the ICAF, May 13-14, 1971 (also published as AFFDL-TR-71-89, July 1971)

2. Hinders, U. A., "F-111 Design Experience - Use of High Strength Steel," ASD, WPAFB, OH, AIAA paper,70-884, presented at AIAA 2nd Aircraft Design and Operations meeting Los Angeles, CA, July 20-22, 1970

3. Tupper, N., "Fracture Mechanics Design Requirements - Review and Reflection," in this book

4. Packman, P. L., Vanderbilt University; Pearson, H. J., Owens, J. S., Lockheed/GA; Young, G., AFML, "The Application of a Fracture Mechanics - NDT Design Criterion for Aerospace Structures," WESTEC Conf, March 10, 1969, Los Angeles, CA

5. Wood, H. A., Engle, R. M., Haglage, T. L., AFFDL, WPAFB, OH, "The Analysis of Crack Propagation under Variable Amplitude Loading in Support of the F-111 Recovery Program, TM-71-3-FBR, Dec 1971

6. Bryan,D. F., The Boeing Co., "The B-52G-H Wing Cyclic Test Program," presented at the Air Force Conference on Fatigue and Fracture of Aircraft Structures and Materials, Dec 15-18, 1969 (AFFDL-TR-70-144)

7. Ekvall, J. C., Lockheed California Co., "Progress Report, LAC/002995, April 30 1971, Contract No. F33615-71-C-1324, "Engineering Criteria and Analysis Methodology for the Approval of Potential Fracture Resistant Primary Aircraft Structures," AFFDL, WPAFB, OH.

8. Engle, R. M., "CRACKS: A FORTRAN IV Digital Computer Program for CRACK Propagation Analysis," Air Force Flight Dynamics Laboratory, TR-70-107, Oct 1970

9. Willenborg, J. D., Engle, R. M., Wood, H. A., "A Crack Growth Retardation Model Using an Effective Stress Concept," Air Force Flight Dynamics Laboratory, TM-FBR-71-1, Jan 1971

10. Feddersen, C. E., Moon, D. P., "A Compilation and Evaluation of Crack Behavior Information on D6ac Steel Plate and Forging Materials for the F-111 Aircraft," Defense Metals Information Center, Battelle, Columbus Labs, June 25, 1971

APPLICATION OF FRACTURE MECHANICS
TO AIRCRAFT STRUCTURE

George E. Fitch, Jr.
North American Rockwell
B-1 Division
Los Angeles, California

ABSTRACT

Current and future concepts of fracture mechanics
criteria for aircraft structural design are discussed
along with a brief historical background establishing
the need for such criteria. The application of the
criteria is approached from the standpoint of impact-
ing on the selection of materials, configurations,
and operating stress levels during the early design
stages of an air vehicle structure.

The important analysis features, primarily associated with subcritical flaw growth, are presented.
Preliminary test results are shown that illustrate the
effects of flaw geometry and location on crack growth
under constant amplitude and spectrum loading, with
and without aggressive environments.

APPLICATION OF FRACTURE MECHANICS
TO AIRCRAFT STRUCTURE

Fracture mechanics, which originated with Griffith's
application to glass (1) in the early 1920's, found very
little practical application in engineering until the late

311

1930's and early 1940's when George Irwin made use of the
new discipline to solve the failure problems encountered in
welds of steel ships. The aircraft industry was introduced
to the concepts of flawed strength analysis in the 1950's
with the Comet, the first commercial jet transport. About
this same period of time, others were able to solve large
rocket motor case fracture problems using fracture mechanics.
(2) Also at this time the new concept was applied in material selection and sizing in the brazed steel honeycomb construction on the B-70. In 1959, the concepts of subcritical
flaw growth were formulated in part by Paris. (3) Then in
the late 1960's, the phenomena of fracture occurred on the
F-111 and was used extensively by General Dynamics in their
recovery program. (4)

New Specification. With this background, the Air Force
prepared a specification requiring design and analysis of
the B-1 structure to strength and life goals using the principles of linear elastic fracture mechanics. The primary
objective of the new specification is to achieve flight
safety with additional benefits to be derived in maintenance,
particularly for safe life structure.

Design Requirements. The new criteria emphasizes the
use of materials with good fracture toughness characteristics,
residual strength and subcritical flaw growth. More important, however, is the encouragement to use damage tolerant
design configurations, meaning multi-load path redundant
structural assemblies with specified levels of residual
static strength after failure of a single principal element.

Damage Tolerance. Structure that is to be classed as
damage tolerant must withstand 100% of limit load with a
single principal element broken. To visualize the impact
of this criteria, envision a simple structural member that
has been divided into two separate but equal load sharing
members. The damage tolerant residual strength requires one
of the two members to carry limit load that is two-thirds
of the total ultimate load. This amounts to a direct penalty

of 33-1/3% on the cross-sectional area requirements of the
two members. To offset this type of weight impact, of course,
it is imperative to use innovative design concepts that divide
the load bearing among several members, not two, without loss
of inspectability.

Life Requirements. To provide additional incentives
to the designer to use multi-load path concepts, the fatigue and
crack growth characteristics required of different types of
structure were graduated. Structure that is not damage
tolerant must be capable of containing crack growth from a
determinable initial flaw size to critical crack length defined at limit load within the air vehicle lifetime. Structure that is damage tolerant but not readily inspectable
must satisfy a less stringent life requirement that is the
combination of crack growth in the single principal element
and the fatigue life of the remaining structure after failure
of the single principal element.

Structure that is both damage tolerant and readily inspectable is required only to possess a fatigue life equal
to one-quarter air vehicle lifetime after failure of a single
principal element. These requirements are summarized in Fig.
1. The conditions that constitute readily inspectable structure are defined in the specification.

Initial Flaw Size. The specification allows the use
of initial flaw size of 0.150 inch in the critical dimension
for the flaw, without the use of any special nondestructive
testing (NDT) procedures. If special NDT procedures are to
be used, smaller initial flaw sizes may be used provided
they are demonstrated by an NDT demonstration test to specified probability levels of detection and confidence. The
demonstration involves the use of realistic specimens containing crack life defects processed by actual NDT production
procedures by production inspection personnel.

• DESIRABILITY OF "DAMAGE-TOLERANT" DESIGN CONFIGURATION

• ALLOWS FOR "SAFE-LIFE" DESIGN CONCEPT

• EMPHASIS ON "INSPECTABILITY"

• SELECTION OF MATERIAL

CRACKLIFE ≃ LIFE FROM a_{init} TO a_{crit}

DESIGN CRITERIA CATEGORIES

CONFIG \ ACCESS	DAMAGE TOLERANT RESIDUAL STRENGTH > 100% LIMIT LOAD	NOT DAMAGE TOLERANT (EITHER MONOLITHIC OR DOES NOT MEET RES STRENGTH RQMT)
READILY INSPECTABLE	FATIGUE LIFE REMAINING STRUCT > 1 / 4 A / V LIFETIME X SF	CRACK LIFE > 1 A / V LIFETIME
NOT READILY INSPECTABLE	FATIGUE LIFE (REMAINING STRUCT) ÷ 2.0 + CRACK LIFE > 1 A / V LIFETIME	

SF = 1.0   LEAK BEFORE BREAK
    = 2.0   OTHERWISE

Fig. 1. Fracture mechanics design requirements

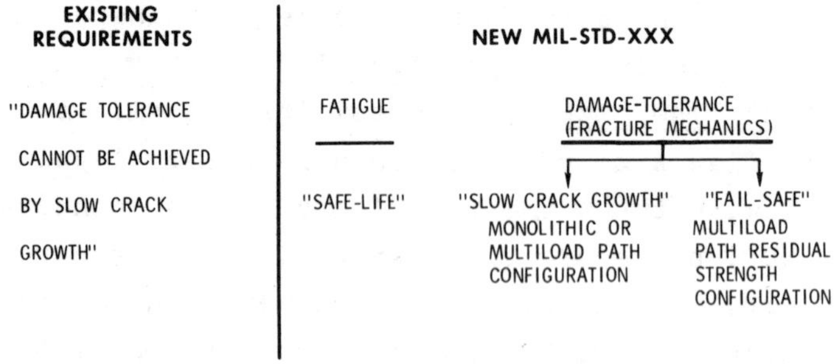

EXISTING REQUIREMENTS		NEW MIL-STD-XXX
"DAMAGE TOLERANCE CANNOT BE ACHIEVED BY SLOW CRACK GROWTH"	FATIGUE ⎯⎯ "SAFE-LIFE"	DAMAGE-TOLERANCE (FRACTURE MECHANICS)

DAMAGE-TOLERANCE (FRACTURE MECHANICS)

"SLOW CRACK GROWTH" MONOLITHIC OR MULTILOAD PATH CONFIGURATION

"FAIL-SAFE" MULTILOAD PATH RESIDUAL STRENGTH CONFIGURATION

Fig. 2. Evolving fracture mechanics and fatigue criteria

Analysis and Test Requirements. The new specification requires the application of the relatively new discipline of linear elastic fracture mechanics to analyze the sub-critical flaw growth characteristics of the critical tension elements of the primary structure. The assumption is made that the initial crack-like defects are in the most unfavorable location and orientation with respect to the direction of principal stress. The growth characteristics must consider the realistic cyclic load spectrum of stresses at that location in addition to the actual environment.

In addition to the material property tests for the determination of fracture toughness (K_{Ic}) and subcritical flaw growth rates, testing is required to substantiate the analysis. Proof-of-conformance tests are required for crack growth as well as residual strength.

New Emerging Criteria. It is apparent that the criteria invoked considers that the multi-load path configuration and structure is the only method of achieving damage tolerance. This is indeed the case as described by early editions of the ASIP document (5) which states that damage tolerance cannot be achieved by slow crack growth. However, when the USAF criteria branch and the industry advisory groups attacked the problem on integrating the new fracture mechanics criteria to the existing ASIP requirements, it was properly recognized that slow crack is a valid form of damage tolerance.

This new approach allows monolithic structure to compete with multi-load path structure on at least an equal conceptual basis. The best design configuration in a given situation then can be determined by the usual cost-strength-weight effectiveness factors without having to consider significant variations of flight safety among the different candidates. The concept also puts crack initiation fatigue life in the proper perspective with respect to crack growth and damage tolerance, as shown in Fig. 2. The fatigue requirements must bear the burden for ensuring minimum maintenance long life

	F_{tu}	F_{ty}	K_{I_c} (RW)
	KSI	KSI	KSI $\sqrt{IN.}$
ALUMINUM			
2024-T851	68	59	20
7075-T651	72	62	24
7075-T73	67	62	30
2219-T851	60	45	33
TITANIUM			
6AL-4V ANN	130	120	50
6AL-4V RA OR D / B	130	120	75
6AL-4V STA	130		40
STEEL			
HP 9Ni-4Co-0.20C	180	190	130
HP 9Ni-4Co-0.30C	220	185	100
300M	280	235	60
PH 13-8Mo H1000	205	190	70
PH 14-8Mo H1050	185	175	75
D6 AC	220	185	88

Fig. 3. Typical material properties

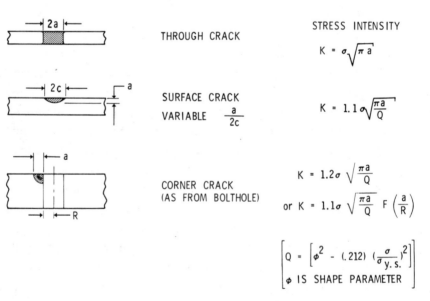

THROUGH CRACK

STRESS INTENSITY

$$K = \sigma \sqrt{\pi a}$$

SURFACE CRACK
VARIABLE $\dfrac{a}{2c}$

$$K = 1.1 \sigma \sqrt{\dfrac{\pi a}{Q}}$$

CORNER CRACK
(AS FROM BOLTHOLE)

$$K = 1.2 \sigma \sqrt{\dfrac{\pi a}{Q}}$$

$$\text{or } K = 1.1 \sigma \sqrt{\dfrac{\pi a}{Q}} \ F\left(\dfrac{a}{R}\right)$$

$$\left[\begin{array}{l} Q = \left[\phi^2 - (.212)\left(\dfrac{\sigma}{\sigma_{y.s.}}\right)^2\right] \\ \phi \text{ IS SHAPE PARAMETER} \end{array}\right]$$

Fig. 4. Typical flaw models

structure while damage tolerance requirements provide for flight safety.

Fracture Control. The fracture control procedures included in the B-1 specification are concentrated on the control of materials and their properties. This is somewhat reduced in scope from the total fracture control plans preferred by many experts for application to aerospace structures.

The prior existence of adequate static strength and fatigue strength criteria for military aircraft procurement has pre-empted the necessity for the more comprehensive approaches that tended to integrate the fracture mechanics approach into the static and fatigue requirements. The control procedures require the use of fracture toughness testing in material procurement, and a processing cycle to assure that materials with properties lower than those used in design are not used in the airplane structure.

Design Analysis Procedure. The main emphasis of these requirements, from an analytical standpoint, is subcritical flaw growth from initial length to critical length. The procedure requires integration of crack growth rate curves using the realistic stress spectrum at detail locations in the air vehicle structure. The critical length of the crack is determined by the critical stress intensity factors and the limit operating stress on the structural member. Selection of material with adequate toughness then is an important initial consideration in the design process. A list of materials and their strength characteristics together with K_{Ic}, the critical plane strain stress intensity factor, provides a basis for such a choice. Such a listing is presented in Fig. 3 for materials typical of those used in the B-1 program.

Flaw Models. The various types of flaws that are prevalent in aircraft structures have different stress intensity factors and will therefore grow at different rates. The flaw types typical of those encountered are shown in Fig. 4. The

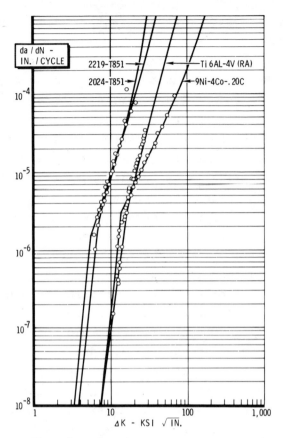

Fig. 5.   Crack growth rate data

through crack is a severe configuration that can grow rapidly.
A surface flaw has a stress intensity factor that depends
primarily on the aspect ratio (a/2c) of the flaw. Bolt holes
and other stress concentration factors create stress fields
in which corner cracks and surface flaws have high stress
intensity factors. For typical aircraft structures the corner
crack or midplane crack from a bolt hole is most common and
has maximum impact in the fracture mechanics analysis.

Crack Growth Rate. Crack growth rate curves are customarily plotted on a log-log scale as da/dN versus ΔK range
of stress intensity factor. Various curve fitting equations
are in use at present. For convenience of integration those
techniques that account for the range ratio (R) effects have
been widely used. A typical plot of fatigue-crack growth
data is shown in Fig. 5 for four materials at a range ratio
of zero, fitted with two branches of Forman equation exponents
and coefficients. Consideration is being given to fitting
with equations of the hyperbolic tangent form that will fair
into the critical stress intensity asymptote at the upper
end of the curve, and into the threshold value for crack
growth (K_{th}) at the lower end of the curve. Environment
plays an important role in crack growth rate of the various
materials. When aggressive environments are present during
subcritical flaw growth, then cyclic frequency also becomes
an important variable. Therefore, realistic environments
and frequency of load application must be used to collect
empirical crack growth rate data for use in predicting crack
growth in real structures.

Crack Growth Curves. Using the flaw model and the local
stress spectrum, the da/dN curve can be integrated to produce
crack growth curves such as shown in Fig. 6. Curves for
various operating stress levels can be calculated. These
curves are useful for showing graphically the effect of
initial flaw size (a) and fracture toughness (K_{Ic}). For small

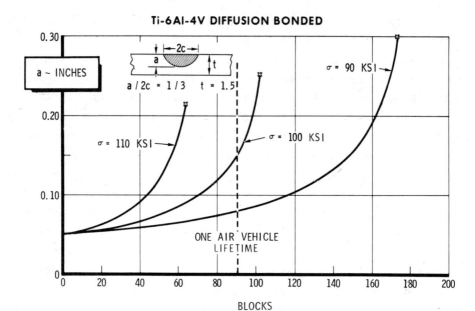

Fig. 6.   Crack growth curves

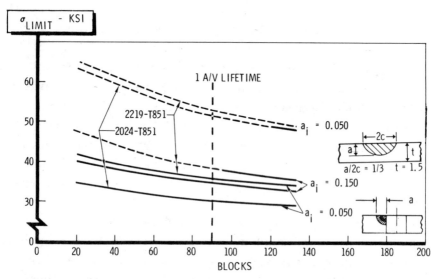

Fig. 7.   Allowable operating stress for crack growth

initial flaw sizes or low operating stress levels the growth
curve is initially of flat slope; the slope of the curve increases rapidly as critical conditions are approached. For
larger initial flaw sizes, or higher operating stresses, the
initial slope of the growth curve is high and critical conditions are approached rapidly.

Crack Growth Allowable Curves. The crack growth curves
at various stress levels can be replotted as stress versus
life curves and the stress can be scaled to represent limit
load operating stress, maximum spectrum stress or any convenient definable value pertinent to the detail design. Figure 7 shows such a plot in terms of limit load stress for
two materials, two flaw models, and two initial crack lengths.
Note that the increase of the initial size of a surface flaw
from 0.050 in. to 0.150 in. makes this flaw model virtually
as severe as the corner crack from a bolt hole with an initial
size of 0.050 in. The fracture mechanics analyst can use
the crack growth allowable curves to inform the designer that
the static strength design is either adequate or requires
modifications to meet crack growth requirements. The original
crack growth curves, Fig. 6, can be used to determine the
size of initial flaw that will just grow to critical length
in one air vehicle lifetime. The above procedures are applied to the critical tension material of the primary air
frame including the lower cover of the wing, the upper crown
structure of the fuselage, and both covers of the vertical
and horizontal stabilizers. On the B-1, most of the weight
impact has been due to applying the damage tolerance multi-
load path concepts to critical structures such as the wing
pivot. However, appreciable weight increases have been encountered due to the application of the requirement for
crack growth to one air vehicle lifetime. Most of the impact is in the lower cover of the wing outer panel and wing
carry-through structure. Except for the material properties,

BOLTHOLE AND SURFACE

S/N 8-13
MATL: 2024-T851 ALUMINUM
SPECTRUM: WING ~ G-A-G
ONLY
MAX STRESS: 33 KSI

S/N 8-35
MATL: 2024-T851 ALUMINUM
SPECTRUM: FUSELAGE
MAX STRESS: 18 KSI

S/N 8-17
MATL: 2024-T851 ALUMINUM
SPECTRUM: WING ~ COMPLETE
MAX STRESS: 25 KSI

S/N 9-5
MATL: 2219-T851 ALUMINUM
SPECTRUM: CONSTANT AMPLI.
MAX STRESS: 8 KSI & 16 KSI
(MARKING STRESS): 4 KSI
AND 8 KSI

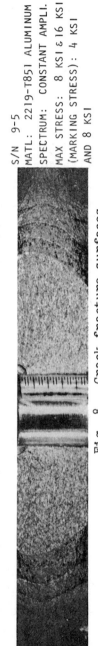

Fig. 8. Crack fracture surfaces

and the air vehicle spectrum, the single most important variable in the exercise of the criteria is the initial flaw size.

Test Programs. Element and component tests are utilized to verify analysis during design development. Proof-of-conformance testing is accomplished on full-scale design verification test specimens representing critical air frame components such as the crew module, wing and wing carry-through structure, and the empennage-aft fuselage.

Small Element Tests. Analysis verification tests are performed on specimens that are 4 inches wide and 0.50 inches thick at the test section. This specimen is used for surface flaws as well as bolt hole corner cracks. Figure 8 shows fracture surfaces of some of these test specimens. The top fracture surface shows a surface flaw tested under spectrum loading of fairly high stress intensity. Note the stable crack shape and lack of tendency to "tunnel" at the midplane. The third fracture surface from the top illustrates the tendency to "tunnel".

Surface Flaw Versus Bolt Hole Corner Crack. The rapid growth of a bolt hole corner crack is shown in Fig. 9. The total life of the part-through surface flaw of the same initial depth for a low stress intensity fuselage spectrum was almost twice that of the bolt hole crack.

Effect of Aspect Ratio. The surface flaw used for the previous comparison had an initial aspect ratio (a/2c) of 1 to 6. Figure 10 shows that the shallow flaw (a/2c = 1/6) grows much more rapidly than a flaw with initial aspect ratio of ½, a semi-circular flaw. The tests to date have shown that shallow flaws grow rapidly but change aspect ratios as they grow until arriving at a stable shape between a/2c of 1/3 to ½ under axial loading.

Environmental Effects. The effect of two aggressive environments on fatigue crack growth is compared to dry air in Fig. 11 for 2219-T851 aluminum. Although a definite trend

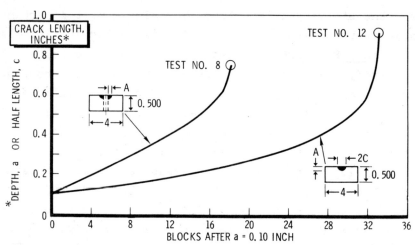

- COMPARISON OF CRACK GROWTH RATES OF A 6:1 ASPECT RATIO SURFACE FLAW AND A SEMICIRCULAR CORNER FLAW IN AN OPEN HOLE SUBJECTED TO THE SAME SPECTRUM
- FUSELAGE SPECTRUM, 5 BLOCKS = 1 A/V LIFE
- MAXIMUM SPECTRUM STRESS = 16 KSI
- 2024-T851 ALUMINUM PLATE

Fig. 9.   Comparison of crack growth, bolthole corner crack and surface flaw

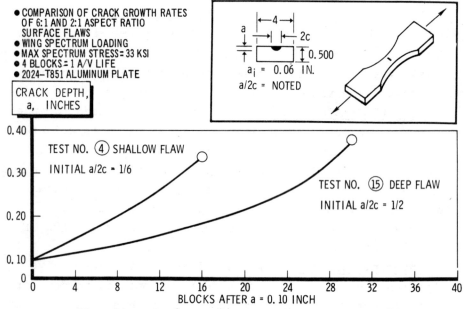

Fig. 10.   Shallow flaw vs deep flaw growth

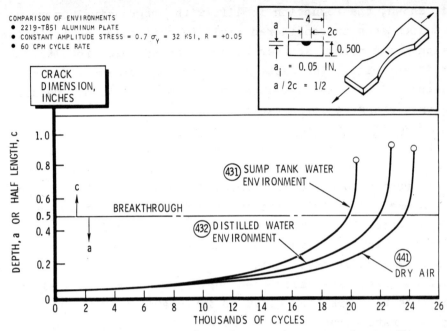

Fig. 11. Effect of environment on crack growth

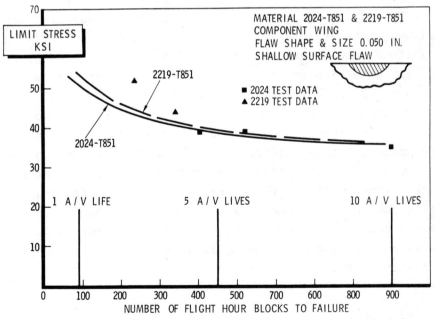

Fig. 12. Crack life allowable stresses vs test data

is shown, the reduction in life with progressively more severe
environments is considered small in this case and is in fact
within the normal scatter of crack growth test results for
this material. The tests shown were performed at a test frequency of 60 cpm. A greater reduction in life may result
when testing to lower cyclic frequency.

   Verification of Crack Growth Allowables. Crack life
data for 2024-T851 and 2219-T851 aluminum are shown in Fig.
12 in relation to the crack growth allowables determined by
integration to the da/dN versus K curves. At lives longer
than one air vehicle lifetime the agreement is good whereas
for shorter lives the test data are conservative; i.e., indicates higher allowables, compared to analytical results.
This particular test series is for surface flaws with initial
a/2c of 1/6. The calculated curves are conservative in part
because they are the result of integrations of the crack
growth rate curve that did not attempt to account for retardation effects due to variable amplitude spectrum loading.

   Retardation Effects. A computer program has been developed that accounts for the retarding effect of variable
amplitude load sequences. Figures 13 and 14 show comparisons
of test data with predicted crack growth curves with and
without the retardation effect factored into the analysis.
The retardation effect is variable as shown by the two charts
and is most dependent on the high to low load ratios that
are present in the spectrum. The model upon which the retardation is based utilizes the residual stress in the plastic
zone at the crack tip for mathematical representation. The
basic concept of the model was to develop a model that would
depend upon known material properties and therefore not require empirical correction as is necessary with other retardation methods.

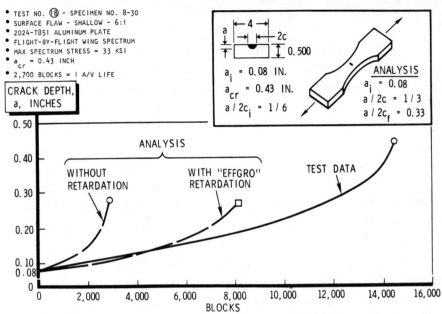

Fig. 13. Effect of retardation on predicted crack growth flight-by-flight spectrum

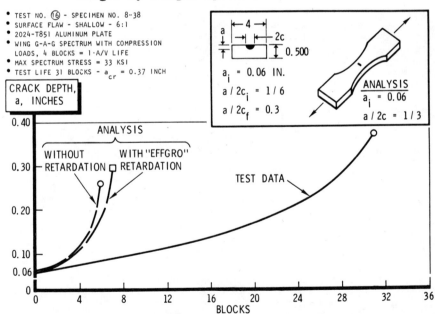

Fig. 14. Effect of retardation on predicted crack growth block loading spectrum

SUMMARY

In summary, a criteria for design and analysis of
critical air frame structure has been developed. The criteria
emphasizes subcritical flaw growth from an initial size to
critical crack length defined at limit load. With empirically
determined fracture properties for each structural material,
analytical procedures based on the stress intensity factor
concept of linear fracture mechanics are adequate to calculate
the crack growth life of structures with pre-existing flaws.
Application of the procedures has resulted in weight impacts
to critical structural components of the B-1 air frame. The
fracture mechanics requirements, in general, closely compete
with and often supplant the crack-initiation fatigue requirements for design impact. The most sensitive parameter
in the process appears to be the initial flaw size that is
to be determined by nondestructive inspection techniques.

References

1. Griffith, A. A., "The Phenomena of Rupture and Flow in Solids", Transactions of Royal Society of London V221, 1921. pp 163-198

2. Shannon, J. and W. Brown, "Progress in Fracture Mechanics", Machine Design, Mar. 5, 1970

3. Paris, P. et al, "A Rational Analytic Theory of Fatigue". Unpublished, 1959

4. Buntin, W. B., "Concept and Conduct of Proof Test of F-111 Production Aircraft". Presented to Royal Aeronautical Society, 27 Oct 1971

5. ASD 66-57 Air Force Aircraft Structural Integrity Program Requirements, February 1969

6. AFFDL-TR 71-89, Fracture Control Procedures for Aircraft Structural Integrity, Howard A. Wood, July 1971

TOUGHNESS CRITERIA AT THE
STRUCTURES/MATERIALS INTERFACE

Charles E. Feddersen
Project Leader
Structural Materials Division
Battelle's Columbus Laboratories

ABSTRACT

Several general facets of crack behavior and
damage tolerance are reviewed from both a structures
and a materials perspective. Since the achievement
of an effective level of structural damage tolerance
in practical hardware applications requires a balance
between materials capabilities and structural design
criteria, the critical interface between some of the
detail assumptions of mechanics and the actual factors
of materials processing are examined. In general,
the problem of developing damage-resistant hardware
cannot be solved solely from a single perspective.
Both the structures and the materials specialists
need a better understanding and greater appreciation
of the subtleties of their complementary technologies.

INTRODUCTION

Crack behavior is a physical phenomenon that is truly at
the interface of the structures and the materials technologies.
This is evidenced in the fact that the regularity of cracking

that is noted on the macroscopic scale is known to be an accumulation of microscopic damage processes.

Metallic materials generally are polycrystalline aggregates whose strength is dependent on the integrity of complex micromechanical cohesive forces. In contrast, the structural applications in which these materials are utilized are, of necessity, analyzed in terms of an idealized macromechanical continuum. Thus, to develop a coherent understanding of crack behavior, it is necessary to bridge the interface between these two technologies.

It is the objective of this presentation to describe, in engineering terms, a general perspective on crack behavior and structural damage tolerance to broaden the view of both the metallurgist and the mechanist. Four steps are taken in this presentation. First, an overview of the structural damage problem is presented. Second, the modes of crack behavior particularly significant to structural problems are discussed. Third, the problems of materials characterization and design allowables are considered. Fourth, the implication of these details in potential design applications are interpreted. Concluding remarks on research areas are presented in the final summary.

DESIGN FOR STRUCTURAL DAMAGE TOLERANCE

To design adequately for damage tolerance, the objectives for a safe and useful service life must be smoothly meshed with the damage constraints intrinsic to both the material and the structure. The design and service experience cycle whereby this is accomplished is illustrated in Fig. 1. The iteration and feedback implied in this flow chart reflect the learning process of an industry and can be applied quite generally.

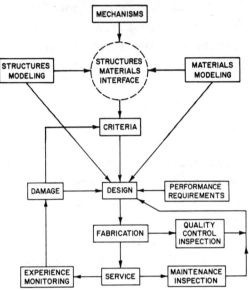

Fig. 1. Design and experience cycle of structural damage tolerance

TYPE	SOURCE	EXAMPLE
ACCIDENTAL	FABRICATION	MACHINING MARKS, TOOL CUTS, BURRS
	HANDLING	PUNCTURES SCRATCHES DROPPED HARDWARE
OPERATIONAL, OR IN-SERVICE	INTERNAL TO HARDWARE (INITIATION— PROPAGATION)	FATIGUE CORROSION STRESS CORROSION SUSTAINED LOAD, VISCOELASTIC, OR "CREEP"
	EXTERNAL	DEBRIS IMPINGEMENT HANDLING COMBAT DAMAGE

Fig. 2. Forms of structural damage

The upper portion of this chart represents the fracture and flaw propagation research and technology that is the central focus of this presentation. The lower portion of the chart is the more obvious flow of the engineering-manufacturing-service cycle characteristic of most production systems.

Two particular portions of this chart bear further elaboration at the outset of this discussion. One is the "damage" block. The other is the "mechanism/criterion" axis of the upper quadripole. It is this axis that forms the interface between structures and materials.

Forms of Structural Damage. The occurrence of damage in a structure is an unavoidable result of its fabrication and service. The nature of this damage is cited in the display of Fig. 2. The damage may be either critical at its initial occurrence or the site for crack initiation and propagation to critical fracture instability at a later time. The principal task of designing for damage tolerance is to evaluate these potential damage forms in terms of fracture and flaw propagation technology. Herein is the role of mechanisms and criteria.

Mechanisms and Criteria. In the upper quadripole of Fig. 1, mechanisms and criteria are counterpoised at the structures-materials interface. In the rational problem of structural design for damage tolerance, it is important to make a careful distinction between mechanisms and criteria. A mechanism is the actual physical process that is manifested as crack extension, be it stable or unstable. In contrast, a criterion is the logical analytical statement that describes or determines the propensity for that mechanism to be effective. Generally, the acknowledgment of a mechanism reflects our understanding of the physical world. For a fixed set of conditions, a mechanism cannot be eliminated; however, it can be controlled. The means of control is the establishment of criteria in this instance, damage-control criteria.

A proper balance in the understanding of mechanisms and criteria is the keystone to effective structural damage tolerance. Herein is the crux, or focal point of this presentation -- to recognize our knowledge of crack-behavior mechanisms and our ability to establish damage-tolerance criteria.

Basic Crack-Extension Mechanisms. When all of the damage processes are characterized, screened, and modeled, they may be segregated into one of two general categories. These are (a) energy instability and (b) strain instability. Energy instability refers to the regional instability at the crack tip wherein a volumetric limit to the plastic distortion, sustainable by the material and configuration, is encountered, and unstable crack advance is precipitated by redistribution of the strain energy. Strain instability refers to a more localized instability at the crack tip, wherein local ligaments reach a limiting elongation and crack advance is precipitated by the sequential transfer of crack-tip strains.

In the first category are those processes related to the Griffith (1) concept that, when the structural energy made available or released through crack extension is greater than that required to generate a new crack surface, crack extension proceeds in an unstable fashion. This may be expressed as

$$U_{release} > U_{crack\ extension} \tag{1}$$

This mechanism is fundamental to the Irwin (2) concept of the strain energy release rate, G, or equivalently the stress intensity factor, K, which are related as

$$K^2 = GE \tag{2}$$

where E = elastic modulus. For the idealized case of a central crack of half length, a, in an infinite plate under a remote tensile stress, S, expression 2 above becomes

$$K^2 = GE = S^2(\pi a) \tag{3}$$

The second category is concerned primarily with those situations in which crack extension is controlled by a limiting localized strain, dominantly plastic strain. This category

is associated with the Neuber (3) notch concepts and Wells'
(4) concept of crack opening displacement, δ.

In a real sense, these categories are not completely
independent; rather, they tend to define interdependent domains
of material behavior. For example, at low stress levels where
crack opening displacement, stress-intensity factor, and
strain energy release rates can be related by

$$\delta = \frac{K^2}{EY} = \frac{G}{Y} \tag{4}$$

where Y = tensile yield strength. This interrelationship is
more than coincidental. By Griffith-Irwin concepts, the plastic region at the crack tip is defined as a circular region
whose radius, r_y, may be expressed as

$$r_y = a \left(\frac{K}{Y}\right)^2 = a \left(\frac{GE}{Y^2}\right) \tag{5}$$

The unit volume, or area, of such a region may be expressed as

$$\text{Area} = \pi(r_y)^2 \sim \frac{(GE)^2}{Y^4} \tag{6}$$

such that the strain energy release rate may be interpreted
more generically as

$$G \sim \frac{Y^2}{E}(\text{Area})^{\frac{1}{2}} = Y \cdot \varepsilon_y \cdot r = Y \cdot \bar{r} \tag{7}$$

where $\varepsilon_y = Y/E$
   r = general measure of plastic zone radius
   $\bar{r} = \varepsilon_y \cdot r$.

The correlation between δ and some critically deformed liga-
ment, $\bar{r}$, is obvious.

These features are displayed schematically in Fig. 3.
The wedge-, circular-, and butterfly-shaped plastic zones can
be identified conceptually by a characteristic measure, r.

This strong interface between strain and energy instability has been inferred and demonstrated experimentally by a
number of investigators. It is commonly recognized that all
real structural materials do exhibit some degree (albeit a

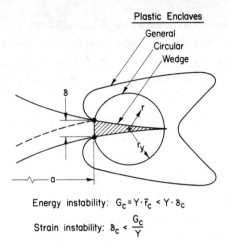

Energy instability: $G_c = Y \cdot \bar{r}_c < Y \cdot \delta_c$

Strain instability: $\delta_c < \dfrac{G_c}{Y}$

Fig. 3.   Idealized crack tip features

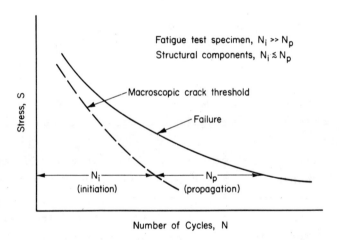

Fig. 4.   Fatigue crack initiation and development

very small degree) of plastic distortion at the crack tip
under load. It also has been confirmed recently that within
the plastic zone very intense deformations relatable to crack
opening displacement concepts exist directly adjacent to the
crack tip.

    <u>Criteria</u>. Criteria for crack behavior may be established
on one of two bases. Either they may be established from
an absolute understanding of the limits to the fundamental
mechanisms involved, or they may evolve merely from the experience or intuitive familiarity of dealing with a particular
damage process. That is, criteria may be rational or empirical. More specifically, there are instances of the crack
behavior modes, subsequently described, wherein very definite
and reliable bounds are known. There also are instances where
apparent synergistic behavior clouds our understanding and
one must make an arbitrary, hopefully conservative, judgment
of the critical limits. At the present time, it is most important to recognize the limitations of our knowledge of crack
behavior. While many aspects of crack behavior can be characterized discretely, many other aspects still require "ad
hoc" evaluation.

    And this is where we seem to find ourselves on many oc-
casions -- groping for a better means of quantifying some
mechanical behavior. It is a purpose of this presentation
to point out some of the critical mechanism/criteria areas
in crack behavior and to portray the understanding that is
necessary to effectively and efficiently cross the structures/
materials interface.

MODES OF CRACK BEHAVIOR

    As cracks initiate and extend by fatigue, stress cor-
rosion, or other material damage processes, they eventually
transcend the microscopic scale and reach the macroscopic

scale of concern to engineers. Regardless of their extension,
however, cracks continue to be a macroscopic accumulation of
microscopic damage that must be characterized "in the large"
by the basic instability mechanisms previously described.

In this portion of the presentation, an engineering
categorization of crack extension processes is described.
It is the intent of this section to illustrate the engineer's
perspective and describe the interpretive tools available
for characterizing the respective processes. These are current, but not necessarily fixed, concepts. In fact, it is
a purpose of this presentation to suggest and encourage more
advanced approaches that may have broader generality.

Crack Initiation. Crack initiation may begin with either
the discrete occurrence of some mechanical damage or as the
nucleation and accumulation of material damage from a fatigue
or corrosion process. An illustration of the latter case for
fatigue is shown in Fig. 4. A generalized S-N curve applicable
to either a small-size laboratory fatigue specimen or a larger
structural component is shown.

For engineering purposes, the initiation stage is complete,
and a macroscopic crack is existent when the crack is visible
to the naked eye or under 10X magnification. This is labeled
as the threshold or initiation of macroscopic cracking.

In small-size laboratory fatigue specimens, crack initiation and specimen failure may be nearly synonymous. However,
in larger structural components, the existence of a crack does
not necessarily imply imminent failure of the component. Substantial and useful structural life is accountable in the
cyclic crack extension or propagation that can be tolerated
prior to reaching conditions critical for fracture.

Crack Propagation. In highly critical structural components, the central focus of lifetime analysis is on the
crack-propagation phase following the initiation of a crack.
Representation of this behavior for a fatigue environment is

illustrated in Fig. 5. An analogous illustration can be created for stress-corrosion behavior.

As a physical or mechanical phenomenon, fatigue-crack propagation is noted as the growth or extension of a crack under cyclic loading. Experimental data of this type generally are defined as crack-growth data and are displayed in a crack-growth curve, as illustrated in the left-hand portion of Fig. 5.

Since the crack-growth curve is dependent on both crack length and applied load or stress level, the presentation of crack-growth curves is not the most concise means of representing crack behavior in a material. As with most dynamic processes, the rate behavior or slope, $\Delta a/\Delta N$, of the crack-growth curve provides a more fundamental characterization of the behavior. In general, the fatigue-crack propagation rate behavior can be evaluated as a function of some cyclic damage index, as illustrated in the right-hand portion of Fig. 5.

At least three regimes of crack-propagation behavior are evident. There appears first to be a threshold cyclic-damage index below which a fatigue crack will not propagate. This is then followed by a regime of stable and regular increase of the propagation rate. Finally, prior to fracture, a distinct tearing process may be noted with each applied cycle of loading.

The influence of various forms of the cyclic-damage index are illustrated in Fig. 6. The parametric influence of stress ratio is shown by the different layering of rate curves for each cyclic-damage index. It is interesting to note that if one utilizes the crack-opening-displacement relation of expression (4) in the form of an incremental operator, i.e.,

$$\Delta\delta = \frac{2K \cdot \Delta K}{EY} \tag{8}$$

and then uses this operator simply in the consistent dimensional form of $(K \cdot \Delta K)^{\frac{1}{2}}$, a significant consolidation of data can be obtained. However, since the absolute interrelationship

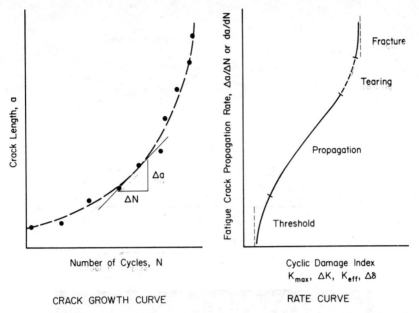

Fig. 5. Representation of fatigue crack growth behavior

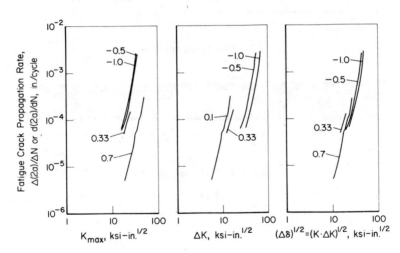

Fig. 6. Comparison of damage indexes for fatigue-crack propagation (From NASA TN D-5390)

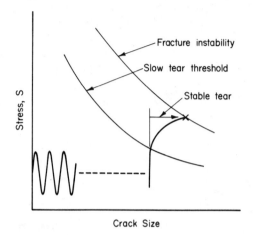

Fig. 7.   Terminal crack behavior

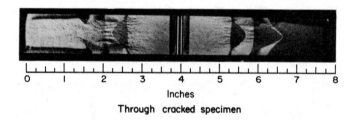

Inches
Through cracked specimen

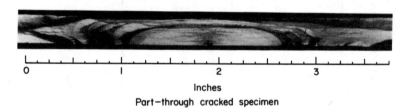

Inches
Part—through cracked specimen

Fig. 8.   Stable tear or crack extension prior to fracture

of these indexes has not been established in a rigorous
quantitative fashion, these illustrations are provided only
to demonstrate the variations that can be encountered in
analytical evaluations. In this instance, the data are for
center-crack tension panels wherein the full crack length,
2a, is denoted on the rate axis.

Terminal Behavior. The terminal stage of crack life includes not only fracture instability, but also a phase of
stable tear distinctly different from the fatigue process.
This interaction is shown in Fig. 7.

The existence of stable tear is illustrated in Fig. 8
and is shown for both center-crack and surface-flaw configurations. The dark textured areas indicate the stable tear
areas of crack extension that resulted from near-fracture
loading. The light textured areas represent subsequent
fatigue cracking accomplished at lower load levels to mark
the stable tear behavior.

MATERIALS CHARACTERIZATION

To successfully interpret and apply the generalized
knowledge of crack behavior, it is necessary to recognize
some basic aspects of materials and mechanics that are really
inseparable. These are outlined in the following subsections.

Basic Material Behavior. The crack-tip-extension process
is dependent on the localized deformation of the material
adjacent to the crack tip. This distortion is a very complex
process and is a manifestation of the fundamental elastic-
plastic characteristics of the material. A conceptual relationship between the stress-strain behavior of a material
and the associated zones of plastic deformation is illustrated
in Fig. 9.

In an ideally elastic-perfectly plastic material, the
lack of strain hardening limits the development of the plastic

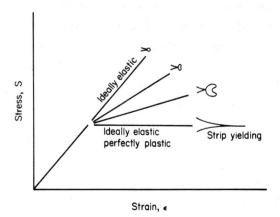

Fig. 9.   Stress-strain behavior and plastic zones in
          metallic materials

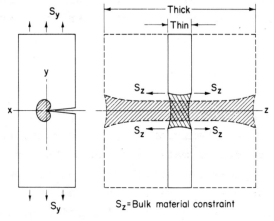

Fig. 10.   Influence of stress state or thickness on plastic
           zone development

zone to one dimension in the crack plane as shown. When strain
hardening is introduced, the initial plastic zone is a nucleus
for successive expansion of the plastic zone in two dimensions
as indicated by the "butterfly" shapes. In the limit of quasi-
elastic behavior, there is, at the crack tip, a small circular
zone of plastic deformation defined by the distortion-energy
theory.

This overly simplified illustration reflects qualitatively
the influence of the intrinsic ductility and the limiting
strain behavior of the material. Even when this is well characterized, it can be strongly affected by stress state and
geometric factors.

Stress State and Geometric Factors. At the interface
of materials and structures, the influence of stress state
and geometry are inseparable from the intrinsic material characteristics. It is important to recognize that although stress
state is not necessarily equivalent to the bulk size of a
material, the apparent effect of these two characteristics
may be indistinguishable for all practical purposes. A pic-
torial illustration of this apparent equivalency is shown in
Fig. 10. In essence, thick-section materials support varying
degrees of triaxiality at the crack tip due to shear lag in
the thickness direction, thereby constraining plastic-zone
development. In contrast, thin-section materials are largely
restricted to planar, or two dimensional, stress distributions.

Processing Factors. To further illustrate that toughness
characterization is neither entirely a mechanics problem nor
simply a materials problem, the effects of processing variables should be considered. The integrity of the microstructure of a material can be dependent upon the amount of mechanical work or reduction that is applied to the product form.
This may be the mechanical reduction of sheet or plate rolling,
the extrusion process, or forging. Subsequent thermal processing is also a discrete factor. Furthermore, the relative

roles of these processes appear to vary with the base metal
and alloys under consideration.

For example, titanium appears to be a material that is
particularly sensitive to the initial reduction process. In
the very thin sheet forms that have undergone extensive reduction, very regular quasi-plane-stress elastic fracture in
terms of K, or energy instability criterion, is noted. In
the thicker sections, however, where one would expect even
more regular and predictable behavior due to plane strain
stress states, there actually can be a rather perplexing in-
consistency in material toughness levels. It has been noted
in evaluating fracture toughness by means of the compact-
tension specimen test method ASTM E-399 that toughness actually increases to some degree with size. This, of course,
is contrary to the strict mechanical concept of stress-state
effects due to bulk material size. Although part of this
irregularity can be attributed to the nominal level of applied
load or stress, notable exceptions do remain. Recognizing
that thickness, at least in the case of titanium, is inversely proportional to reduction or contained mechanical
work, one is frequently led to the conclusion that the different specimen sizes also can reflect distinctly different
material product forms, as implied by Fig. 11. This is not
always fully appreciated by the mechanist. The aspect of
bulk size is a mutually important characterization problem
to both the analyst and the metallurgist.

In contrast, the 4000 series of low-alloy steels appears
to be most sensitive to the final thermal processing. A
broad range of tensile yield and ultimate strengths in these
materials can be obtained by appropriate quenching and tempering operations. The fracture toughness also can exhibit
a broad variation with this treatment, particularly the
rapidity of the quenching operation. This has been well documented in the fabrication experience of the F-111 aircraft.

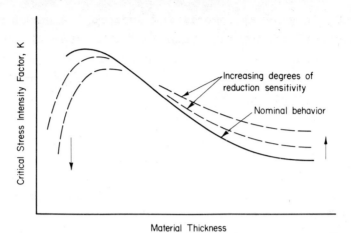

Fig. 11.   Influence of reduction on fracture behavior of
reduction-sensitive materials

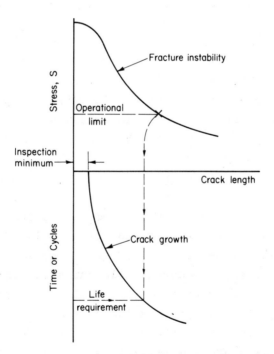

Fig. 12.   Service life determination

Thus, in general, processing factors are another inseparable part of distinguishing and characterizing material toughness. They are neither a negligible nor a primary element; rather, they are an essential constituent in considering toughness criteria.

APPLICATION TO DESIGN

The initial overview of structural damage tolerance presented in Fig. 1 depicts the flow and feedback cycle as a simple and obvious process. The implementation of this phase, however, is far from that.

The basic service life determination is diagrammed in Fig. 12. The operational limit in conjunction with the service life requirements determine the inspection limits, or proof test limits. This presumes an intimate and reliable knowledge of crack growth and fracture instability characteristics. While, as indicated by the companion presentations in this volume, there is a lot known about these properties, there also remains an intensive effort to interpret, consolidate, and standardize this information on a basic level as design allowables. Two of these problem areas are cited in the following sections.

Variance in Fatigue-Crack Propagation Rate Analysis. Scatter in experimental data can be the result of both material variation and experimental error. In either case, a dispersion range, or scatter band, of data is always expected in a practical engineering evaluation of material behavior.

In particular, for damage-tolerant structural design and structural life prediction, a concise statistical evaluation of fatigue-crack propagation data is very desirable. However, since most of the prominent rate models for fatigue-crack propagation are semi-empirical, there are intrinsic, unavoidable variations in the basic parameters that can be very misleading to the resulting behavioral interpretations. It is the purpose of this discussion to elucidate some of these factors.

Broad experimental observations, along with sound but simplistic concepts, of the dominant variables have led most investigators to consider fatigue-crack propagation as an exponential process that can be characterized by numerical parameters that are not physically measurable quantities. However, it is sometimes inferred that the resultant parameters or characteristic constants are indeed physical constants. Furthermore, it is often inferred that these parameters may be subject only to the usual 10, 20, or 50 per cent variation such as is encountered in other reference mechanical properties. In reality, because of the mathematical construction of the model, the variations that can be encountered may range well over an order of magnitude in numerical value. As a result, when one uses these constants to rank material behavior, the tremendous excursions in the numerical values of the associated constants often leads one to believe there is no correlation in the result when, indeed, the actual physical results may be nearly identical. This may be best illustrated in a consideration of the Paris model of fatigue-crack propagation, namely

$$\Delta a/\Delta N = C(\Delta K)^n$$

where ΔK is the cyclic-damage index, as displayed in Fig. 13.

It is not difficult to find large bodies of fatigue-crack propagation data that on a rate basis display the behavior illustrated in this figure. Here, it can be seen that a scatter band or dispersion range between 25 and 30 per cent of the logarithmic rate cycle may occur over a single logarithmic cycle of variation in domain of the independent variable. From a practical point of view, this band would be considered a tight consistent scatter band of data. However, an empirical evaluation of some subsets of this band may

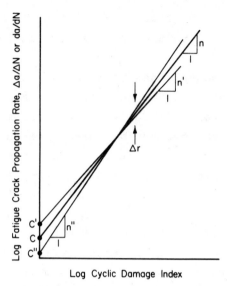

Fig. 13. Variances in fatigue-crack propagation rate analyses

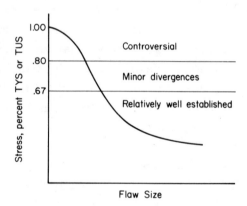

Fig. 14. Regimes of confidence in fracture modeling

suggest no correlation among the data when viewed from an analysis of the rate parameters above.

If a large quantity of data are found with a regular dispersion throughout this band, a representative average rate line may be represented simply by the parameters C and n. However, if one looked at selected constituent subsets of these data, extreme pairs of rate parameters (C', n' and C'', n'') could also be noted. Because of the resultant large numerical differences in the absolute values of C' and C'' and of n' and n'', one may erroneously conclude that the behavior of subsets is grossly different when, indeed, nearly identical behavior is being represented.

Assuming there is a dispersion range, Δr, the change in slope from the mean to either extreme is

$$\Delta n = \Delta r / \Delta \log (\Delta K)$$

An analogous relation exists for ΔC. If ΔK ranges from 10 to 50, or about 70 per cent of a log cycle with a dispersion range of 30 per cent, the variation between the extreme slopes may be

$$2\Delta n \approx .86$$

and the range of variation of the coefficients may be

$$2\Delta C \approx 14$$

or more than an order of magnitude.

Current Limits on Fracture Analysis. Similar variations exist in regard to our confidence in fracture analysis. In the lower ranges of elastic stresses, the concepts of linear elastic-fracture mechanics appear to be valid and very useful. As the boundary between elastic and plastic material behavior is transcended, increasing divergences in the mechanistic analysis of fracture mechanics are encountered. A qualitative display of the relative confidence in fracture analysis is illustrated in Fig. 14.

CONCLUSIONS

For many years, the inherent plasticity characteristics
of relatively low-strength materials allowed a measure of
"forgiveness" of damage in structures. The available plastic
deformation provided a safety net, a relief valve, or even
a margin for error in the process of design synthesis. However, as performance requirements are increased, a maximum
advantage must be taken of all material characteristics. As
a result, it is necessary to make a refined analysis and application of all aspects of the materials and structures
technologies. This is particularly important with regard to
damage tolerance. It is necessary to understand, in detail,
the loadings, the stress analysis, and the material behavior.

But most fundamentally important is an accurate understanding of the balance between criteria and the mechanisms.
As our understanding of cracking mechanisms advances, the
criteria must be adapted in as flexible a fashion as possible
to obtain the maximum effectiveness of damage tolerant structural designs. The descriptions presented herein reflect
today's level of technology. Tomorrow, we hope it will be
considerably advanced.

References

1. Griffith, A. A., "The Phenomena of Rupture and Flow in Solids", Transactions, Royal Soc., London, Vol 221, 1920

2. Irwin, G. R., "Analysis of Stresses and Strains Near the End of a Crack Traversing a Plate", Journal of Applied Mechanics, Vol 24, No. 3, 1957, pp 361-364

3. Neuber, H., "Theory of Notch Stresses: Principles for Exact Stress Calculations", J. W. Edwards, Ann Arbor, Michigan, 1946

4. Wells, A. A., "Unstable Crack Propagation in Metals", Proceedings of the Crack Propagation Symposium, Cranfield (1962)

APPLICATION OF FRACTURE MECHANICS
TO THE DESIGN OF DAMAGE-TOLERANT
STIFFENED AIRCRAFT STRUCTURE

T. Swift
Senior Engineer Scientist
Douglas Aircraft Company
McDonnell Douglas Corporation
Long Beach, California

ABSTRACT

Finite element analysis methods to determine
the effects of stiffeners on the crack tip stress
intensity factors are described in detail with
emphasis on stiffener attachment stiffness. Existing methods of analysis, which assume compatibility of strain between the stiffener and the
sheet using rigid attachments, can result in considerable error. Advanced computer technology has
made it possible, through finite element analysis
methods, to determine the effects of attachment
flexibility on stress distributions in cracked
stiffened structure. Examples are given to illustrate the difference between rigid attachment and
flexible attachment assumptions. The effects of
bond delamination on the crack tip stress intensity
and stiffener stress distribution are included.
Crack growth retardation due to the plastic
zone formed on high load cycles and its effect on
propagation under spectrum loading are considered.

It is shown that for 2024-T3 material, crack growth
retardation is offset to a large degree by slow
stable growth during the high load cycle and that
the amount of stable growth is dependent on the
stress intensity factor and plastic zone size of
the previous load history. It is also shown that
the stress intensity at the threshold of slow stable
growth is not only a material property but depends
almost entirely on the past load history.

Some difficulties are explained when flat panel
tests are used to predict the residual strength of
curved, stiffened structure containing cracks.
Crack growth in flat panels is compared to circumferential crack growth in a curved panel subjected
to biaxial loads and pressure.

INTRODUCTION

In the past, the fail-safe design of aircraft structures
incorporating the single element failure concept has proved
inadequate. The introduction of fracture mechanics into aircraft design analysis methods has helped to overcome this
inadequacy to some extent. Plane strain fracture mechanics
has almost become a science with the introduction of ASTM
standard testing techniques, but much of the art remains with
plane stress fracture of thin sheet components. This paper
describes some of the methods used in applying linear elastic
plane stress fracture mechanics to the design of stiffened,
thin sheet fuselage structure.

Modern jet transport aircraft are normally designed for
120,000 hours which, based on a scatter factor of two, represent 60,000 hours of crack-free service. (1) Imperfections
in manufacturing, such as badly driven rivets, mismatch of
parts causing residual stresses, and damage received in

service, can all reduce fatigue life. Therefore, the possibility of fatigue cracks occurring in service cannot be ignored. Tremendous advances made in recent years enable the
prediction, within reasonable limits, of the residual strength
of fatigue-cracked structure. Continued work in this area
is required, however, due to the complexity of introducing
plane stress fracture mechanics into the design of pressurized,
thin stiffened sheet aircraft structure. This paper concen-
trates on three areas in which it is believed that significant error is introduced by present methods of analysis to
predict crack propagation and residual strength of cracked-
stiffened panels, i.e:

(a)   Effect of attachment flexibility
(b)   Threshold of slow stable crack growth
(c)   Flat panel versus curved panel testing

The attachment of the stiffener to the sheet and its
flexibility are important in the prediction of stress distributions in stiffened cracked panels. The assumption that
the attachment is rigid and that the strains in the stiffener
and skin are compatible can lead to considerable error.

The stress intensity at the threshold of slow stable
crack growth often has been thought of as entirely a property
of the material. It is, in fact, a function of the past
loading history and the plastic zone ahead of the crack tip,
introduced during previous loading cycles. The results of
crack growth and residual strength tests on flat stiffened
panels are presented, including the effects of high load
cycles and slow stable crack growth. Crack growth rates da/dN
versus the stress intensity factor range are presented
for 2024-T3 clad sheet wide panels up to ΔK values of 160
ksi$\sqrt{\text{inch}}$, approaching K_c for the material.

When flat panels are used to predict the residual strength
of curved, stiffened fuselage structure subjected to pressure
loads, considerable error may be introduced and unconservative allowables obtained.

THE EFFECTS OF ATTACHMENT FLEXIBILITY

Residual Strength of Cracked Stiffened Panels. A finite element method of analysis to determine the residual strength of centrally-cracked stiffened panels has been previously described in Ref 2 and 3. The method is based on the Matrix Force Method of Structural Analysis (4,5) and uses the Fortran Matrix Abstraction Technique FORMAT (6) to solve the necessary matrix operations. Stress distributions throughout the panel are determined as a function of crack length. Other methods have been proposed to determine the effect of stiffeners on the crack tip stress intensity in a cracked panel, but the majority of these assume strain compatibility between the stiffener and the sheet to which it is attached. This can only be true if the attachment is infinitely rigid. In conventional aircraft structure this is never the case and the attachment is always flexible to some degree.

The stress intensity at the tip of the crack and the net section stress ahead of a crack tip are reduced when stiffeners are provided. As the crack extends, part of the load is transferred to the stiffeners and the remaining load is transferred to the skin ahead of the crack. If the stiffeners-to-skin attachment is infinitely flexible, no load will be transferred into the stiffener and the panel will behave like an unstiffened panel with no reduction in crack tip stress intensity. If, however, the attachment is rigid, a large portion of the load from the cracked sheet will be transferred to the stiffener, thus reducing the stress ahead of the crack tip with a consequent reduction in the crack tip stress intensity factor. It can be seen then that attachment flexibility must be accounted for if the proper stress distributions are to be determined.

Attachment flexibility is easily accounted for in the finite element analysis methods referred to above. The following equations illustrate how this is done.

The crack tip stress intensity for a stiffened panel containing a central crack is given by

$$K = \frac{\sigma C}{R_{ct}} \sqrt{W \overline{\text{Tan} \ (\pi a/W)}}$$

(1)

Where

K   = stress intensity factor, ksi$\sqrt{\text{inch}}$

σ = gross applied stress at the boundary, ksi

C   = width correction factor (7) $1.0 + 0.3(2a/W)^2$

W   = panel width, inch

a   = half crack length, inch

R_{ct} = $\dfrac{\sigma_{yct} \ \text{in unstiffened panel}}{\sigma_{yct} \ \text{in stiffened panel}}$

σ_{yct} = stress in the vicinity of the crack tip in the direction of loading and normal to the crack.

The R_{ct} is determined by finite element analysis methods described in the following.

Figure 1 presents a simulated panel containing a transverse or circumferential crack. The panel is divided into a series of discrete bars and shear panels as shown in Fig. 1(a). Only a quarter of the panel is required due to symmetry as illustrated in Fig. 1(b). Loads are applied at the top of the panel to represent a uniform stress level and reactions are provided at the bottom. The propagating crack is simulated by successive disconnection of the reactions from the center of the panel through an element modification procedure described in the Appendix. Up to 12 modifications are normally made in one computer run. The FORMAT program not only includes the capability to disconnect reactions but can also be used to modify the stiffness of elements automatically. The crack tip stress is defined as the bar stress adjacent to the last reaction disconnected as shown in Fig. 1(c). Crack tip stresses are determined for both unstiffened and stiffened panels having the same grid size, and ratios taken of the crack tip stresses to determine R_{ct}. It is

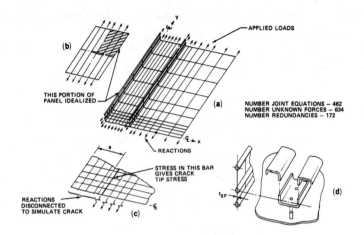

Fig. 1.   Panel idealization

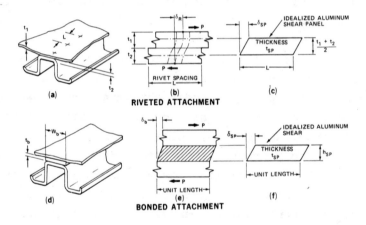

Fig. 2.   Attachment idealization

obvious that a finite element analysis method, or in fact
any other method, will not give the true stress at the crack
tip. But this is not necessary since only the ratio of
stresses in the region of the crack tip is required when Eq
1 is used. The rivet flexibility is included by simulating
the rivet to a shear panel as illustrated in Fig. 1(d).
Simple tests are performed (3) to determine the rivet stiffness.

An empirical fit to the test data for aluminum alloy
sheet can be expressed by

$$\delta_R = \frac{P}{E_A d}\left[A + B\left(d/t_1 + d/t_2\right)\right]$$

(2)

Where

δ_R	=	rivet deflection, in.
P	=	applied load, lb
E_A	=	modulus of aluminum, psi
d	=	rivet diameter, in.
t_1 and t_2	=	thickness of the joined sheets, in.
A	=	constant, 5.0 for aluminum rivets and 1.666 for steel attachments
B	=	constant, 0.8 for aluminum rivets and 0.86 for steel attachments.

Referring to Fig. 2(a), 2(b), and 2(c), the thickness
t_{sp} of the idealized shear panel of height $(t_1 + t_2)/2$ is
determined by equating the attachment deflection δ_R to δ_{sp},
the deflection of the idealized shear panel.

$$\delta_{sp} = \frac{P}{Lt_{sp}G_A}\left(\frac{t_1 + t_2}{2}\right)$$

Where

G_A = shear modulus for aluminum, psi

$\delta_R = \delta_{sp}$

Therefore, for riveted joints $t_{sp} = \dfrac{E_A d(t_1 + t_2)}{2LG_A\{A + B(d/t_1 + d/t_2)\}}$ (3)

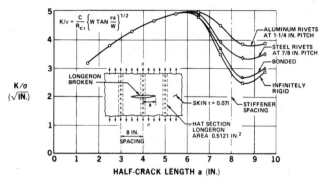

Fig. 3. Crack tip stress intensity factor -- crack length with variable stiffener to skin attachment

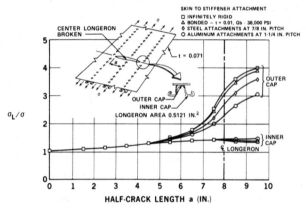

Fig. 4. Outer longeron cap stresses vs crack length for various longeron attachments

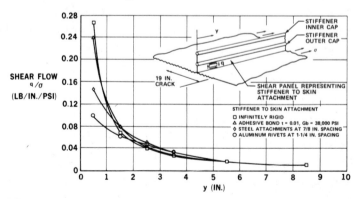

Fig. 5. Stiffener to skin attachment shear flow

Adhesive bonded joints are treated in a similar fashion. Referring to Fig. 2(d), 2(e), and 2(f), the thickness t_{sp} of the idealized shear panel of height h_{sp} is determined by equating the bond deflection δ_b to the idealized shear panel deflection δ_{sp}

$$\delta_b = \frac{Pt_b}{W_b G_b}$$

Where

W_b = bond width, inch

t_b = bond thickness, inch

G_b = shear modulus of adhesive bond material, psi

$\delta_b = \delta_{sp}$

Therefore, for a bonded joint $t_{sp} = \dfrac{h_{sp} W_b G_b}{G_A t_b}$ (4)

The height h_{sp} would normally equal the bond thickness t_b. However, if a parametric study is required, it is often advantageous to obtain a unit solution with shear panel height constant and then modify the shear panel stiffness by changing its thickness using the element modification procedure outlined in the Appendix. In this way, any combination of crack length and stiffness up to a total of 12 can be made in one computer run.

Analysis Results. In order to illustrate the effect of attachment stiffness, an analysis was performed on a panel 0.071-inch thick, having hat section stiffeners at 8-inch spacing with an area 0.5121 square inch. The idealization for the panel was similar to that shown in Fig. 1 with the center longeron assumed to be broken. Figures 3, 4, and 5 show the analysis results. Four different skin attachments were considered:

(a) Infinitely rigid

(b) Adhesive bond 1.0 inch wide, 0.01 inch thick with shear modulus G_b of 38,000 psi

(c) 3/16-inch diameter steel attachments at 7/8-inch spacing

(d) 3/16-inch diameter aluminum attachments at 1¼-inch spacing

Figure 3 shows the crack tip stress intensity factor K, per unit gross stress, as a function of crack length. It can be seen that as the crack approaches the stiffener, the stress intensity is reduced. The lowest stress intensity factor occurs just beyond the stiffener for the infinitely rigid stiffener to skin attachment. This case assumes compatibility of strain between the stiffener and the sheet which is an assumption often made for other methods. In practice, however, appreciable deflection takes place in the rivets, resulting in a lower load transfer into the stiffener and a consequent increase in crack tip stress intensity. Considerable error may therefore be present with the rigid attachment assumption.

Figure 4 shows outer stiffener stress as a function of crack length for the four cases considered. The highest load transfer into the stiffener occurs with the rigid attachment. Outer and inner cap stresses are shown, indicating considerable bending in the stiffener due to eccentricity of load application from the sheet. The stiffener to skin attachment shear flow is shown in Fig. 5 for the first 8-½ inches of idealized shear panel from the crack. It can be seen that the intensity of shear load is extremely high in the vicinity of the crack, particularly for the rigid and adhesively-bonded connection. The distributions are, of course, based on elastic analysis and do not show the effects of yielding of the first attachments on the remaining shear load distribution. This is shown in Ref 3. The analysis results show that increasing the attachment stiffness increases skin strength but decreases stiffener strength. Care must be exercised, therefore, when choosing an attachment to obtain a balanced design. To illustrate this point, the gross residual strength of the panel, based on both skin fracture and stiffener strength criteria, is shown in Fig. 6. The skin fracture criteria have been plotted for two different skin materials:

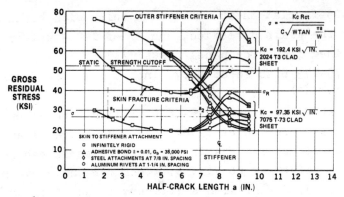

Fig. 6.   Gross residual strength vs crack length

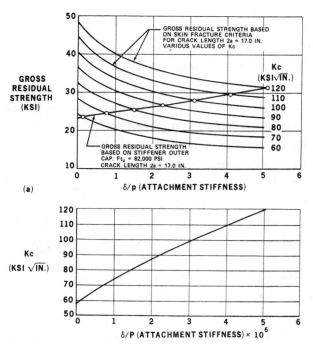

(a)

(b) OPTIMUM ATTACHMENT STIFFNESS vs Kc FOR SIMULTANEOUS
FAILURE OF SKIN AND STIFFENER

Fig. 7.   Optimum attachment stiffness

(a).   2024-T3 clad sheet 0.071 inch thick with crack normal
       to the grain direction, and K_c of 192.4 ksi$\sqrt{\text{in}}$. ob-
       tained from wide panel tests[2].

(b).   7075-T73 clad sheet 0.071 inch thick with K_c of 97.35
       ksi$\sqrt{\text{in}}$.[2].

The stiffeners are 7075-T6 extrusion with allowable based
on outer cap strength of 82,000 psi. The significance of
the curves illustrating skin fracture criteria can be explained by referring to Fig. 6. Consider the curve plotted
for K_c = 97.35ksi$\sqrt{\text{in}}$. with stiffeners attached by an infinitely rigid connection. If the panel contains a crack
of length a_1 and a gross stress of σ is applied, then fast
fracture will occur and the crack will be arrested at a crack
length a_2.

The residual strength of the panel is given by σ_R at
the peak of the curve. Compatibility between skin fracture
and stiffener strength criteria exists when the stiffener
allowable strength coincides with the skin residual strength
at the peak of the skin residual strength curve.

The residual strength of the 2024-T3 panel, based on
skin criteria, is extremely high compared to the stiffener
criteria, particularly for infinitely rigid or bonded attachment where the residual strength is higher than the static
gross strength without crack. The design from a residual
strength standpoint is more compatible when aluminum rivets
at 1-¼-inch spacing are used. Even so, failure of the panel
would be precipitated by stiffener failure.

Figure 6 indicates that 7075-T73 skin material produces
a more compatible design when combined with 7075-T6 extrusion
for flat panels with the damage tolerance considered here.
The configurations which show the least difference between
skin and stiffener strength criteria are those two with steel
or aluminum fasteners. Figure 7(a) shows gross residual
strength based on skin criteria for the same panel containing

a crack of length 2a = 17 inches with a broken center longeron.
(The peak of the residual strength curve is at 17 inches.
See Fig. 6.) Gross strength is plotted against stiffener-
to-skin attachment stiffness for various values of K_c. The
stiffener strength curve is shown plotted over the curves.
The intersection of the curves (illustrated by circles) indicates the optimum attachment stiffness for simultaneous
failure of skin and stiffener. Figure 7(b) shows optimum
attachment stiffness versus K_c derived from curves shown in
Fig. 7(a).

Bond Delamination. Considerable reduction in crack
tip stress intensity is shown with bonded stiffeners, as
illustrated in Fig. 3. This is due to the high relative
stiffness of the adhesive bond when compared to aluminum
attachments. However, the load transfer through the bond
material into the stiffener is extremely concentrated near
the vicinity of the crack, as illustrated in Fig. 5. This
high concentration of shear load may cause bond delamination
in the vicinity of the crack, thus reducing the effectivity
of the stiffener. The effects of bond delamination can be
easily accounted for in the FORMAT finite element analysis
by using the element modification procedure outlined in the
Appendix. The shear panels, which simulate the attachment
of the stiffener to the skin, can be disconnected automatically during the crack propagation phase to represent
bond delamination. The effects of delamination on the stress
intensity factor are shown in Fig. 8 for 1 inch and 2 inches
of delamination on each side of the crack. Considerable increase in the crack tip stress intensity factor is shown
with increasing delamination.

When delamination exceeds 1.5 inches on each side of
the crack, the strength of the bonded panel will be lower
than a panel with riveted stiffeners. Figure 9 shows that
increasing bond delamination decreases the stiffener outer
cap stress considerably and increases the inner cap stress
slightly.

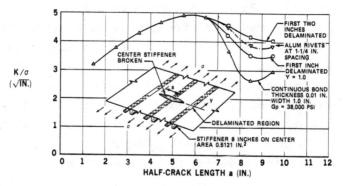

Fig. 8. Crack tip stress intensity vs crack length with
         varying degrees of bond delamination

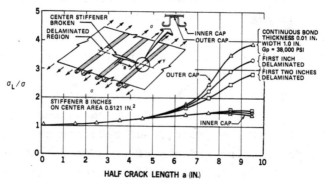

Fig. 9. Effect of bond delamination on outer stiffener stress

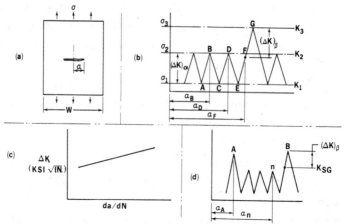

Fig. 10. Threshold of slow stable crack growth

Correlation. A considerable amount of testing was performed on flat stiffened panels with transverse and longitudinal cracks, under uniaxial loading, and large curved
panels, under biaxial loading combined with pressure to correlate the FORMAT finite element analytical methods. Much
of this correlation appears in Ref 2 and 3. The shape of
the skin residual strength curve for both transverse and
longitudinal cracks was substantiated, particularly with 7075-
T73 skin, which is more susceptible to fast fracture than
2024-T3. Stiffener stress distributions, as a function of
crack length, were correlated with strain gage results. Other
important data were obtained during this test program which
were not included in Ref 2 and 3. Some of these data are
discussed in this paper.

THE THRESHOLD OF SLOW STABLE CRACK GROWTH

Many equations have been proposed to determine the crack
propagation rate under constant amplitude loading. Two of
the most useful ones are those proposed by Paris [8] and
Forman [9], respectively:

$$da/dN = C(\Delta K)^n \tag{5}$$
$$da/dN = \frac{C(\Delta K)^n}{(1 - R) K_c - \Delta K} \tag{6}$$

Both of these equations have been integrated into computer programs to determine crack propagation under spectrum
loading. [10] A method has been proposed to determine the
effect of crack growth retardation due to high intermittent
load cycles based on a reduced effective stress concept. [11]
It is noted in this report that considerable conservatism
exists in crack growth studies when this phenomenon is neglected. When considering materials with high ductibility
such as 2024-T3, however, this conservatism may be offset
to some extent by slow stable growth during the high load
cycle. The use of Eq 5 and 6 in which parameters C and n

have been determined from constant amplitude testing, in conjunction with the retardation model of Ref 11, may be insufficient to accurately predict the overall retardation effect. It is suggested that the effect of slow stable growth is significant and should be accounted for, particularly with 2024-T3 material.

Consider the panel shown in Fig. 10(a) which contains a center, through crack that has been subjected to constant amplitude cyclic loading. During the load phase from A to B shown in Fig. 10(b), the gross stress is increased from σ_1 to σ_2. At stress σ_2 the crack tip stress intensity from Eq 1 is

$$K_B = \frac{\sigma C}{R_{ct}} \sqrt{W Tan(\pi a_B/W)} \tag{7}$$

A plastic zone is formed at the crack tip of radius $\frac{1}{2}\pi$ $(K_B/\sigma_{ys})^2$ where σ_{ys} is the material yield strength. The plastic zone is surrounded by elastically strained material. Reducing the stress to σ_1 at C causes a residual compressive stress to be imposed at the crack tip from the elastic material surrounding the plastic zone. On re-application of the load at C, the residual stress will not be entirely relieved until a crack tip stress intensity equal to K_B is reached a little before the peak at D. At the peak D the crack tip stress intensity will be

$$K_D = \frac{\sigma_2 C}{R_{ct}} \sqrt{W Tan(\pi a_D/W)} \tag{8}$$

The stress intensity factor range from C to D will be called $(\Delta K)_\alpha$ and associated with this ΔK will be a certain growth rate da/dN. For this particular type of growth rate, associated with constant amplitude stress, the zone ahead of the crack tip is always subjected to residual compressive stress imposed by the plastic zone from the previous load cycle. This kind of growth is normally seen plotted as ΔK versus da/dN, on a log-log scale, similar to Fig. 10(c).

Empirical or semi-empirical equations such as 5 and 6 are written to fit the test data. As the gross stress level is increased from point E, the crack tip will again be subjected to residual compressive stress until a stress intensity K_D is reached at point F, which will be at a stress slightly less than σ_2 (little error would be involved in assuming σ_2). The crack growth from E to F would be $(\Delta K)_\alpha$-type growth, which is subject to residual stress from the previous load cycle. If the stress is increased to σ_3 at point G, the zone ahead of the crack tip will be completely relieved of residual stress at point F, and the crack growth from E to G will not be the same kind of growth associated with residual stress from the previous load cycle. The stress intensity range from F (nearly equal to D) to G will be called $(\Delta K)_\beta$. The crack growth associated with $(\Delta K)_\beta$ is far more severe than that associated with $(\Delta K)_\alpha$ and can be several hundred times as great, depending on K_2 and $(\Delta K)_\beta$. This residual stress-free growth is defined as slow stable growth in this paper.

Suppose now that the history of load application has not been at a constant amplitude before the high load cycle was applied, and that a previous high load cycle A was applied followed by constant amplitude cycles, as shown in Fig. 10(d). The crack propagation will be retarded until

$$a_n + \frac{1}{2\pi}\left(\frac{K_n}{\sigma_{ys}}\right)^2 = a_A + \frac{1}{2\pi}\left(\frac{K_A}{\sigma_{ys}}\right)^2 \tag{9}$$

$$\text{if} \quad a_n + \frac{1}{2\pi}\left(\frac{K_n}{\sigma_{ys}}\right)^2 < a_A + \frac{1}{2\pi}\left(\frac{K_A}{\sigma_{ys}}\right)^2$$

then stable growth will not start to occur on the B high load cycle at a stress intensity K_n and will only start to occur when Eq 9 is satisfied.

$$\text{If} \quad a_n + \frac{1}{2\pi}\left(\frac{K_n}{\sigma_{ys}}\right)^2 > a_A + \frac{1}{2\pi}\left(\frac{K_A}{\sigma_{ys}}\right)^2$$

then slow growth will start at a stress intensity K_n.

Let K_{SG} be the stress intensity at the threshold of slow stable growth on the high load cycle B. Then, to satisfy Eq 9

$$K_{SG} = \sigma_{ys} \sqrt{2\pi\{a_A - a_n + \tfrac{1}{2}\pi (K_A/\sigma_{ys})^2\}} \qquad (10)$$

and $(\Delta K)_\beta = K_B - K_{SG}$ \qquad (11)

The K's in each case are determined from Eq 1. The authors of Ref 9 suggest an additional crack growth curve to account for the transition from 90-degree tensile to 45-degree shear-type cracking. A third curve is suggested here to account for slow stable crack growth when spectrum type loading is being considered.

Test Program. Crack propagation and residual strength tests were performed on some large, flat, stiffened panels as part of the test program described. The panels were 120 inches long and 60 inches wide, stiffened with frames and longerons to represent typical fuselage structure. A description of four of these panels, made with 0.071 2024-T3 clad sheet, is shown in Table 1. Dimensions of the stiffeners are shown in Fig. 11 of Ref 2 and cross-referenced in Table 1 of this paper. The panels were analyzed by FORMAT finite element analysis and the results appear in Table 4 of Ref 3, where values of crack tip stress ratio R_{ct} and stiffener stress are given as a function of crack length. Panels 1,2,3, and 4 correspond to cases 17,15,20, and 19 of Ref 3, respectively. The panels were tested in a servo-hydraulic universal testing machine capable of applying alternating loads up to 1.5 million pounds. Figure 11 shows two panels mounted in the machine.

Two tests were performed on each panel to simulate transverse or circumferential cracks with a broken center longeron. Uniaxial loads were applied to simulate shell inertia bending stresses and axial stresses due to pressure. Prior to the start of each test, one longeron was completely sawcut through and a crack starter slot with sharp ends placed in the skin

Table 1

Sixty-Inch-Wide Flat Panel Configuration Longeron, Spacing 8 Inches (Skin Material 0.071 2024-T3 Clad Sheet - Longerons, 7075-T6 Extrusion)

(SKIN MATERIAL 0.071 2024-T3 CLAD SHEET, LONGERONS, 7075-T6 EXTRUSION)

PANEL NO.	LONGERON TYPE	LONGERON NET AREA (SQ IN.)	LONGERON GROSS AREA (SQ IN.)	RIVET TYPE AND SPACING	CONFIGURATION (1)
1	HAT	0.5121	0.5471	NAS 1097 DD6 1-1/4 IN. SPACING 1 ROW	7
2	HAT	0.3029	0.312	NAS 1097 DD6 1-1/4 IN. SPACING 1 ROW	6
3	TEE	0.4865	0.545	RV 5170-6 7075 T73 1-1/4 IN. SPACING 2 ROWS	9
4	TEE	0.2895	0.336	RV 5170-6 7075 T73 1-1/4 IN. SPACING 2 ROWS	8

(1) REFERENCE 2, FIGURE 11.

Fig. 11.   Test panels mounted in 1.5-million-lb machine

directly over the longeron cut. The skin cracks were propagated to pre-determined lengths under constant amplitude stress
levels and then higher loads were applied to represent fail-
safe stresses. The main purpose of the tests was to determine
if there was any tendency to cause a fast fracture in the
skin, and if such a tendency existed, were the longerons
adequate as natural crack stoppers. The panels were repaired
after the first test and tested to failure during the second
test. Figure 12 shows Panel 1 after the second test.

  Test Results. The results of testing on the four 2024-
T3 panels are shown in Fig. 13 through 20. Material properties are shown in Table 2. During the first test on Panel
1, static loads were applied, increasing in magnitude as
shown in Fig. 13. Slow stable crack growth was measured at
such increment during static load application. Considerable
retardation in crack propagation was experienced when cycling
was resumed after each high static load application. Fast
fracture of the skin did not occur during any of the high
load cycles, and the highest crack tip stress intensity
factor applied was 147.5 ksi$\sqrt{\text{in}}$.

  Figure 14 shows the results of the second test on Panel
1. Higher cyclic stresses were applied and also static load
applications with higher crack tip stress intensity factors.
The highest K value reached without fast fracture was 168
ksi$\sqrt{\text{in}}$. at Point F. During Test 1 of Panel 2, the load was
cycled by hand to give a maximum gross stress of 34.05 ksi
with stress ratio equal to zero. Seventeen such cycles were
applied which gave some $(\Delta K)_\alpha$-type crack growth data at extremely high stress intensity factors.

  Crack growth versus cycles is shown in Fig. 15. The
highest stress intensity applied during this operation was
163.5 ksi$\sqrt{\text{in}}$. As the crack tip approaches the stiffener,
the intensity factor K is reduced for the same gross stress,
due to load transfer into the stiffener. Figure 16 shows the
sawtooth appearance of the fracture during the 17 high load
cycles.

Fig. 12. Panel 1 after final failure

Table 2

Material Properties

PANEL NO.	2024-T3 0.071 CLAD SHEET		7075-T6 EXTRUDED LONGERONS	
	Ft_u (KSI)	Ft_y (KSI)	Ft_u (KSI)	Ft_y (KSI)
1	66.658	45.486	84.248	75.663
2	66.434	45.581	86.084	78.645
3	66.227	45.502	81.838	75.967
4	66.271	46.033	86.065	79.672

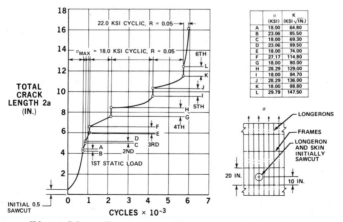

	σ (KSI)	K (KSI $\sqrt{\text{IN.}}$)
A	18.00	64.80
B	23.06	85.50
C	18.00	69.30
D	23.06	89.50
E	18.00	74.00
F	27.17	114.80
G	18.00	80.00
H	28.29	129.00
I	18.00	84.70
J	28.29	136.00
K	18.00	88.80
L	29.79	147.50

Fig. 13. Test results, panel 1, test 1

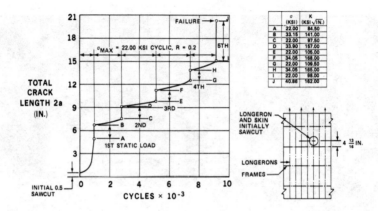

Fig. 14.   Test results, panel 1, test 2

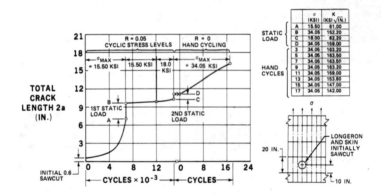

Fig. 15.   Test results, panel 2, test 1

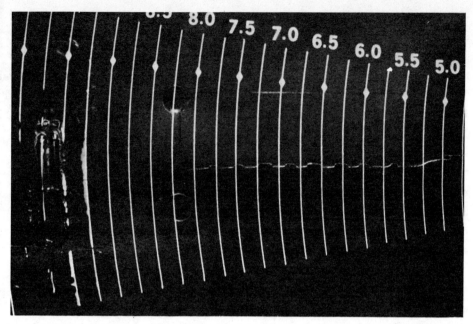

Fig. 16.   Saw tooth appearance of crack during propagation
          at high-stress intensity

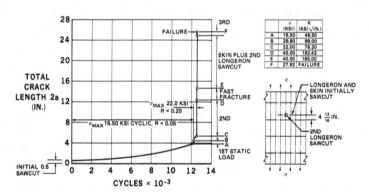

Fig. 17.   Test results, panel 2, test 2

The only fast fracture experienced on the 2024-T3 panels
occurred during Test 2 of Panel 2. The results are shown
in Fig. 17. Fast fracture occurred at a gross stress of 40.0
ksi and a crack length of 12.41 inches giving a critical stress
intensity factor K_c and fracture toughness for the material of
192.43 ksi$\sqrt{\text{in}}$. The fast fracture was arrested at a crack
length of 14.75 inches. At this point, a further longeron
was saw cut and the skin crack extended symmetrically about
two broken longerons to 25.0 inches. Final failure occurred
at a gross stress of 27.92 ksi and a crack length of 25.69
inches. Hand cycling at high stress intensity factors was
performed on Panel 3, Test 1, and on Panel 4, Tests 1 and 2
as shown in Fig. 21. During Test 2 of Panels 3 and 4, a
second longeron was saw cut and the skin damage extended to
three bays. The gross stress at failure of Panels 3 and 4
was 34.29 ksi and 30.97 ksi, respectively.

Verification of Eq 10, which gives the stress intensity
at the onset slow stable growth as a function of the plastic
zone size from the previous high load cycle, is shown in Fig.
22(a). It can be readily seen that the onset of slow growth
is a function of previous load history and does not occur
at a constant value. Figure 22(b) shows an enlargement of
the crack growth versus hand cycles for Panel 4, Test 2,
illustrated in Fig. 21. A previous high load cycle had been
applied at point B of Fig. 21 up to a gross stress of 40.05
ksi and stress intensity of 190 ksi$\sqrt{\text{in}}$. Hand cycles at a
gross stress of 36.0 ksi were subsequently applied with growth
rate retarded by the previous high load. Figure 22 shows
a sharp increase in growth rate, as retardation ceases, at
a crack length of 12.86 inches. The crack length at which
retardation should cease (predicted from Eq 9 and 10) is
12.96 inches, indicating close agreement between analysis
and test.

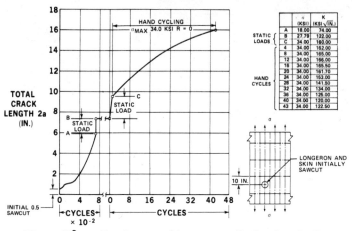

Fig. 18.   Test results, panel 3, test 1

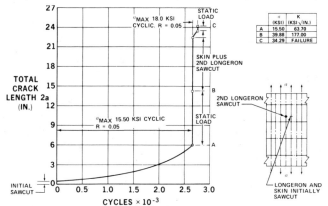

Fig. 19.   Test results, panel 3, test 2

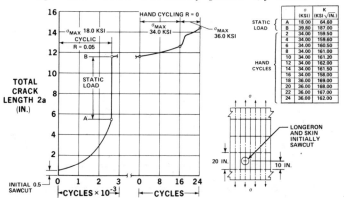

Fig. 20.   Test results, panel 4, test 1

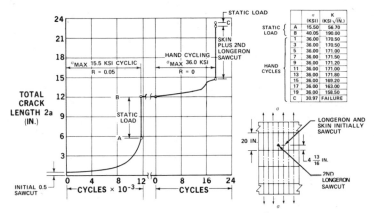

Fig. 21.   Test results, panel 4, test 2

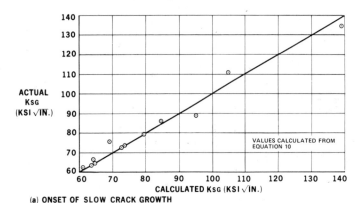

(a) ONSET OF SLOW CRACK GROWTH

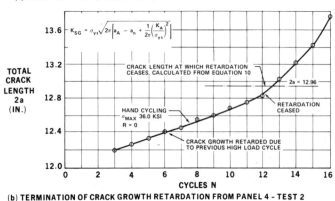

(b) TERMINATION OF CRACK GROWTH RETARDATION FROM PANEL 4 - TEST 2

Fig. 22.   Onset of slow growth and crack growth retardation

Figure 23 shows crack growth rate da/dN versus ΔK taken from all the tests. The data shown are not subjected to retardation due to high load cycles, having been tested by Eq 9 and 10. The data are $(\Delta K)_\alpha$-type growth data where each cycle is subjected to pre-load from the previous load cycle, or constant cycle data. Values are shown up to extremely high ΔK values where K is approaching K_c for the material. Equations of the Paris form, such as Eq 5, have been written to fit the data and it can be seen that a different equation is necessary when stress intensities approaching instability are applied. Figure 24 shows the same data with an equation of the Forman type, such as Eq 6, written to fit the data. It can be seen that a better fit is obtained in the region where stress intensities are approaching K_c for the material.

All of the stable growth data obtained from the panels have been plotted against stress intensity factor K, given by Eq 1. Curve A of Fig. 25 represents data with the skin crack 4-13/16 inches from the lateral frame stiffeners and Curve B represents data for the crack midway between stiffeners. Considerably more lateral buckling of the sheet is experienced for the type A crack which causes a greater amount of crack extension per ksi√in. of stress intensity factor change due to interaction of Mode III-type stress intensity. The significance of the curves can be illustrated by the following example.

Consider the lower edge of the scatter band, Curve A. The crack is stable under a stress intensity of 100 ksi√in. If the load is increased, slow growth will take place, and at 130 ksi√in., with ΔK equal to 30 ksi√in., the half crack extension Δa will be 0.5 inch.

Because of the similarity of the slow stable growth curve to a stress strain curve, an equation similar to the Ramberg-Osgood equation (12) has been used to fit the lower edge of the scatter band. This equation is represented by the dotted line in Fig. 25.

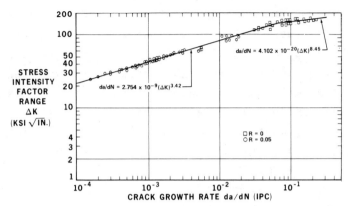

Fig. 23. Crack growth rate, 2024-T3 clad sheet 0.071-thick fitted to Paris' equation

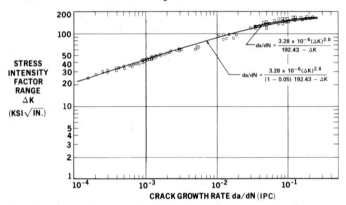

Fig. 24. Crack growth rate, 2024-T3 clad sheet 0.071-thick fitted to Forman's equation

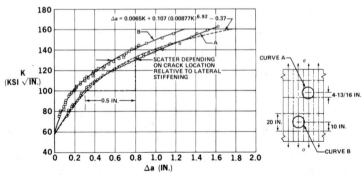

Fig. 25. Slow growth vs stress intensity factor (2024-T3 clad sheet)

The onset of slow stable crack growth is shown to be
at K = 57 ksi√in. But this is due to the limitations of the
test data. It is hypothesized that slow stable growth would
start as soon as load is applied, provided a fatigue crack
could be formed at a maximum stress intensity of zero, which
would be difficult. It has been shown by Eq 10 that the onset of slow stable growth is a function of the stress level
previously applied. For example, if the maximum stress intensity at which crack propagation has taken place were 2
ksi√in., then the onset of slow growth would be 2 ksi√in.,
and if the crack had been propagated at a maximum stress intensity of 30 ksi√in., the onset of slow growth would be
30 ksi√in. In view of this, the family of curves has been
plotted as shown in Fig. 26. These curves are based on
Curve A of Fig. 25 and give the amount of half-crack extension
per cycle versus stress intensity factor range $(\Delta K)_\beta$ as a
function of the stress intensity at the onset of slow stable
growth K_{SG}. It can be readily seen by comparing the $(\Delta K)_\beta$-
type growth of Fig. 25 and 26 to the $(\Delta K)_\alpha$ -type growth of
Fig. 23 and 24 that considerable error would be experienced
if an equation such as Forman's equation were used for spectrum loading, where the parameters had been obtained from
constant amplitude data. Considering Fig. 10(b), cycle EG,
Forman's equation could be used from E to F, but between
points F and G where stable growth is taking place, data such
as that shown in Fig. 25 should be used. The dividing line
between $(\Delta K)_\beta$ and $(\Delta K)_\alpha$ types of growth should be determined
by an equation such as Eq 10. The error may not be as pro-
nounced in more brittle materials with lower fracture toughness values, but it is suggested that this phenomenon needs
to be accounted for in crack propagation analysis of ductile
materials such as 2024-T3.

In recent publications (13,14), the onset of slow stable
growth has been included in the residual strength diagram

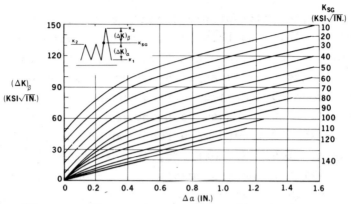

Fig. 26.   Slow growth vs stress intensity factor range based
on curve A

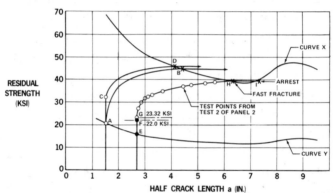

Fig. 27.   Gross residual strength and the threshold of slow
crack growth

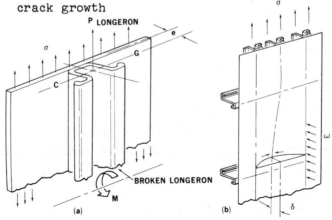

Fig. 28.   Center longeron bending

for skin fracture criterion. This diagram shows two curves,
one of which is based on K_c, the fracture toughness of the
material, and the other based on K_1 described in Ref 14 as
the threshold of slow crack growth and referred to in this
paper as K_{SG}. However, the lower curve, describing the crack
length at which stable growth is initiated, cannot be entirely a function of the material properties but in fact must
be a function of the previous loading history.

Consider Fig. 27. The upper Curve x has been plotted
for Test Panel 2 using a fracture toughness value K_c of 192.43
ksi√in. determined from Test 2, shown in Fig. 17, and R_{ct}
values from Table 4, Ref 3, for Case 15. The lower curve
is plotted for the stress intensity at the threshold of slow
stable growth, shown in Fig. 25 as 57 ksi√in. which was limited
by test data and may be lower, as previously explained.

Consider the hypothetical case where a crack had been
propagated at a gross constant amplitude maximum stress of
20.4 ksi, or lower, to a half-crack length a of 1.5 inches.
On increasing the gross stress level, slow growth will start
to take place at 20.4 ksi (as shown by point A of Fig. 27)
and follow curve AB (obtained from Fig. 26) until point B
is reached, where fast fracture will occur. If on the other
hand the previous maximum constant amplitude stress was 32.0
ksi, then slow growth would not start until 32.0 ksi had
been reached at point C in Fig. 27 and would follow curve
CD where fast fracture would take place at D. This hypothesis
is substantiated to some extent by the results of Test 2 on
Panel 2 shown in Fig. 17. A crack had been propagated to
a half-crack length a of 2.69 inches at a maximum gross stress
of 22.0 ksi. Static load was gradually applied from zero
and slow-crack growth started to occur at 23.32 ksi shown
by point G in Fig. 27. Theoretically, to satisfy Eq 9 and
10, slow growth should have occurred at 22 ksi at point E,
but the error is small. It did not, however, start at E on
curve Y. Slow growth continued as the gross stress was

increased (as shown by test points in Fig. 27) until at point
H, fast fracture occurred and the crack was arrested at point
I.

Curve Y, therefore, has meaning only if the intersection
of the maximum gross stress at which previous propagation
has taken place and the half-crack length fall below the curve.
It has been previously pointed out that the threshold of slow
growth may in fact be as low as the lowest stress level at
which it is possible to manufacture a fatigue crack.

FLAT PANEL VERSUS CURVED PANEL TESTING

Residual strength and crack propagation tests often are
performed on flat, stiffened panels to simulate fatigue-
damaged curved pressurized fuselage structure. This method
of testing panels loaded uniaxially is far more inexpensive
than testing large curved stiffened panels under biaxial
loading conditions combined with pressure. Much can be learned
from the results of flat panel testing, but care must be exercised in the interpretation of results. For example, the
bulging effect caused by pressure loading when a longitudinal
crack is propagated in a pressurized shell cannot be exactly
simulated by flat panel testing. The bulging causes an increase in crack tip stress intensity, particularly when the
crack tips are in the region midway between stiffeners. Tests
are often performed on flat panels and the results adjusted
by bulging coefficients similar to the one proposed in Ref 15

$$(K_c)_{CURVED} = \frac{(K_c)_{FLAT}}{(1+10a/R)} \tag{12}$$

It has been shown by curved panel testing conducted at
Douglas that when a two-bay longitudinal crack is propagated
with the center frame intact, the stress intensity at the
crack tip can be approximated to Eq 12, provided the total
crack length is divided by two. The center stiffener remaining

intact reduces the bulging to a degree equivalent to a one-
bay crack. This bulging coefficient, however, is only valid
when the crack tip is sufficiently remote from the stiffener.
It has been found that with a full two-bay crack, when the
crack tips are in the vicinity of the outboard stiffener,
the bulging may be ignored and flat panel data used to determine residual strength. It should be noted, however, that
this has only been substantiated on panels with titanium
crack stoppers located at frame positions which help to reduce bulging in the vicinity of the frame.

A second phenomenon exists when transverse cracks are
propagated in flat panels to simulate a circumferential crack
in a pressurized fuselage shell. This phenomenon exists
when a two-bay crack is present with the center longeron
failed and when the loading is applied in a uniaxial direction. Figure 28(a) shows that at some distance from the
crack, the longeron load P is acting at the centroid of the
section. This load is eventually reacted by the skin ahead
of the crack tip and is thus transferred a distance $\underline{e}$, which
causes the longeron to bend inward. The induced bending in
the center longeron, for a uniaxial loading condition, causes
a membrane action in the skin to load the outer longerons
as shown in Fig. 28(b). The resultant bending in the outer
longerons tends to cancel out the bending caused by transfer
of load from the cracked sheet. Tests on flat panels have
shown that in most cases the outer longeron bending is almost
entirely canceled out by this secondary effect. This results
in a higher allowable load, particularly if the panel is
stiffener critical. If this allowable is used for curved,
stiffened structure, subjected to internal pressure, the
resultant allowable will be unconservative since the phenomenon does not exist on curved panels subjected to pressure.
The inward bending of the longeron is entirely canceled out
by the internal pressure, and thus outer longeron bending
due to transfer of load from the cracked sheet does exist,

as shown in Fig. 29. Extreme care should, therefore, be
exercised when flat panel results are used to predict curved
panel allowable stresses. It will be noticed in Fig. 28(b)
that buckling of the sheet will introduce Mode III stress
intensity in addition to Mode I. Higher stress intensities
result from this buckling and are higher when the crack is
close to the lateral stiffener. The center longeron, canti-
levered about the upper frame, allows more buckling than if
the crack were mid-bay, where the cantilever is not as long.
This effect is reflected in the slow crack growth data of
Fig. 25, where slow growth is greater with the crack closer
to the frame.

Figure 30 shows a comparison between crack growth in
a curved panel subjected to biaxial load combined with pressure, and that of a flat panel. The crack in the skin extends into two bays, and the center longeron is broken in
each case. The panels are both made from 2024-T3 clad sheet
0.071-inch thick with identical frames and longeron stiffeners. The longeron has a net area of 0.3029 square inch
with a configuration similar to Configuration 6 in Fig. 11,
Ref 2. Stress intensity factors can be determined from the
data for Case 15 in Table 4, Ref 3. The gross average axial
stress levels are the same in each case with the same stress
ratio except that the curved panel is also subjected to a
cyclic maximum pressure of 9.3 psi. The crack growth is
faster in the curved panel due to the skin working at a higher
stress than the longeron. In a pressurized shell, where the
skin is biaxially loaded and the stiffeners are uniaxially
loaded, the skin works at a higher stress than the longeron
due to strain compatibility. For the panel in question the
skin axial stress is given by

$$\sigma_{x_s} = 9.183N_x + 1.1332N_\phi \tag{13}$$

and the longeron stress by

$$\sigma_{x_L} = 8.902N_x - 2.058N_\phi \tag{14}$$

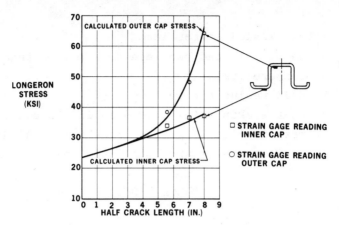

Fig. 29.   Outer longeron stress distribution from curved panel
tests

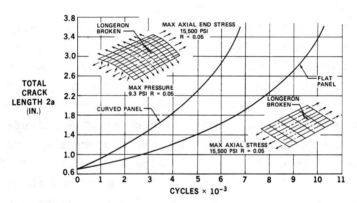

Fig. 30.   Comparison of crack propagation curved vs flat panels,
skin material 2024-T3

where

N_x = the axial load per inch

N_ϕ = the radial load per inch due to hoop tension = PR

P = pressure (psi)

R = shell radius (in.)

In this case, the skin axial stress is 16,920 psi and the longeron stress is 12,930 psi, whereas the skin and longeron stress in the flat panels are both 15,500 psi.

CONCLUSIONS

The effects of attachment flexibility on the stress intensity factors in stiffened panels are significant and should be accounted for in crack propagation and residual strength analysis. The threshold of slow stable crack growth and the amount of growth in 2024-T3 clad sheet is almost entirely a function of the past load history. Crack growth during high load cycles, where preload from the previous cycle has been relieved, is an order of magnitude greater than the type of growth experienced during constant amplitude loading and should be accounted for in spectrum crack growth analysis. Care should be exercised when using the results of flat panel tests to predict allowable stresses for curved sheet structure.

Acknowledgment. The author wishes to express his appreciation to R. E. Darling and R. G. Eastin who performed some of the computer analyses included in this paper.

References

1. Stone, M., "Structural Reliability Through Detail Design and Development Testing," Air Force Conference on Fatigue and Fracture of Aircraft Structures and Materials, Miami Beach, Florida, 15-18 December 1969, AFFDL TR-70-144

2. Swift, T. and Wang, D. Y., "Damage Tolerant Design -- Analysis Methods and Test Verification of Fuselage Structure," Air Force Conference on Fatigue and Fracture of Aircraft Structures and Materials, Miami, Florida, 15-18 December 1969, AFFDL TR-70-144

3. Swift, T., "Development of the Fail-Safe Design Features of the DC-10," ASTM Symposium on Damage Tolerance in Aircraft Structures, Toronto, Ontario, Canada, 21-26 June 1970, ASTM STP-486

4. Denke, P. H., "A General Digital Computer Analysis of Statically Indeterminate Structures," Douglas Paper 834, September 1959

5. Denke, P. H., "A Computerized Static and Dynamic Structural Analysis System; Part III, Engineering Aspects and Mathematical Formulation of the Problem," Douglas Paper 3213, presented to the SAE International Automotive Congress and Exposition, January 1965

6. Pickard, J. and Morris, R. C., "FORMAT II -- Second Version of Fortran Matrix Abstraction Technique," AFFDL-TR-66-207 Vol I and Vol III

7. Allen, F. C., "Stress Analysis of Centrally Cracked Plates", presented to ASTM Committee E-24, March 1969

8. Paris, P. and Erdogen, F., "A Critical Analysis of Crack Propagation Laws," Journal of Basic Engineering-Trans. of ASME, Series D. Vol 85, December 1963

9. Foreman, R. G., Kearney, V. E. and Engle, R. M., "Numerical Analysis of Crack Propagation in Cyclic Loaded Structures," Journal of Basic Engineering - Trans. of ASME, Vol 89, September 1967

10. Engle, R. M., "Cracks - A Fortran IV Digital Computer Program for Crack Propagation Analysis," AFFDL-TR-70-107, October 1970

11. Willenborg, J., Engle, R. M., Wood, H. A., "A Crack Growth Retardation Model Using an Effective Stress Concept," TM 71-1-FBR Air Force Flight Dynamic Laboratory.

12. Ramberg and Osgood, "Description of Stress Strain Curves of 3 Parameters," NACA TN 902

13. Vlieger, H., "Residual Strength of Cracked Stiffened Panels," National Aerospace Laboratory NLR, The Netherlands, NLR TR 71004u

14. Broek, D., "Concepts in Fail-Safe Design of Aircraft Structures," Battelle Memorial Institute, March 1971

15. Kuhn, P., "Notch Effects on Fatigue and Static Strength," Published in Current Aeronautical Fatigue Problems, Pergamon Press.

APPENDIX

FORMAT II ANALYSIS

Unit Solution

A unit solution to the stress distributions in an uncracked idealized panel is obtained using the Force Matrix Method of structural analysis.[4, 5] This method is based on the formulation of matric equations of equilibrium and Maxwell-Mohr equations of continuity. A solution to the matric equations is obtained using the Second Version of Fortran Matrix Abstraction Technique (FORMAT II).[6] The basic matric equations solved in the unit solution by FORMAT II are:

$$F = f_x X + f_O \tag{A1}$$

$$\Delta = f_O^T D f_O \tag{A2}$$

where

F = Matrix of element forces in the statically indeterminate structure resulting from unit values of external loads

Δ = Matrix of deflections in the statically indeterminate structure resulting from unit values of external loads

f_x = Matrix of element forces resulting from unit values of the redundancies

f_O = Matrix of statically determinate element forces resulting from unit values of external loads

$X = -(f_x^T D f_x)^{-1} (f_x^T D f_O)$

D = Matrix of element flexibilities

The superscript T represents transposition of the matrix.

The matrix of element forces in the statically indeterminate structure due to external loads is:

$$FKO1 = F.KO \tag{A3}$$

The matrix of deflections in the statically indeterminate structure due to external loads is:

$$DEFKO1 = \Delta.KO \tag{A4}$$

where KO is the matrix of external loads.

The matrices required from the unit solution to be used in the second stage or modification analysis are:

Equation (A1)

Equation (A2)

f_x

$\delta_{xx}^{-1} = (f_x^T D f_x)^{-1}$

f_O

D

The matrix of element forces – Equation (A1) takes the form:

$$F = \begin{bmatrix} \text{Reactions} \\ \text{Bar Forces} \\ \text{Panel Forces} \end{bmatrix}_m^n$$

where m is the number of element forces and n is the number of external load vectors. Typical values of m and n are:

$$\left. \begin{array}{l} m = 1087 \\ n = 43 \end{array} \right\} \text{1-Bay Longitudinal Crack}$$

$$\left. \begin{array}{l} m = 1233 \\ n = 47 \end{array} \right\} \text{2-Bay Longitudinal Crack}$$

$$\left. \begin{array}{l} m = 1043 \\ n = 39 \end{array} \right\} \text{For idealization of Figure 1}$$

Extractor matrices are also required in the modification analysis to extract the reactions, bar forces, panel shear forces and panel shear flows from the matrix F. These matrices are defined in the unit analysis and saved for use in the modification analysis. They are defined as follows:

GR = Reaction extractor matrix

GB = Transposed bar force extractor matrix

GP = Panel shear force extractor matrix

GPF = Panel shear flow extractor matrix

Element Modification

The effects of crack propagation in the sheet are determined by disconnecting the reactions in the skin at the horizontal centerline as illustrated in Figure 1. This function is performed by an element modification procedure which requires the solution to the following matric equations:

$$FM = FKO1 + FE.C.EO \tag{A5}$$

$$DM = DEFKO1 + DE.C.EO \tag{A6}$$

where

FM = Matrix of element forces in modified structure

DM = Matrix of element deflections in modified structure

FKO1 = Matrix of element forces in unmodified structure

DEFKO1 = Matrix of element deflections in unmodified structure

FE = Matrix of element forces in unmodified structure due to unit deformations of elements to be modified

DE = Element deflections in unmodified structure due to unit deformations of elements to be modified

C = Column extractor matrix

FE = $-f_x \delta_{xx}^{-1} f_x^T$ EM

δ_{xx}^{-1} = $(f_x^T D f_x)^{-1}$ called DXXINV

EM = Matrix defining unit deformations of elements to be modified

f_x is re-defined FX

f_O is re-defined FO

$$FE = -FX.DXXINV.FX^T.EM \qquad (A7)$$

$$DE = FO^T (D.FE + EM) \qquad (A8)$$

$$EO = \left[(\Delta D_{mm})^{-1} - R.FE.C \right]^{-1} R.FKO1$$
$$= A^{-1}.R.FKO1 \qquad (A9)$$

R is a row extractor matrix

$$(\Delta D_{mm})^{-1} = \left[D(D_{mii}/D_{ii} - 1) \right]^{-1}$$

D_{mii} = Original value of area, thickness or I value of element to be modified

D_{ii} = Modified value of area, thickness or I value of element to be modified

D = Value of original element flexibility obtained from D matrix of original run

For multiple modification, the basic equations are expanded as shown. Three modifications are demonstrated.

$$A = \left[(\Delta D_{mm})^{-1} - (Rmm_1.FE.Cmm_1 \right.$$
$$\left. + Rmm_2.FE.Cmm_2 + Rmm_3.FE.Cmm_3) \right]$$

$$EOM = A^{-1} (Rmm_1 + Rmm_2 + Rmm_3)FKO1$$

$$FMM = \left[FKO1 : FKO1 : FKO1 \right]$$
$$+ FE \left[Cmm_1 EOM : Cmm_2 EOM : Cmm_3 EOM \right]$$

$$DMM = \left[DEFKO1 : DEFKO1 : DEFKO1 \right]$$
$$+ DE \left[Cmm_1 EQM : Cmm_2 EOM : Cmm_3 EOM \right]$$

These equations, written generally for r modifications, are:

$$A = (\Delta D_{mm})^{-1} - \sum (Rmm_r.FE.Cmm_r) \qquad (A10)$$

$$EOM = A^{-1} \sum (Rmm_r)FKO1 \qquad (A11)$$

$$FMM = \left[FKO1 : FKO1 ------ \right]_r$$
$$+ FE \left[Cmm_1 EOM : Cmm_2 EOM --- \right]_r \qquad (A12)$$

$$DMM = \left[DEFKO1 : DEFKO1--- \right]_r$$
$$+ DE \left[Cmm_1 EOM : Cmm_2 EOM--- \right]_r \qquad (A13)$$

For a problem which includes only disconnecting reactions, ΔD_{mm} is infinitely large $[(\Delta D_{mm})^{-1} = 0]$ and is therefore neglected. However, the capability exists to change bar areas and panel thicknesses by retaining ΔD_{mm}.

The number of modifications in any one computer run is generally 12. This means that successive disconnections of 12 reactions take place in one computer run. The solution to the modification matric equations is obtained using the FORMAT II abstraction instructions. [6]

To familiarize the reader with the solution to the equations, an example is given for four modifications using FORMAT abstraction statements for disconnect only $-(\Delta D_{mm})^{-1} = 0$

	FKO1	= F.MULT.KO
	DEFKO1	= DELTA.MULT.KO
Equation (A7)	FXTEM	= FX. TMULT.EM
	XEM	= −DXXINV.MULT.FXTEM
	FE	= FX.MULT.XEM
Equation (A8)	DFE	= D.MULT.FE
	DFEM	= DFE.ADD.EM
	DE	= FO.TMULT.DFEM
Equation (A10)	RFWUN	= RMMWUN.MULT.FE
	AWUN	= RFWUN.MULT.CMMWUN
	RFTWO	= RMMTWO.MULT.FE
	ATWO	= RFTWO.MULT.CMMTWO
	SUMWUN	= −AWUN.ADD.−ATWO
	RFTRE	= RMMTRE.MULT.FE
	ATRE	= RFTRE.MULT.CMMTRE
	SUMTWO	= −ATRE.ADD.SUMWUN
	RFFOR	= RMMFOR.MULT.FE
	AFOR	= RFFOR.MULT.CMMFOR
	A	= AFOR.ADD.SUMTWO

Let $\Sigma (RMM_r) = RMT$

Equation (A11) $\begin{cases}\end{cases}$

SWUN	= RMMWUN.ADD.RMMTWO
STWO	= SWUN.ADD.RMMTRE
RMT	= STWO.ADD.RMMFOR
RMTFKO	= RMT.MULT.FKO1
EOM	= A.SEQEL.RMTFKO

Let EMM   = Cmm_1 EOM: Cmm_2 EOM, etc.

Equation (A12) $\begin{cases}\end{cases}$

EKWUN	= CMMWUN.MULT.EOM
EKTWO	= CMMTWO.MULT.EOM
ADWUN	= EKWUN.ADJOIN.EKTWO
EKTRE	= CMMTRE.MULT.EOM
ADTWO	= ADWUN.ADJOIN.EKTRE
EKFOR	= CMMFOR.MULT.EOM
EMM	= ADTWO.ADJOIN.EKFOR

Let FOM   = [FKO1: FKO1 —]

B	= FKO1.RENAME.
BWUN	= FKO1.ADJOIN.B
BTWO	= BWUN.ADJOIN.B
FOM	= BTWO.ADJOIN.B
FEEMM	= FE.MULT.EMM
FMM	= FOM.ADD.FEEMM

Let DOM   = DEFKO1: DEFKO1—

C	= DEFKO1.RENAME
CWUN	= DEFKO1.ADJOIN.C
CTWO	= CWUN.ADJOIN.C
DOM	= CTWO.ADJOIN.C
DEEMM	= DE.MULT.EMM
DMM	= DOM.ADD.DEEMM

FMM is the matrix of element forces in the modified structure:

$$\text{FMM} = \quad m \begin{bmatrix} \text{Reactions} \\ \text{Bar Forces} \\ \text{Panel Forces} \end{bmatrix}^n$$

Reactions, bar forces, panel forces and shear flows can be extracted from this matrix using extractor matrices GR, GBT, GP, GPF saved from the unit analysis.

Joint external reactions:	FREACT	= GR.MULT.FMM
Bar forces:	FBAR	= GBT.TMULT.FMM
Panel shear forces:	FPANEL	= GP.MULT.FMM
Panel shear flows:	FFLOW	= GPF.MULT.FMM

The four basic input matrices to the modification program are RMMr, CMMr, EM and KO. RMMr and CMMr are row and column extractor matrices for the multiple modification procedure. EM is a matrix of unit deflections for the elements to be modified. KO is a matrix of external loads.

A simple example will serve to illustrate the form of these matrices. Consider the idealization of Figure 1. Suppose it is required to disconnect, one at a time, the first four reactions from the vertical centerline in the skin, to simulate a propagating crack for three different loading conditions. There will be four RMM and CMM matrices, one EM matrix and one KO matrix. The fourth RMM and CMM matrices only are shown for illustration. The row and column sizes for these matrices m and n are:

rm = Number of rows in the RMM matrix: total number of modifications to be made (10 in the example)

rn = Number of columns in the RMM matrix: total number of element forces (1043 for the idealization of Figure 1)

cm = Number of rows in the CMM matrix: number of elements to be modified (4 in the example, i.e., 4 reactions)

cn = Number of columns in the CMM matrix: total number of element modifications to be made (10 in the example)

em = Number of rows in the EM matrix: total number of element forces (1043 in the example)

en = Number of columns in the EM matrix: number of elements to be modified (4 in the example)

km = Number of rows in the KO matrix: number of load vectors (39 for the idealization of Figure 1)

kn = Number of columns in the KO matrix: number of load cases considered (3 in the example)

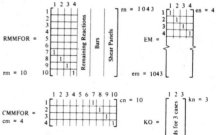

APPLICATION OF DAMAGE TOLERANCE CRITERIA
TO MULTI-PLANK WING COVER DESIGN

O. L. Freyre, L. W. Lassiter
J. A. Aberson, J. M. McKinney
Advanced Structures Department
Lockheed-Georgia Company

ABSTRACT

Design trends that bear on structural integrity are reviewed to provide a background for evaluating the function of a fracture control system. Damage tolerance criteria are considered within the overall perspective of achieving a reliable and efficient structure. The ramifications of implementing fracture control on a multi-plank wing cover design are discussed.

DESIGN TRENDS IN STRUCTURAL INTEGRITY

The performance of aircraft structures in operational environments has been monitored over a long period of time and has covered a large variety of airplanes. Collected data have been evaluated in the past where the performance of the structure was compared with the performance of other major subsystems comprising the airplane. As late as 1963, it was generally agreed that, historically, aircraft structures had demonstrated greater reliability than any other subsystem of an airplane, particularly when results were reviewed in terms of causes for mission aborts. However, it will be

397

recalled that in the years preceding this period, serious
difficulties were encountered, in which structural fatigue
posed a potential threat to the effectiveness of a strategic
bomber system and where several British Comet airplanes were
lost as a result of the catastrophic failure of the pressurized fuselage. These incidents combined to create a new
awareness and concern for structural integrity.

A number of related efforts were originated to cope
with these emerging conditions. In essence, the Air Force
structural integrity program was initiated in 1958 with the
preparation and distribution of the WCLS-TM 58-4, "Detail
Requirements for Structural Fatigue Certification Programs."
Military Specifications and Civil Air Regulations also were
revised to incorporate specific requirements directed at providing a control on the minimum level of structural integrity
that was to be incorporated in a new design. Requirements
in this area have continued to expand through an evolutionary
process on the basis of problems encountered on subsequent
programs. The purpose of this paper is to consider the implication of recently proposed damage tolerance criteria on
the multi-plank wing cover design concept. Results also will
be interpreted from the point of view of the efficiency of
the design concept in meeting the specified criteria.

Before getting into the details of the damage tolerance
of the panelized structural concept, a brief review of design
trends that have had an influence on structural integrity
may be helpful. In general, it can be said that greater demands are being placed on the structure and that the structures engineer is meeting these additional requirements by
increasing the efficiency of the structure. This has been
accomplished through the development of advanced stress-
analysis methods, which permit closer margins, and by fully
exploiting the strength properties of materials. These improvements have gone hand-in-hand with advances in materials

development. However, apart from generalities, specific
assessments can be made to quantify the influence of structural design requirements on structural integrity. Some of
these conditions will be discussed.

A comparison of the design utilization requirements of
a turbo-prop transport and a heavy logistic jet transport
reveals several interesting features. For example, the initial mission profiles and utilization rates established for
these particular airplanes show that the latter spends only
6% more time at cruise altitude than the former. The amount
of time spent in climb, descent, and low-altitude operations
is surprisingly similar for both airplanes. One may be in-
clined to make a case for assuming that long-range transports
are less susceptible to fatigue because they spend less time
at the lower altitudes where gust exposure is more severe.
In the case noted, the premise is open to question. Considering that the level-flight maximum speed of the jet transport
is about 1.2 times that of the older transport and that both
types of airplanes have a design fatigue-life goal of 30,000
flight hours, it can be seen that the gust load exposure of
the advanced system can be more severe than that of the older
system. Attention is called to the fact that the statistical
distribution of gust occurrence is based on data collected
in terms of miles flown; therefore, the product of speed and
time determine the level of gust exposure. High-speed, low-
level dash and aerial refueling requirements contribute further to increasing the significance of fatigue, fatigue crack
growth, and fracture in the design of new aircraft structures.

The influence of design load factor also can be shown
to be a significant parameter in the development of a new
design. Design and operational criteria considered in this
study corresponded to low-load-factor airplanes such as sub-
sonic strategic bombers and cargo/transport type aircraft.
Maximum design limit load factor for this category of airplanes

ranges from 2.00 to 3.00. It is interesting to observe the
degree to which fatigue and related problems become significant design considerations as the design limit load factor
is reduced. To illustrate, consider three structures with
similar usage that have a constant or uniform detail design
quality and where a constant level of exploitation of material strength properties is maintained; that is, the tensile
stress level at maximum ultimate load is the same irrespec-
tive of the design limit load factor requirement. Under the
conditions posed, Table 1 shows the results of analyses for
specific cases where 7075-T6511 aluminum structures designed
for 2.50-g's and 2.00-g's had predicted fatigue lives on the
order of 29% and 7%, respectively, of the fatigue life of
the 3.00-g airplane.

In terms of design cut-off stresses, the same line of
thought shows that, to achieve the fatigue life indicated
for the 3.00-g airplane, the design ultimate tensile stress
for the 2.50-g and 2.00-g airplanes must be reduced by 16%
and 32%, respectively, below the cut-off stress used for the
baseline airplane.

Premature fatigue crack initiation resulting from the
use of high design stresses or as a result of material flaws
and fabrication errors expands the scope of the problem to
the point where consideration must be given to the residual
strength of a damaged structure. The use of high-strength
materials, where toughness has often not kept pace with the
improvements in other strength properties, has combined with
other trends in aircraft development to require that greater
attention be given in the selection of materials and structural arrangements in order to maintain appropriate levels
of structural integrity.

Table 1

Influence of Design Limit Load Factor on Fatigue

Design Limit Load Factor	Fatigue Life Ratio for Constant Design Cut-Off Stress	Reduction in Design Cut-Off Stress for Constant Fatigue Life
3.00*	1.00	0
2.50	0.29	16%
2.00	0.07	32%

*Baseline Airplane

DAMAGE TOLERANCE CRITERIA

The damage tolerance criteria considered herein are
taken from requirements specified in the work statement of
Ref 1, which applies to an Air Force study of a wing carry-
through structure. In general, damage tolerance is assumed
to be achieved either through the fail-safe design concept
that utilizes crack stoppers and alternate load paths or
through the realization of slow or controlled crack growth.
By way of reference, the specific requirements are illus-
tratively defined in Fig. 1(a), 1(b) and 1(c). A 0.15 inch
flaw is assumed to exist in a principal structural element
in each case. For fail-safe designs, the crack growth period
and/or the fatigue life of the remaining structure, subsequent to the loss of a principal structural element, is
specified as a function of the inspectability of the component. In readily inspectable fail-safe designs, the remaining structure must be capable of successfully sustaining fatigue loads for ¼ lifetime after the failure of a
principal structural element. A factor of 1 may be used in
the fatigue assessments of integral fuel tank structure where
fuel leakage can aid in uncovering the existence of cracks
(provided a leak-before-break criterion is applicable).
Evaluations in other areas require a factor of 2.

Fail-safe structures that are not readily inspectable
require that the crack growth period from the initial flaw,
along with the fatigue life of the remaining structure after
the loss of a principal structural element, must exceed the
design life requirement of the airplane. The fatigue evaluation in this case must include a factor of 2, as shown in
Fig. 1(b).

In monolithic and non-fail-safe designs, the slow-crack-
growth requirement specifies that a crack emanating from an
initial flaw shall not grow to critical proportions within
the design life of the structure.

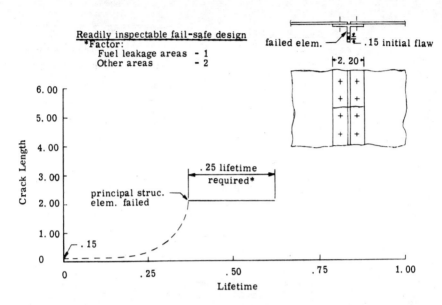

Fig. 1(a).   Damage tolerance criteria.   Readily inspectable
fail-safe design

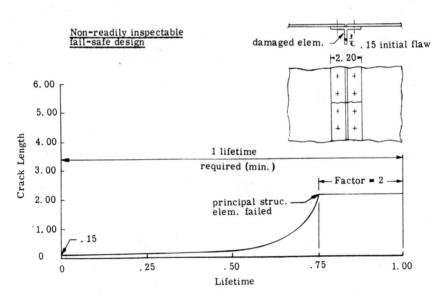

Fig. 1(b).   Damage tolerance criteria.   Non-readily inspectable
fail-safe design

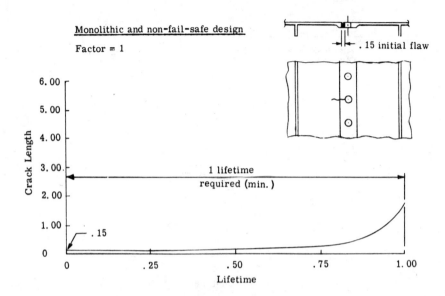

Fig. 1(c).   Damage tolerance criteria.   Monolithic and non-fail-safe design

In the succeeding sections a limited parametric analysis will be utilized to illustrate the approach used in the design of plank structure to conform to the appropriate fracture criteria for a fail-safe structural concept. On the basis of residual strength, the criteria also specify that, after failure of a single plank, the remaining structure must be capable of sustaining either limit load or the maximum load in the fatigue load spectrum, whichever is greater.

FRACTURE CONTROL IN MULTI-PLANK WING COVER DESIGN

In the evolution of a new design, many factors compete to the degree that the end product of necessity becomes a compromise. Fracture considerations are, of course, extremely important, but so, too, are weight, cost maintainability, etc. Thus it is not enough to achieve the desired fracture control, per se; it must be achieved while meeting all of the other design requirements as well.

Design Requirements. Certain design and operational functions are particularly affected by fracture control practices. Consider the following, for example:

(a). Weight - Weight control is generally a major concern in all aircraft development programs. The incremental improvement in airplane performance as a function of structural efficiency requires that changes in design criteria be evaluated in terms of the effect on structural weight. Damage tolerance criteria influence the material selection process and, therefore, can result in limiting the use and exploitation of certain high-strength materials.

(b). Design Lifetime - Traditional safe-life requirements for military aircraft are not at all diminished by the addition of damage tolerance criteria. On the contrary, damage tolerance expands the fatigue requirements to include a minimum level of endurance for structure containing flaws

or cracks. The additional factors that must be considered
to meet that requirement influence the selection of materials, allowable design stress levels, and structural arrangements.

(c). Maintenance & Inspection - Any effective fracture
control program is certain to bear directly upon the maintenance and inspection requirements established for the vehicle. This is, of course, obvious in the safe-life approach,
but the impact is quite evident in fail-safe structures as
well. In this case reliance is not placed upon knowledge
of crack growth rate for assurance of structural integrity,
but rather upon the ability of the fail-safe design features
to provide positive containment of damage within safe limits.
Even here, however, the mechanics of crack growth influences
operational requirements in terms of establishing the inspection frequency; normal procedure is not to permit a crack
to reach complete failure of an element.

(d). Cost - Fracture control cannot, of course, ignore
cost, which is a critical parameter in any design. Although
the cost aspect is not treated as a parameter in this paper,
attention is called to the fact that some of the approaches
for achieving damage tolerance in structures have a direct
bearing on cost. For example, multiple elements and alternate
load paths increase the number of parts to be fabricated,
handled, and assembled. Quality Assurance functions must
also be expanded at all stages in the manufacturing process.
Some phases of fleet operating costs, such as inspection,
can be expected to increase. In addition, down time for the
more elaborate inspection requirements reduces the availability of the airplane to the using command.

Parametric Analysis. The basic panel configuration
selected for analysis is shown schematically in Fig. 2. It
consists of a three-bay assembly with a lap splice made up
of a single row of mechanical fasteners. Riser configuration
effects were not considered in the detail stress analysis.

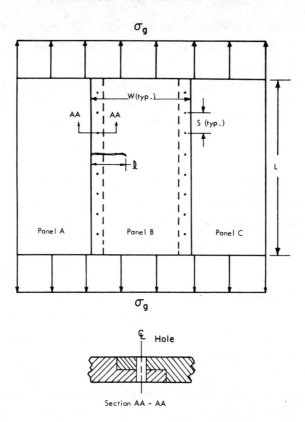

Fig. 2. Cover configuration used in parametric analysis

Modeling of the riser was accomplished by considering the
riser area to be concentrated in an axial element in the
plane of the panel.

The range of values in the parametric studies was
selected primarily to evaluate the influence of parameter
variations on the damage tolerance property of panelized
structure. On this basis, it is emphasized that the purpose of the analysis is to illustrate trends; the results
are not intended to be used as design information.

Four aspects of the cover performance are of concern
in the parametric evaluation. They are: (a) the time required to initiate a fatigue crack in Panel "B" (safe-life
concept), (b) the time required for a crack emanating from
a 0.15 inch flaw in Panel B to propagate across Panel B,
(c) the time required to initiate a crack in Panel A as the
crack in Panel B is growing across its width, and, (d) the
residual strength of the adjacent panels with the center
panel completely failed.

The first item is simply a normal fatigue analysis in
which nominal stress levels and stress concentration effects
are considered. Maximum allowable stress levels under design
ultimate load conditions are established to reflect the safe-
life requirements. These analyses are based on the assumption that the maximum stress concentration in a typical panel
is on the order of 4.0. Item (c) is treated in a similar
manner except that the initial nominal stress levels in the
fatigue spectrum are amplified due to load redistribution
as the crack progresses across the center panel. All fatigue
analyses are based on materials data taken from Ref 2. The
second item is handled within the framework of linear elastic
fracture mechanics by numerically integrating Forman's equation, taken from Ref 3, for the spectrum given in Table 2,
to obtain a prediction of crack length versus flight hours.
A static-strength, finite-element analysis, including

Table 2

Stress Spectrum* Used in Fatigue and
Crack Growth Analysis

Load Block	Mean Gross Stress,** psi	Alternating Gross Stress,** psi	Applied Cycles***
1	495	9239	3206
2	1366	14,516	4367
3	3189	5405	4428
4	9333	5221	22,440
5	9341	7862	260
6	9340	11,892	5
7	14,397	3976	38,460
8	14,450	7468	440
9	14,408	11,630	5
10	15,610	2482	140,000
11	17,683	3293	69,765
12	17,756	8028	220
13	17,678	12,240	5

   * Corresponding to a design stress level of 78 ksi
  ** Stresses in 7075-T6 Aluminum material only; correspond-
     ing titanium stresses are increased by a factor of 130/82
 *** Per 30,000 flight hours (1 lifetime).

Table 3

Parameters Used in Linear Parametric Analysis

Wing Cover Material	Panel Width, W	Splice Thickness, t	Fastener Spacing/Diameter Ratios (S/D)	Splice-Thickness/Fastener-Diameter Ratio (t/D)	Splice "Spring Constant", K
7075-T6 Aluminum Extrusion	10",25"	.1",.25",.4"	3, 5	0.4,0.7,1.0	200,000 lb_f/in 500,000 lb_f/in 800,000 lb_f/in
Titanium (Ti 6Al-4V) Annealed Extrusion	10",25"	.1",.25",.4"	3, 5	0.4	500,000 lb_f/in 800,000 lb_f/in 1,100,000 lb_f/in

plasticity effects, is used to evaluate the condition described in item (d). These analyses and the developed results are described briefly in the following sections.

Finite-Element Analysis. Finite-element analyses were
made for a variety of parametric values, the ranges of which
are shown in Table 3. The parameters considered were material; panel width; panel thickness, t; fastener diameter, D,
in terms of t/D; fastener spacing, S, in terms of S/D; and
the spring constant, K, of the joint. The spring constant
is defined as the slope of the load-deflection curve of the
joint and is a collective measure of general factors such
as fastener type, diameter, spacing, sheet material, and
sheet thickness. In using this definition of the constant,
no attempt was made to conduct a rigorous examination or
separation of its constituents, but rather a range of realistic values was assumed.

The purpose of the finite-element analyses was to predict the values and location of peak elastic stresses in
Panels A and C once cracking of B had begun. To obtain these
peak stresses, a finite-element model was constructed to
portray in a physically realistic manner the discrete transfer of load among Panels A, B, and C through the mechanical
fasteners. The first model considered is shown in Fig. 3
and is a highly detailed model of Panels A, B, and C above
the horizontal line of symmetry formed along the crack plane.
The model characterizes the three panels as a network of
constant plane-stress triangular finite elements with the
panels overlapped and joined at discrete locations by fastener
finite elements. These fastener elements can be described
as shear springs joining two structural points and are well
suited for modeling single shear attachments.

To perform analyses for all the variations listed in
Table 3, use of the model shown by Fig. 3 would have resulted
in excessive computer costs. Therefore, in order to obtain

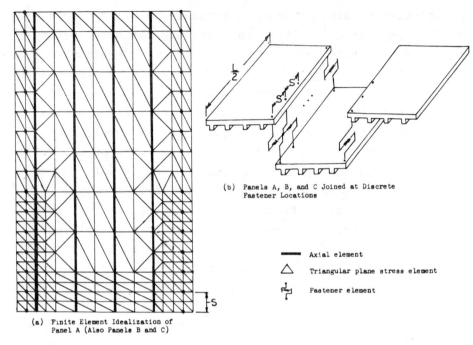

(b) Panels A, B, and C Joined at Discrete
    Fastener Locations

────── Axial element

△ Triangular plane stress element

⊏⊐ Fastener element

(a) Finite Element Idealization of
    Panel A (Also Panels B and C)

Fig. 3. Detailed finite element model

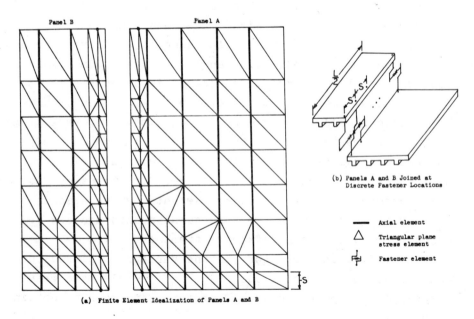

Panel B   Panel A

(b) Panels A and B Joined at
    Discrete Fastener Locations

────── Axial element

△ Triangular plane
   stress element

⊏⊐ Fastener element

(a) Finite Element Idealization of Panels A and B

Fig. 4. Coarse finite element model

an analysis for all the cases at reasonable costs, a less
detailed model was constructed. This model, shown by Fig.
4, was constructed by considering a quadrant formed by the
horizontal line of symmetry along the crack and a vertical
line along the center of Panel B. Carefully selected cases
were analyzed using both the detail and coarse model, and
the results were compared. Using these comparisons, a set
of extrapolation constants based on thickness, spacing, spring
constant, and crack length was obtained. The extrapolation
constants were applied to the results of the coarse model
analyses to provide a sufficiently accurate representation
of the location and value of peak stresses in Panel A. All
cases in Table 3 were analyzed in this way and peak stresses
predicted for various lengths of crack in Panel B for a constant uniaxial tension in the panels as shown on Fig. 2.

To predict the actual locations and values of peak
stresses from the constant stress-values obtained for the
triangles and bars in the analysis involved an averaging and
interpolation procedure. A set of average "stress-at-a-point"
values was obtained by a weighted averaging of the stress
components between two adjoining triangles and assigning
these averaged values to be located at the mid-point of the
triangles' common sides. The weighting factor for each triangle was total area of adjoining triangles per area of triangle. A set of point values thus obtained provided a stress
field topography from which isostress lines, peaks, and val-
leys were linearly interpolated. Experience gained through
use of nodal averaging techniques and the mid-point technique
has shown the mid-point technique to be easier to apply,
computationally more efficient, and as accurate as any nodal
scheme. Also, boundary forces and interpolated stresses were
examined to substantiate that the results are generally applicable to a wing box comprised of a continuous series of
panels.

In general, the techniques and procedures associated
with utilizing a detail model to allow extrapolation of results from a coarse working model are considered to be
neither new nor clever, but they are considered to be practical. The use of fastener elements, however, is relatively
new in structural analysis and provides the analyst not only
with the capability of characterizing the discrete nature
of load transfer between panels through joint fasteners,
but with the individual fastener forces as well. These
forces can prove to be significant both in the prediction
of stress intensity factors and in the prediction of the
mode of failure of the three-panel configuration. More will
be said about this in a later section on residual strength.

Fatigue/Fracture Analysis. The analyses presented relate directly to the damage tolerance criteria discussed
previously. Only the criteria for readily inspectable and
non-readily inspectable fail-safe structure are considered.
The criterion for monolithic or non-fail-safe designs will
not be dealt with in this paper.

The criterion for the readily inspectable case is illustrated schematically in Fig. 5. The basic difference between this criterion and the one for non-readily inspectable
structure is the nature of the endpoints specified in their
respective statements. The former may be regarded as a
floating-endpoint specification and the latter, a fixed-
endpoint specification. In this context, the term "floating
endpoint" refers to the absence of a specific total life requirement, prior to the initiation of a crack in the adjacent
structure, but subsequent to the loss of a principal structural element. By contrast, the criterion for non-readily
inspectable structure exhibits a "fixed endpoint" characteristic in that a total life requirement is specified during
which a crack may progress across a principal structural
element, provided the adjacent structure remains crack-free.

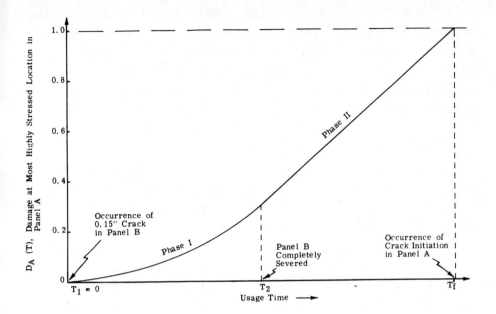

Fig. 5. Hypothetical accumulation of damage in panel A

The difference between the characteristics of these two criteria alters the basic approach to the fatigue/fracture analyses required. For structure that is not readily inspectable, the period of crack growth in the flawed structure is included in the specified period during which the adjacent structure must remain uncracked. Therefore, the fatigue damage accumulated by this adjacent structure during and after the crack growth period must be taken into account.

For readily inspectable structure, the specified period of one-quarter lifetime does not include the crack growth period. Therefore, the changing local stress in the adjacent structure associated with crack growth in a principal structural element does not have to be considered in the fatigue-damage calculation of the adjacent structure. As a result, a conventional local fatigue analysis of the adjacent structure can be performed and the controlling parameters adjusted to permit the design to meet the prescribed damage tolerance criterion.

Referring to Fig. 5, the damage tolerance criterion for readily inspectable structure can be expressed as

$$(T_f' - T_2) \geq \begin{Bmatrix} 1/4 \\ 1/2 \end{Bmatrix} \text{ lifetime in } \begin{Bmatrix} \text{fuel} \\ \text{non-fuel} \end{Bmatrix} \text{ leakage areas} \qquad (1$$

The results of the fatigue/fracture analysis for readily inspectable 7075-T6 aluminum structure are presented in Fig. 6 and 7. Figure 6 displays results for 10-inch-wide panels, while Fig. 7 shows comparable results for 25-inch-wide panels.

Each of these figures displays design stress level versus splice thickness for various values of normalized spacing, S/D, and thickness, t/D. These plots represent the extremities of the envelope defined by inequality (1). The plots allow correlation of the allowable value(s) of design stress level for readily inspectable structure in fuel leakage areas with corresponding values in non-fuel leakage areas. It can be seen from these plots that the additional fatigue endurance can be achieved with very little decrease of design stress level.

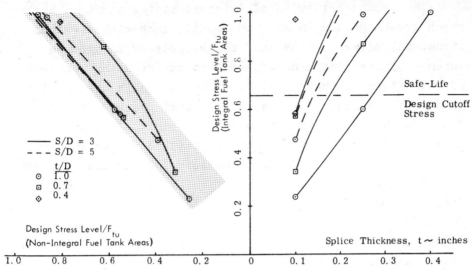

Fig. 6.   Influence of design stress level on damage tolerance
          criteria for readily inspectable 10-in.-wide 7075-T6
          aluminum wing panels (K = 500,000 lb$_f$ in.)

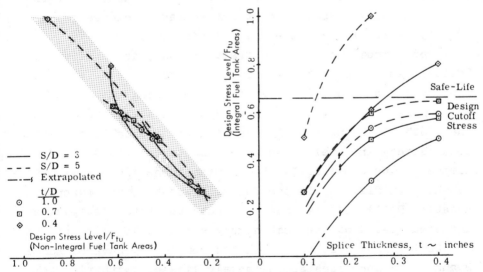

Fig. 7.   Influence of design stress level on damage tolerance
          criterion for readily inspectable 25-in.-wide 7075-T6
          aluminum wing planks (K = 500,000 lb$_f$ in.)

The second criterion of interest states simply that the
crack growth period in any non-readily inspectable principal
structural element, plus half the calculated fatigue endurance of the remaining adjacent structure after the loss
of this element, must equal or exceed a single design lifetime of the vehicle. It is assumed that cracking initiates
from a 0.15-inch initial flaw in the principal structural
element. This criterion can be related to the schematic
shown on Fig. 5. The damaged "principal structural element"
is Panel B shown on Fig. 8. At zero time, designated T_1 on
Fig. 5, Panel B is assumed to contain a 0.15-inch edge crack.
Crack growth emanating from the flaw will occur under operating conditions until Panel B is completely failed at some
point in time designated T_2.

During Phase II, i.e., after Panel B has completely
failed, the damage imposed on Panel A accumulates at a constant rate. As a result, early cracking occurs in Panel A
at some value of time, T_f'. The damage tolerance criterion
for non-readily inspectable structure can be expressed as

$$(T_2 - T_1) + 1/2 \ (T_f' - T_2) \geq 1 \ \text{Lifetime.} \tag{2}$$

For purposes of fatigue/fracture analysis considerations,
Phases I and II are used to describe damage accumulation in
Panel A during and after significant cracking occurs in Panel
B. During Phase I, the crack in Panel B is growing across
the width of the panel. As cracking progresses, the maximum
local stress in Panel A increases and causes the fatigue
damage in the panel $D_A(T)$ to increase non-linearly with time
as shown in Fig. 5. In the following sequel, the functional
notation $D_A(T)$ will be used to denote the total fatigue damage accumulated at the most highly stressed location of Panel
A. During Phase II, the crack has completely severed Panel
B and $D_A(T)$ increases approximately linearly with time in
accordance with Miner's linear cumulative damage hypothesis.

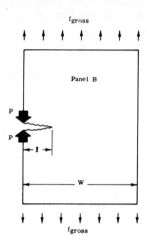

Fig. 8.   Model of cracked panel B

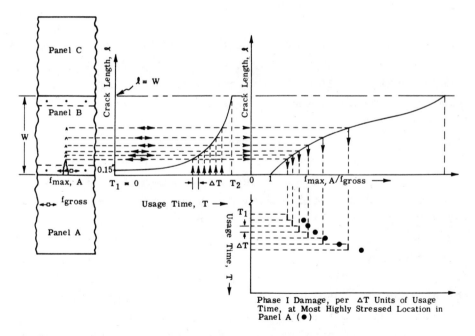

Fig. 9.   Schematic of sequence used to calculate phase I damage
accumulation in panel A

Phase I damage can be estimated by calculating an amplified stress spectra for Panel A corresponding to equal, discrete intervals of flight time and using these data to determine the damage accumulated by Panel A during each interval.
This concept is depicted schematically in Fig. 9. The total
damage imposed on Panel A is then simply the sum of these
individual damages.

The crack-growth curves used in the analysis were obtained by numerically integrating Forman's equation considering stress intensities based on an edge-crack model super-
posed on a restrained-crack model as shown in Fig. 8. In
the figure, f_{gross} denotes the gross stress applied to Panel
B, and P denotes the restraining force, per splice unit
thickness, offered by the adjacent attaching fasteners. An
estimate of P can be made by summing the fastener forces obtained from the finite-element analysis discussed in the
preceding section. The results of superposing these two
solutions are the tabular correction factors given in Table 4.

The plots of stress versus crack length depicted in Fig.
9 were obtained using the load redistribution effects determined from the linear finite-element analysis described
in the preceding section. Figures 10 through 13 display
examples of redistribution effects in terms of maximum local
stress in a panel versus crack length in the adjacent panel.
These figures show, respectively, the comparative effects
of material, splice-thickness/fastener-diameter ratio,
fastener-spacing/fastener-diameter ratio, and splice spring
constant.

Returning to Fig. 9, values of crack length corresponding
to certain pre-selected values of time are determined from
the appropriate crack-growth curve. These lengths then are
used to determine the local stress magnification factor,
$f_{max, A}/f_{gross}$. Assuming this magnification factor to maintain a constant value during any given interval of time, ΔT,

Table 4

Tabular Correction Factors* Used in Crack Growth Analyses

ℓ/W	$\beta_P^{**}(\ell/W)$	$\beta_f^{***}(\ell/W)$
0	--	2.000
.05	2.46	2.032
.10	2.36	2.099
.15	2.29	2.218
.20	2.21	2.402
.25	2.16	2.637
.30	2.10	2.930
.35	2.07	3.298
.40	2.07	3.744
.45	2.07	4.303
.50	2.07	4.996
.55	2.07	5.898
.60	2.07	7.097
.65	2.05	8.781
.70	1.98	11.291

$$*K_I = f_{gross}\sqrt{\pi\ell}\beta_f(\ell/W) - (P/\sqrt{W})\,\beta_P(\ell/W)$$

** Reference 4

*** Reference 5

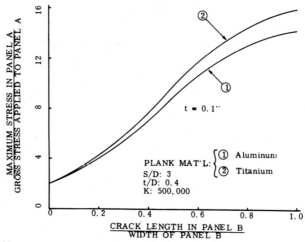

Fig. 10.   Wing cover panel maximum stress variation caused by
a growing crack in an adjacent panel (B) -- material
variation

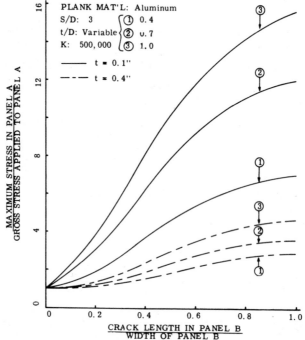

Fig. 11.   Wing cover panel maximum stress variation caused by
a growing crack in an adjacent panel (B) -- t, t/D
variation

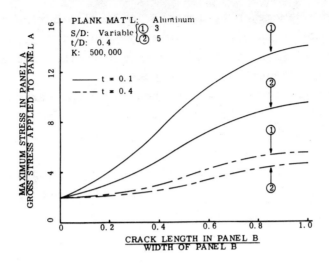

Fig. 12. Wing cover panel maximum stress variation caused by
a growing crack in an adjacent panel (B) -- t, S/D
variation

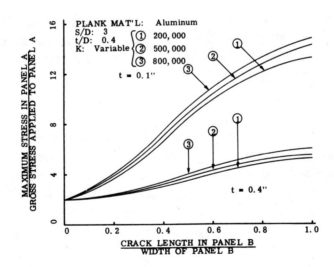

Fig. 13. Wing cover panel maximum stress variation caused by
a growing crack in an adjacent panel (B) -- t, K
variation

the fatigue damage, n/N, imposed on Panel A during this interval can be calculated. One per cent of a 30,000-flight-hour target design lifetime was chosen as the time interval for the work presented in this paper.

Phase II damage is calculated using the maximum value of $f_{max, A}/f_{gross}$. The total amount of time required to initiate a crack in Panel A, T_f', can now be estimated. This can be done by using Miner's cumulative damage rule and demanding that the total damage imposed on Panel A during Phases I and II be unity. The resulting expression for T_f' is

$$T_f' = (T_2 - T_1) + \frac{1 - D_1}{D_{II\ 1}} \qquad (3)$$

where T_1, T_2 and T_f' are defined on Fig. 5, and D_I and $D_{II\ 1}$ denote damages accumulated by Panel A during Phases I and II, respectively; D_I is the total damage absorbed during Phase I, and $D_{II\ 1}$ is the damage absorbed per unit flight hour.

As mentioned previously, T_1, the beginning of Phase I, is assigned a reference value of zero for the results presented herein. Furthermore, the results of the crack-growth analyses yield values of T_2 for the several conditions considered. Therefore, once T_f' is calculated from Eq 3, it can be used in the inequality (2) to determine whether or not the criterion has been met. The results for non-readily inspectable structure are shown in Fig. 14. Comparable results for mill-annealed Ti 6Al-4V panels are not plotted. An identical analysis for this material indicated that the crack-growth phase exceeded 30,000 flight hours for all cases examined. In other words, in terms of inequality (1), $T_2 - T_1 \geq 1$ lifetime.

Residual Strength. Nonlinear finite-element analysis of the model shown by Fig. 3 was performed for a number of selected configurations, Table 3, to predict the full static

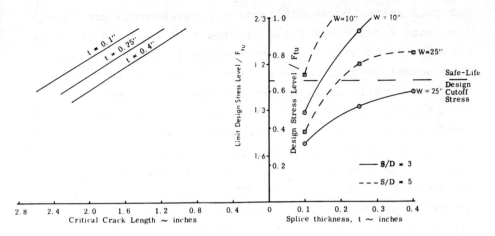

Fig. 14. Influence of design stress level on damage tolerance criteria for non-readily inspectable 10-in. and 25-in.-wide 7075-T6 aluminum wing panels (t/D = 0.4, K = 500,000 lb$_f$in.)

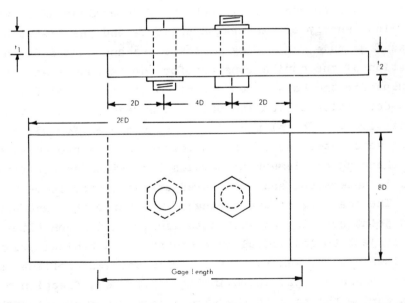

Fig. 15. Typical joint configuration used for load-deflection test

residual strength capability of the three-panel configuration once Panel B was fully cracked through. The analysis
method used to make these predictions is a finite-element
incremental loading procedure wherein the constant uniaxial
tension is built up in discrete steps. After each step in
the incremental method, material properties, fastener spring
constants, and geometry of the three panels are modified to
account for yielding of material and fasteners and displace-
ments of the model's joints. This modified model then is
loaded by the next increment of load and analyzed. This procedure of analysis-modification-analysis continues until
either an instability occurs in the model or all the defined
load is placed on the structure. The Lockheed-Georgia
Company has used this analysis method in project environments to accurately predict residual strength for both wing
spar and span-wise splice configurations.

Yielding and subsequent modification of material properties for the triangular elements were determined using the
von Mises energy of distortion criteria and the Prandtl-
Reuss flow rule. Yielding of fasteners and bars and modification of the spring constant for the fasteners and axial
modulus for the bars were determined directly from fastener
load-deflection curves and uniaxial stress-strain curves,
respectively. The slopes of the above curves for all element
types were determined from a Ramberg-Osgood representation.
The changing of element properties for triangles and axials
is well understood and considered standard practice.

The changing of the spring constant for the fasteners
is a joint quantity as stated earlier, and its constituents
are subject to individual interpretation. A typical joint
specimen used to generate an experimental load-deflection
curve resembles that shown in Fig. 15. The deflection measured during the test is the elongation of the gage length.
This elongation is comprised of three main types of deformation:

(a) plate extension, (b) fastener shear deformation, and
(c) bearing of the fasteners into the plates. The determination of the spring constant, K, for the joint depends on the
approach to be followed in the analysis. Since the plate
and fasteners are modeled separately, as shown by Fig. 3,
it is logical to remove that part of the gage deflection due
to plate extension and thus obtain a load-deflection curve
characterizing the fasteners. The slope of such a modified
curve will provide a value for K that combines the deformation characteristics of fastener shear and bearing. It was
this type of curve that was used in the residual strength
analyses. Figure 16 illustrates the gage and modified curves
for Case 1 in Table 5. Two aspects were considered in predicting the residual load-carrying capacity of the three-
panel configuration: overall yielding of the joint and strain
at the critical location. To illustrate these factors, Fig.
17 was prepared to show the progression of the yield pattern
for the strain in the applied stress direction for the critical location, the first effective fastener in Panel A, and
a plot of fastener loads along the joint between A and B as
the nominal applied stress is increased. Results shown are
for Case 5 of Table 5. The failure criteria are based on
an ultimate uniaxial strain of 8% for the 7075-T6 aluminum
alloy. From the figure, it can be observed that the size
of the yielded portion of the panel, the strain at the critical region, and the fastener distribution all indicate a
probable residual strength, σ_{ult}, of around 52000 PSI with
a failure mode of crack extension through A. In a similar
manner all cases listed in Table 5 were analyzed and the
residual strength capacity predicted.

Table 5

Cases Analyzed in Residual Strength Study

Case No.	Material	Width (in)	t (in)	S/D	S (in)	t/D	D	$\frac{K}{\times 10^{-5}}$ (lbs/in)	σ_{ult} (psi)	$\frac{\sigma_{ult}}{F_{tu}} \times 100$
1	Aluminum	25	.25	2.45	1.071	.57	.438	5	22000	26.8
2	Aluminum	25	.25	4.08	1.785	.57	.438	5	34000	41.5
3	Aluminum	25	.25	3.00	1.875	.40	.625	5	33000	40.3
4	Aluminum	25	.25	5.00	3.125	.40	.625	5	46000	56.1
5	Aluminum	10	.25	4.08	1.785	.57	.438	5	52000	63.5
6	Titanium	25	.25	2.45	1.071	.57	.438	5	35000	26.9
7	Titanium	25	.25	4.08	1.785	.57	.438	5	55000	42.4

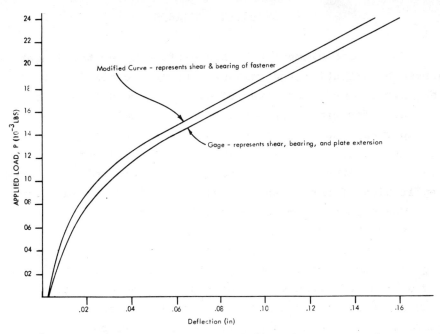

Fig. 16.   Gage and modified load-deflection curves for case 1
            of Table 5

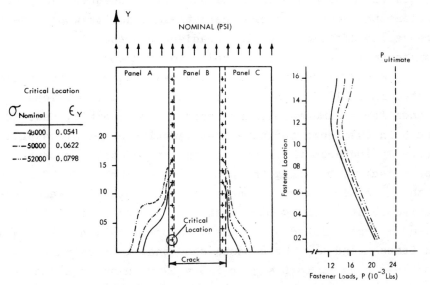

Fig. 17.   Residual strength analysis of case 5 of Table 5

CONCLUDING REMARKS

The finite-element analyses performed for the linear stress distribution and residual strength cases illustrate the physical modeling power of finite-element methods in general. The capability to model individual fasteners is an important and basic asset that has proved to give very accurate results, particularly for residual strength predictions. Although the analysis methods are well developed, application of the technique has had limited exposure.

The structural models, especially the residual-strength models, contained a relatively large number of elements and displacement degrees of freedom; therefore, their analyses required considerable computer time. The number of elements and degrees of freedom were dictated by the steep displacement and stress gradient in the vicinity of the crack and fasteners. Since all the elements used were constant stress elements, a finer model mesh was required than if linear stress elements had been available. In subsequent investigations the use of higher-order stress elements would increase the efficiency of the gradient representation and consequently reduce the analysis time and costs.

A study of the results of the residual strength analyses listed in Table 5 discloses some general and significant trends for a damage-tolerant design. For example, Cases 2 and 5 in the Table indicate that reducing panel width will markedly increase the residual capacity of the structure. Specifically, reducing the width from 25 inches to 10 inches with all other parameters being held constant increases the fail-safe strength by more than 50%. Another significant trend is established by the results of Cases 1 and 2 as well as Cases 3 and 4. These cases show that increasing the fastener spacing (S/D = 3 to S/D = 5) results in a substantial increase in residual strength (40-55%). Comparison of Cases

1 and 2 with Cases 3 and 4 reveals that increasing fastener diameter (t/D = 0.7 to t/D = 0.4) also results in an increase in residual strength (40-60%). An interesting trade-off of spacing and diameter effects is seen in comparing Case 2 with Case 3. In Case 3 the fasteners have a larger diameter than in Case 2 which tends to cause an increase in strength capability, but the S/D ratio is smaller, which causes a decrease in strength capacity, with the net result that the residual strength for the two cases is virtually equal.

The effect of material choice can be observed from the results of Cases 1 and 2 for aluminum and 6 and 7 for titanium. Although the titanium panels have a greater residual-strength capacity than the aluminum, it can be seen from the σ_{ult}/F_{tu} ratios that the allowable exploitation of material strength properties is approximately the same for comparable designs in the two materials.

In summary, for residual strength considerations, the following design trends can be asserted:

(a). Increasing fastener spacing and diameter increases residual-strength capacity substantially.

(b). Decreasing panel width increases residual strength.

(c). For the conditions analyzed, material effects are not significant when viewed in terms of allowable material strength exploitation.

The fatigue/fracture analyses performed in this study illustrate methodologies that can be used to assess the impact of progressive damage in a structure on the fatigue endurance of adjacent structure. The results of this assessment are presented within the framework of damage tolerance requirements for two types of structure that have been characterized as readily inspectable and non-readily inspectable fail-safe designs.

The results of the linear finite-element analysis are used in the fatigue/fracture analyses described previously.

Specific trends that emerge from this study may be summarized as follows:

(a). Lower splice-thickness/fastener-diameter ratios, (t/D), tend to satisfy more readily the damage tolerance criterion for readily inspectable structures. This trend is illustrated by Fig. 6 and 7, where it can be seen that, for a given splice thickness, t, the permissible design stress level increases for decreasing values of t/D.

(b). Higher fastener spacing/diameter ratios, (S/D), tend to satisfy more readily the damage tolerance criteria in both readily and non-readily inspectable areas. Figures 6, 7 and 14 illustrate this trend. It can be seen in each of these figures that, for a given splice thickness, the curves for S/D = 5 invariably lie above their counterparts for S/D = 3.

(c). The permissible design stress level increases, though with decreasing emphasis,* with increasing splice thickness. Again, this trend is illustrated in Fig. 6, 7 and 14 for both readily and non-readily inspectable structure.

(d). Lower plank widths tend to satisfy more readily the damage tolerance criterion. This can be seen from Fig. 6,7 and 14 by noting that the group of curves in Fig. 6 and 14 for 10-inch panels have, on the whole, higher ordinate values than the 25-inch panels shown in Fig. 7 and 14. Indeed, Fig.

---

* The single exception is the curve for t/D = 1, S/D = 3 of Fig. 6. This curve exhibits a concave upward characteristic which implies an _increasing_ emphasis on the increasing design stress level.

6 shows that the 10-inch wide aluminum planks with splice thicknesses greater than 0.25 inch not only satisfy the damage tolerance criterion for readily inspectable structure, but the safe-life design criterion as well. For non-readily inspectable structure, Fig. 14 shows that 10-inch-wide aluminum planks having splice thicknesses greater than 0.25 inch satisfy both the damage tolerance and the safe-life design criteria.

(e). The group of curves in the left quadrant of Fig. 6 and 7 shows the effect of increasing the scatter factor from 1 (in fuel-leakage areas) to 2 (in non-fuel-leakage areas). These curves show that a very minor decrease in design stress level is required in order to satisfy the more demanding requirement.

(f). The foregoing fatigue/fracture trends apply to aluminum structure only. The results obtained from this study indicate that the mill-annealed Ti-6AL-4V panels satisfy the damage tolerance criteria for both readily and non-readily inspectable structure.

Lastly, the study and its related background considerations reveal several areas where further research and development would be helpful. Some of these are:

(a). Test programs to produce load-deflection data relative to joint behavior.

(b). Further finite-element studies, particularly with elements to permit plate-bending effects to be considered.

(c). Analytic techniques for calculating crack-tip stress intensity factors in the vicinity of an integral riser.

(d). More intensive development of positive crack-stopping techniques for monolithic designs, since such designs are inherently very efficient.

References

1. AFFDL RFQ F33615-71-Q-2233, "Design, Fabricate, Test and Evaluate A Wing Carry-Through Structure for An Advanced Strategic Bomber," 20 April 1971

2. Metallic Materials and Elements for Aerospace Vehicle Structures, MIL-HDBK-5A, Department of Defense, Washington 25, D. C., February 8, 1966

3. Forman, R. G., Kearney, V. E. and Engle, R. M., "Numerical Analysis of Crack Propagation in Cyclic-Loaded Structures," Journal of Basic Engineering-Transactions of the ASME, September 1967

4. Paris, P. C., "A Handbook of Crack Tip Stress Intensity Factors," Lehigh University, Interim Report, June 1960

5. Gerberich, W. W., and Katz, Y., "On a Trigonometric Expression for the Single-Edge Notch Specimen," Engineering Fracture Mechanics, Vol 1, No. 3, April 1969, pp 569, 570.

INFLUENCE OF FRACTURE PARAMETER INTERACTIONS
ON THE DESIGN PROCESS

W. E. Krupp and E. K. Walker
Advanced Design and Research Laboratory
Lockheed California Company
Burbank, California

ABSTRACT

The design of high strength-to-weight structures
of monolithic construction will often be the expedient alternative in spite of problems associated with
designing for adequate damage tolerance. The design,
analysis, and testing for this class of structure
must consider the impact of interactions between key
fracture parameters. A discussion of these key
parameters -- fracture toughness, fatigue life, subcritical crack growth rate -- is followed by an
illustration of how they influence the iterative design process. A design sequence for fracture resistant materials is presented, consisting of (a)
trade-off studies to define the relative importance
of pertinent parameters, (b) simple tests for materials selection, (c) complex tests to evaluate parameter interaction and provide design data, (d) detailed analysis to finalize design, inspection and
operating requirements, and (e) evaluation of service experience to obtain information for future designs.

INTRODUCTION

The design of high strength-to-weight structures of
near monolithic construction will many times prove to be the
expedient alternative in spite of the obvious problems in
designing for adequate damage tolerance. Fracture design,
analysis, and testing for this class of structure must consider the impact of complex interactions between key fracture
parameters such as fracture toughness, fatigue, and environmental crack growth rate. These parameters may combine
either favorably or unfavorably, depending upon the type of
material, environment and load spectrum encountered in the
service application. Thus, structure designed without considering interaction effects may (a) fail prematurely, (b)
require costly maintenance and frequent inspections, or (c)
have excessive weight penalties due to synergistic effects
of applying lower bound fracture behavior.

In addition to the interaction effects of one parameter
modifying the behavior of another, there are also sequential
effects. In a particular application, only some of the fracture parameters may be of importance, as shown in Table I.
Establishing the real importance of each parameter and the
practical limits of control or measurement accuracy required
for each can provide substantial savings in the development
of design data and in subsequent process controls and inspections. As material selection invariably requires trade-
offs between desirable and obtainable properties, knowledge
of the relative importance of fracture parameters to the
specific design problem is necessary for proper material
selection.

It is the objective of this paper to provide preliminary
insight as to the nature of the interactions between fracture parameters and how they influence the iterative design
process. It is hoped that the discussion and suggestions
that follow will guide designers in gathering design informa-

tion and in performing analysis pertinent to reliable performance in specific structural applications. It is also hoped that such analysis will discourage the direct application of simplistic materials screening and material selection test data to design cases beyond their limited scope.

TABLE 1. FACTORS INFLUENCING FRACTURE PARAMETER INTERACTIONS

Physical Influence / Fracture Parameter	High Short Term Static Loads	High Long Term Static Loads	Cyclic Loads	Load Sequencing	Aggressive Environments
Fracture Toughness	✕				
Fatigue Crack Growth Rate			✕	✕	✕
Stress Corrosion Crack Growth Threshold		✕			✕
Stress Corrosion Crack Growth Rate		✕			✕

FRACTURE PARAMETERS

The fracture parameters normally of concern in design of a fracture sensitive structure -- fracture toughness, cyclic and environmental crack growth rate -- have been discussed in depth in the literature (1-4) and elsewhere in this symposium. The discussion below is thus confined to those observations that are necessary to clarify the interrelations between parameters and guide their application to design.

Fracture Toughness. The most commonly measured fracture toughness parameter for a material is the minimum value, the plane strain fracture toughness K_{Ic}, defined by

$$K_{Ic} = Y \, \sigma \, \sqrt{\pi \, a}$$

(1)

where $\underline{a}$ = one-half the crack length, σ = applied stress, and
Y = correction factor to account for plasticity, part and
crack geometry. (1)

Currently recommended test procedures (5) require adequate specimen size and thickness to ensure a substantially
plane strain stress state near the crack tip. The required
test specimen thickness (B), which in turn defines other
specimen dimensions, is based on allowable plastic deformation in the zone ahead of the flaw, using the formula

$$B = 2.5 \left[\frac{K_{Ic}}{\sigma_y} \right]^2 \tag{2}$$

where σ_y = yield stress. Precracking at a low stress is also
required to ensure a high degree of notch activity. (6,7)
Measurement of fracture toughness under plane strain conditions yields lower bound values, as thin sections generally
provide higher toughness values. (8,9) Thus K_{Ic} values may
provide an overly conservative value of toughness, causing
a weight penalty, and data should be developed on the actual
thickness used in the design. Such K_Q tests based on the
actual design thickness may be required anyway to obtain
proper characterization of grain flow or other process variables. While this scheme of testing would seem to be the
only logical alternative, it does pose a problem in that non-
standard testing may require development of new experimental
methods and may add costs in excess of those normal for
material selection and procurement.

If the service loads are significantly above the value
used to determine K_{Ic} then a design value of K_Q for final
flaw size should be evaluated. The influence on K_Q of sustained loads, environments, load sequencing, etc., might be
of interest in some uses. Each of these singularly or in
combination could provide values of $K_Q > K_{Ic}$. If it is de-
cided to use a value of $K_Q > K_{Ic}$ in design, caution should

be exercised in that the designer should substantiate that
there are no circumstances in which the lower bound K_{Ic} could
realistically occur in service. As a matter of design philosophy, calculations should be based on K_{Ic} unless there is substantial supporting evidence for a less conservative value.

Fatigue Crack Growth. Cyclic loading at a sufficiently
high stress level, but below that required for static fracture, will cause an initial flaw to propagate, so that the
stress at which fracture occurs decreases with increasing number of cycles. The most frequently presented records of this
behavior are linear plots of flaw size versus cycles or time
and log-log or log-linear plots of the average growth rate
da/dN versus the stress intensity range ΔK. There are, at
present, no standard test methods for determining crack growth
rates although in general the procedures are similar to
those used for K_{Ic} testing. (10,11) Since cyclic crack growth
tends to occur with less associated plasticity than is present
in static fracture (12), the specimen dimension requirements
do not appear as critical.

A large number of tests have been performed under constant amplitude conditions to demonstrate the effects of
environment, stress ratio, cracking rate, geometry, microstructure and plasticity on crack growth rates. Real service loadings are not in general simple constant amplitude
cycles; rather they vary as the aircraft undergoes various
parts of its mission. Thus much effort has been expended to
develop simple approaches that use constant amplitude test
data to predict spectrum results. The linear cumulative
addition of constant amplitude rates to simulate spectrum
crack growth appears to be subject to as much variation from
a Miner's ratio of unity as in the similar use of constant
amplitude stress versus cycles to failure data for estimating
spectrum fatigue life. (13,14) Published results to date
indicate that the trend of such linear cumulative crack
growth estimates is conservative. (15,16) This has been

ascribed to the retarding effect caused by previous higher
loads. (17,18) Quasi-empirical equations have been developed
by Wheeler (19) and Willenborg et al (20) to account for load
interactions, which may retard or accelerate crack growth.
Both estimate the plasticity effects of higher loads and require these effects to remain in diminishing degree as the
crack grows through the plastically deformed region. Both
equations require determination of material related factors
experimentally using spectrum load crack growth tests. The
best use of such equations at present would be to interpolate
between well-defined spectrum growth rates representing extremes of anticipated load spectra. Crack growth rates also
vary with stress range ratio, R, which is the ratio of minimum cyclic stress to maximum cyclic stress. Equations have
been developed by Forman (21) and Walker (22) to account for
stress range ratio effects. Both equations rely on empirically
defined constants and exponents. In addition to load interaction effects and stress ratio effects, the operating environment can have significant influence on cracking rate. (23,25)
Most available test data have been obtained using a severe
environment and accelerated exposures, so that time compres-
sion effects may be present. Also it has not been established
that environmental effects obtained under constant amplitude
conditions are applicable to spectrum growth rates. If the
environmental effects are rate sensitive (26,27) then the
effects of an average growth rate under spectrum conditions
should differ from those of the constant amplitude components.
Therefore, spectrum load tests should be conducted in a
realistic environment and exploratory tests should be conducted to determine whether extending the time base causes
increased fatigue crack growth rates. There are some indications that in steels, there is a continuing increase in
cracking rate with extended time base. (28) For titanium
(29) and aluminum (30) there appears to be a limit to this
behavior, so that for aluminum and titanium real time effects

of environment on cracking rates may be adequately simulated by laboratory tests. All design assumptions should be verified for each specific application.

Stress Corrosion Crack Growth. Subcritical flaw growth due to the combined action of a sustained tensile load and a corrosive environment can cause cracking and failure in a material that normally would not fail if subjected to separate application of either the load or the environment. Tough materials such as copper alloys, mild steel, stainless steel, and some aluminum alloys display high toughness and exhibit little environmental sensitivity to crack-like defects when subjected to sustained load. Environmental cracking of these materials is generally associated with specific corrodents, e.g., brass-ammonia, stainless steel-acidic chlorides, etc. In these tough materials, cracks often initiate at pits formed by anodic dissolution and the rate of crack propagation is typically governed by electrochemical mechanisms and thus is generally very slow. In contrast is the behavior of high strength materials such as low alloy, quenched and tempered steels, precipitation hardenable steels, and maraging steels, all with yield strengths over 180 ksi, aluminum alloys with yield strengths above 63 ksi, and most commercial titanium alloys. These materials generally exhibit low toughness and greater environmental sensitivity to crack-like defects that are inherent in the microstructure. Here, no specific metal/corrodent couples exist, and such diverse media as sea water, wet air, and organic fluids can cause severe cracking in the same material. Crack initiation often occurs at pre-existing defects, with subsequent crack propagation controlled by the interaction of mechanical and chemical factors instead of electrochemical mechanisms.

The stress level and corresponding stress intensity existing during environmental cracking controls crack growth rate. As the magnitude of the stress intensity factor

increases, crack growth rate increases, reducing the time to
failure. For many alloys there appears to be a limiting or
threshold value of stress and stress intensity below which
environmental cracking does not occur in a finite time period
(i.e., the crack growth rate is not measurable by any known
experimental procedure). The threshold for corrosion cracking
is determined by either successive tests at incrementally
lowered stress levels until a lower bound stress for non-
propagation of a pre-existing fatigue crack in environment
is determined, or by propagation to arrest of a pre-existing
fatigue crack in a specimen designed and loaded to cause a
gradual decrease in the stress intensity ahead of the crack
as the crack propagates. Test procedures are generally modeled
after those for K_{Ic} testing (31) but there are no established
standards. The most important differences in threshold values
seem to arise from variations in the time for the crack to
start moving under load in an aggressive environment. Such
factors as precracking stress level or environment, prior load
history, concentration of the aggressive environment, pH, temperature, material and product form, appear to alter the threshold level as well as initiation time. (31)

Once a crack starts to propagate under sustained load
in an aggressive environment, the rate of growth (da/dt) appears to behave more uniformly in terms of stress-intensity.
(32,33) Thus the rate of propagation of an initiated sustained load crack may be a better measure of environmental
sensitivity than the threshold K_{Iscc}. The sustained load
crack growth rate da/dt may be needed in design even for
cases where tests show extremely long initiation times as the
time required for initiation of sustained load cracking from
fatigue precracks cannot be arbitrarily assumed as a measure
of time required for initiation from natural sources such as
metallurgical defects.

The state of stress at the crack tip has a significant
effect on environmental cracking. Experimental evidence indicates environmental cracking is associated with plane-strain

conditions and is of lesser or no importance under plane-stress conditions. (24) These plane-strain conditions can be adequately supplied by triaxial constraint surrounding severe stress risers. (34) Data on the effect of load history on environmental cracking are limited. It has been shown that pre-exposure to the environment before application of low magnitude loads accelerates environmental cracking rate in titanium and aluminum alloys. (35) This was ascribed to the rupture of the protective oxide film, allowing the corrodent access to the base metal. Other work showed an increase in resistance to environmental cracking after exposure to high sustained loads, presumably due to crack blunting.(36) Thus it would be expected that the effects on sustained load environmental cracking produced by periodic overloads would depend on the delay time before load application and the magnitude of the load excursion.

The stress corrosion cracking threshold may vary in a manner similar to K_{Ic} with prior load history and time. The threshold measurement usually includes both initiation and propagation phases. It is obvious that for long time sustained loadings (pressure vessels) the value of K_{Iscc} (rather than K_{Ic}) may be the key design parameter. However, in complex load histories the significance of K_{Iscc} is not as obvious. If the sustained load portions of the operating stresses are below K_{Iscc} the structure should not be susceptible to sustained load cracking. If the structure is operating periodically at sustained stress above K_{Iscc} for long periods of time (time that approaches the corrosion cracking initiation period) then corrosion cracking rate (da/dt) may need to be considered. For complex conditions of mixed load and environments the significance of K_{Iscc} is not clear and it would be desirable to determine its significance by tests under simulated operating conditions prior to accepting a design penalty. However, it should be noted that there is a general correlation between corrosion susceptibility of uncracked material and the threshold for sustained flaw growth (37) so that high K_{Iscc} values are always desirable.

DESIGN APPROACH

The best method of incorporating fracture parameters will depend on the specific design problem. There are, however, some general rules to use as guidelines. First, the best engineering solution to any design problem is simply to find some way of eliminating the problem or at least greatly decreasing its severity or consequences. Thus first considerations should be given to redundancy, fail-safe designs, high toughness/low cracking rate materials with a high degree of product uniformity and environmental resistance, inspectability, and moderate stress levels. As a generality, whenever fracture mechanics parameters become the critical factors defining the applied loadings or the operating and inspection requirements, the structure will be difficult to maintain and costly to operate. Thus whenever high strength-to-weight monolithic structure becomes the only practical alternative, it is best to examine fracture parameters to assure that the design does not exhibit a propensity for failure by fracture mechanics related mechanisms.

While there are probably many schemes (38-41) to arrive at a reasonable balance between fracture resistance requirements and other design requirements, one general approach to the problem could follow the scheme presented in Fig. 1. This design sequence is detailed in subsequent sections.

Fracture Parameter Evaluation

Determination of Failure Mechanism. After a decision has been reached to employ a high strength monolithic part, it is necessary to determine the sensitivity of the particular design application to fracture parameters. For long life designs, studies such as those outlined in Fig. 2 may quickly

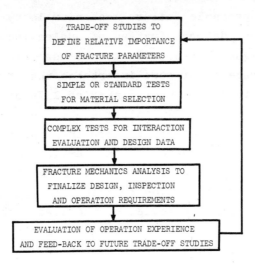

Fig. 1.   Fracture resistant design sequence

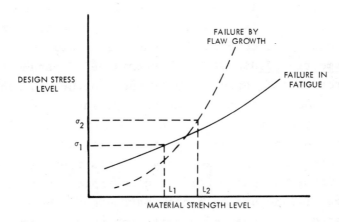

Fig. 2.   Effect of design stress level and material characteristics on prediction of fracture mode

show the most probable failure mechanism is by growth of pre-
existing natural defects instead of nucleation and subsequent
growth of fatigue cracks. Additional analysis may show that
crack growth rate is of more importance than fracture toughness in determining the useful service life of a specific long
life application (Fig. 3). Alternately, initial fracture
toughness may be of primary concern in a short life application (Fig. 4). Examination of the service environment and
fracture parameters may give insight as to the relative importance of stress corrosion cracking and fatigue cracking
(Fig. 5). Similarly, a review of the load spectra should
indicate whether there is a nearly constant amplitude load
spectra (pressure vessel) or an extreme mix of loadings
(fighter aircraft wing). Other factors that must be considered include inspectability, potential for in-service damage,
prior history (maintenance records, failure analyses, accident
reports) and special operational conditions (temperature,
acoustics). In addition, the impact of variations in fracture parameters on operational features should be determined.

Parametric Studies. The performance of parametric studies
should provide a clear picture of the fracture mechanics requirements and how their variation influences the design requirements from both a structural and operational viewpoint.
The details of this parametric study will vary with the design
requirements. A simplified study of this type is shown in
Fig. 6. Since the parametric studies explore the influences
of a range of fracture mechanics parameters, these can usually
be completed by reference to data available in common sources
(books, journal articles, reports) prior to obtaining detailed
information on interactions between variables for specific
materials. From the parametric studies the designer should
arrive at:

    (a). Selection of materials

    (b). Relative importance of each fracture parameter

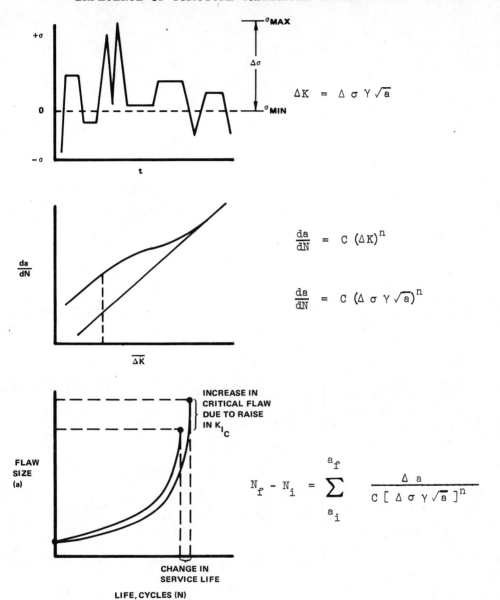

$$\Delta K = \Delta \sigma \, Y \sqrt{a}$$

$$\frac{da}{dN} = C \, (\Delta K)^n$$

$$\frac{da}{dN} = C \, (\Delta \sigma \, Y \sqrt{a})^n$$

$$N_f - N_i = \sum_{a_i}^{a_f} \frac{\Delta a}{C \, [\, \Delta \sigma \, Y \sqrt{a} \,]^n}$$

Fig. 3. Importance of crack growth rate in long service life
    application

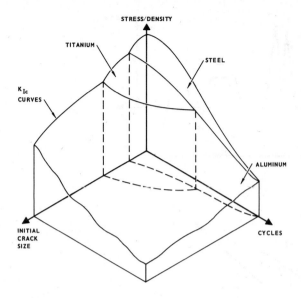

Fig. 4. Importance of K_{Ic} for short life vs long life service
application

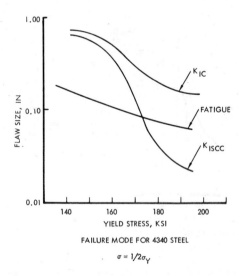

Fig. 5. Importance of stress corrosion threshold in a corrosive
environment

(c). Approximate magnitude of fracture parameters required to meet design needs

(d). Possible trade-offs between initial flaw size,
stress levels, service life

(e). Sensitivity of design to possible variations in
fracture parameters

(f). Probable interactions between variables that are
not defined by simple fracture mechanics test and
thus require further test evaluation before completion of design

(g). Cut-off levels of various parameters where the
design sensitivity shifts to parallel parameters
such as fatigue life of joints, holes, fasteners,
surface corrosion, impact or ballistic damage, etc.

Once the above insight for the design has been obtained
it will be possible to make preliminary material selections
and to detail the test program required for additional data
if any is required.

Nondestructive Inspection. One of the greatest tempta-
tions for a designer attempting to reduce weight in a fracture
sensitive component is to reduce the possible initial flaw
size. This temptation can arise when information is lacking
for assessing the large impact of small initial flaw size on
later operating, maintenance and inspection costs as weighed
against the normal design assumptions that weight and costs
are synonymous and that the materials are free of flaws.

First and most obvious, structure required for long life
under adverse condition of operation and maintenance should
have tolerance for large, easily detectable flaws or comparable structural damage. The resultant weight penalty for
monolithic structure in this category of vehicle will simply
have to be compensated for elsewhere. For this class of
structure the alternatives of redundancy become most attrac-
tive.

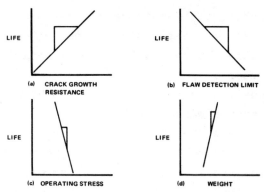

(a) 200% Increase in Crack Growth Resistance   (c) 20% Decrease in Operating Stress
(b) 200% Decrease in Flaw Detection Limit   (d) 20% Increase in Weight

Fig. 6.   Amount of variation in critical fracture parameters
            required to double service life

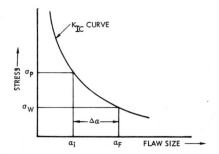

Fig. 7.   Establishment of a minimum flaw size by proof testing

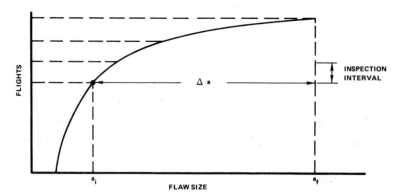

Fig. 8.   Determination of inspection intervals using flaw
            growth data

For structure of short life operated under adverse conditions or for long life structure justifiably operated under "kid glove" conditions, reduction in initial flaw size and consequent reliance on sophisticated nondestructive inspection procedures may be a legitimate alternative. Available inspection procedures and estimates of detectable flaw sizes and types are summarized in Table II. It should be emphasized that flaw detection capability is not absolute, varying with product form, accessibility, test conditions and human factors. The designer is thus well advised to ask guidance from an inspection expert for aid in the parametric studies.

If proof testing is being considered, sustained flaw growth during loading and unloading may occur. (44) This may cause the maximum flaw size passing the proof test to exceed that estimated by K_{Ic} and the peak proof test stress (Fig. 7). This possibility could be evaluated using da/dt and K_{Iscc} data without interaction effects. However, delay effects may occur due to the interaction of peak load plasticity and the decreasing stress field as the specimen is unloaded from the peak proof stress. This could be much the same situation as would occur after a high load from a prior fatigue cycle. This point may be worth investigating prior to accepting a proof test penalty for subcritical flaw growth, since possible flaw growth during proof testing may cause a decrease in proof stress level, leading to a reduction in the amount of guaranteed flaw growth.

Materials Selection Data Acquisition. Once the relative importance of the several fracture parameters is established, preliminary material selection can be accomplished. This would normally involve use of standard laboratory tests to evaluate fracture parameters for candidate materials. The objective of these tests is to give a "first order" evaluation of the suitability of a given material for a specific design application and to provide a basis for material procurement and processing specifications and controls.

Table 2.

Flaw Detectability Limits for Various NDT Techniques (a)

Material	Visual (b)	Magnetic Particle (b)	Penetrant (b)	X-Ray (c)	Ultra-Sonic (c)	Delta Ultra-Sonic (c)
0.25" Extrusion(40)						
7075-T6511	0.03	-	0.25	> 0.50	0.25	-
4340	0.03	0.30	0.35	> 0.50	0.20	-
0.020" Plate(43)						
7075-T6	-	-	0.040	-	0.050	-
Ti-6Al-4V	-	-	0.032	0.070	0.100	-
0.125" Plate(43)						
7075-T6	-	-	0.030	-	-	-
Ti-6Al-4V	-	-	0.050	0.130	0.090	0.034
0.500" Plate(43)						
7075-T6	-	-	-	0.460	0.290	-
Ti-6Al-4V	-	-	0.035	-	0.150	0.090

(a) 100 per cent detection level in laboratory tests. (b) Surface flaws of known location. (c) Both known surface flaws and unknown embedded flaws.

Considerable economy in testing can be achieved if the designer and materials engineer work together to minimize the number of tests on variables of lesser importance to the specific design problem on hand. Emphasis should obviously be placed on those parameters of greatest significance and to those in which possible variation in properties have the greatest impact on desired results. For these cases, the effects of variations in constituent properties, microstructure, primary and secondary processing and fabrication, and in some instances time in service environments should be thoroughly evaluated. It also should be noted that evaluation of only one fracture parameter may not be sufficient to reveal important variations in material behavior. (45,46) While it is probably beyond the scope of the designer to detail test procedures, he can aid the materials engineer by defining variables critical to the design and what load-time-stress interactions are expected, thus providing practical bounds for test variables.

Combining the knowledge of designer, materials engineer and nondestructive inspection specialist can provide guidance as to critical flaw types, orientations and sizes for specific materials and product forms. In this manner, the total number of tests and thus the material selection test program costs can be significantly reduced.

Design Data Acquisition and Substantiation. The acquisition of design data differs in purpose from that of data for material selection and specification. While there is obvious overlap, the object of design data acquisition and substantiation is establishment of material behavior under realistic combinations of environments and loads. These tests will require simulated service conditions to be imposed on either standard fracture specimens, flawed specimens simulating critical areas on monolithic components, or flawed components themselves. (47) Such tests would be too complex and costly to

use in materials screening. They are mandatory however for
quantifying interaction effects, effect of design details,
evaluation of design stress levels, required flaw detection
capability and inspection intervals. Test requirements will
depend on the intended use of the specific design application.
As a minimum, however, interactions between fracture parameters should be evaluated.

Detailed Design Analysis. As in most iterative processes,
this stage of design for fracture prevention bears much similarity to the parametric study discussed previously. However,
by this point in the process, specific material performance
data is on hand and the designer can determine exact bounds
for parametric envelopes and the amount of variation to be
expected. The fracture mechanics analysis outlined in Fig.
3 can be repeated, using specific design stresses, critical
flaw sizes and crack growth rates in lieu of the more general
information previously used. At this point, the main variables for the designer to consider are the operating stress
levels and severity of stress spectrum. The results may be
presented in parametric form (see Fig. 2 and 4) and the consequences of changes in stress levels evaluated. In addition
to flaws existing in the raw materials, the designer must
consider service induced flaws and flaws generated during the
fabrication cycle. Any process that degrades fatigue and
fracture properties must be excluded. Process controls, inspection procedures and frequency of inspection must be specified to guarantee the absence of any flaw that could grow to
critical size during operations. Structures must be inspected
frequently enough so that a crack undetected in one inspection
will not grow to critical size due to service loadings prior
to the next inspection. One criterion (48) requires inspection at one-quarter the time required for a crack to grow from
the minimum inspectable size to critical size, as shown in
Fig. 8. This allows for the possibility of not detecting a
crack during an inspection and the expected statistical scatter

in test results. In addition, the designer must reaffirm
that assumed flaw detection limits are realistic for the
specific procedures and design application involved. As a
final step, the basic design philosophy and data development
test program should be re-examined after the structure is in
operation. This should reveal deficiencies in initial assumptions, gaps in the testing program, indicate promising areas
of research, and add to the data base for future design
efforts.

CONCLUSIONS

The foregoing discussion of fracture parameters and interactions as applied to design poses nothing radically different in the design process. It is simply a matter for the
designer to become aware of the varieties of these relatively
new design parameters so that he can take those steps necessary to successfully incorporate them into the total scheme
of design and analysis. It must be emphasized that fracture
mechanics is intended to augment standard static and current
fatigue structural design techniques. Unfortunately, there
is no new technology that eliminates the requirement for
proper design procedures.

Prevention of fracture in safe-life components has received increased emphasis by government agencies, to the point
where fracture mechanics criteria are being written into con-
tracts. (48,50) In addition, recent court decisions on product liability and implied warranties place a new burden for
safe operation on the original manufacturer. (51,52) These
external stimuli are added to pre-existing internal stimuli
to achieve increased structural reliability, integrity and
efficiency, while minimizing cost and weight impact.

References

1. A. S. Tetelman, A. J. McEvily, Jr., Fracture of Structural Materials, John Wiley & Sons, Inc., 1967

2. H. Liebowitz (ed.), Fracture - An Advanced Treatise, Academic Press, New York, 1968
   Vol   I - Microscopic and Macroscopic Fundamentals
   Vol II - Mathematical Fundamentals
   Vol III - Engineering Fundamentals and Environmental Effects
   Vol IV - Engineering Fracture Design
   Vol   V - Fracture Design of Structures
   Vol VI - Fracture Metals
   Vol VII - Fracture of Nonmetals and Composites

3. T. Yokobori, T. Kawasaki, J. L. Swedlow (eds), Proceedings of the First International Conference on Fracture (Sendai), The Japanese Society for Strength and Fracture of Materials, Tokyo, Japan, 1966
   Vol   I - Mathematical, Physical and Continuum Mechanical Theories
   Vol II - Atomistic, Microstructural and Macroscopic Mechanics
   Vol III - Strength and Fracture of Non-Metallic Materials

4. P. L. Pratt (ed.-in-chief), Fracture 1969 - Proceedings of the Second International Conference on Fracture (Brighton), Chapman and Hall Ltd., London, England, 1969

5. ASTM Standard E-399-70T, "Proposed Method of Test for Plane-Strain Fracture Toughness Testing of High-Strength Metallic Materials," ASTM Standards, Part 31, ASTM, Philadelphia, Pa., pp 911-927, 1970

6. Fracture Toughness Testing and Its Applications, ASTM STP 381, 1965

7. Plane Strain Crack Toughness Testing of High Strength Metallic Materials, ASTM STP 410, 1966

8. R. E. Zinkham, "Anisotropy and Thickness Effects in Fracture of 7075-T6 and T651 Aluminum Alloy," Engineering Fracture Mechanics, Vol 1, pp 275-289, 1968

9. G. R. Irwin, "Fracture Mode Transition for a Crack Traversing a Plate," Transactions of American Soc. for Mech. Engineers, No. 417, June 1960

10. P. Paris, F. Erdogan, "A Critical Analysis of Crack Propagation Laws," _Journal of Basic Engineering, Trans. of ASME_, Series D, Vol 85, pp 528-534, 1963

11. American Society for Testing and Materials, _Fatigue Crack Propagation_, ASTM STP 415, 1967

12. H. H. Johnson, P. C. Paris, "Subcritical Flaw Growth", _Eng. Fracture Mechanics_, Vol 1, p 3, 1968

13. R. Engle, "Cracks -- A Fortran IV Digital Computer Program for Crack Propagation Analysis," AFFDL-TR-70-107, March 1970

14. T. R. Brussat, "An Approach to Predicting the Growth to Failure of Fatigue Cracks Subjected to Arbitrary Uniaxial Cyclic Loading," paper presented at Damage Tolerance in Aircraft Structure Symposium, ASTM 73rd Annual Meeting, Toronto, Canada, June 21-26, 1970

15. R. V. Sanga, T. R. Porter, "Application of Fracture Mechanics for Fatigue Life Prediction," paper presented at Air Force Conference on Fatigue and Fracture of Aircraft Structures and Materials, Miami Beach, Fla., December 1969

16. D. R. Donaldson, W. E. Anderson, "Crack Propagation Behavior of Some Airframe Materials," _Proceedings of Crack Propagation Symposium_, The College of Aeronautics, Cranfield, England, Vol II, September 1961

17. J. Schijve, D. Broek, P. DeRijk, "Fatigue-Crack Propagation Under Variable-Amplitude Loading," NRL-TN M.2094, National Aero and Astronautical Research Institute, 1961

18. C. M. Hudson, H. F. Hardrath, "Investigation of the Effects of Variable-Amplitude Loadings on Fatigue Crack Propagation Patterns," NASA TN D-1803, 1963

19. O. E. Wheeler, "Spectrum Loading and Crack Growth," _Journal of Basic Engineering_, ASME, to be published

20. J. Willenborg, R. M. Engle, H. A. Wood, "A Crack Growth Retardation Model Using an Effective Stress Concept," AFFDL-TM-71-1, January 1971

21. R. G. Forman, V. E. Kearney, R. M. Engle, "Numerical Analysis of Crack Propagation in Cyclic Loaded Structures," _Journal of Basic Engineering_, ASME, pp 459-464, September 1967

22. E. K. Walker, "The Effect of Stress Ratio During Crack Propagation and Fatigue for 2024-T3 and 7075-T6 Aluminum," Effects of Environment and Complex Load History on Fatigue Life, ASTM STP 462, ASTM pp 1-14, 1970

23. M. R. Achter, "Effect of Environments on Fatigue-Crack Propagation," Fatigue Crack Propagation, ASTM STP 415, p 181, 1967

24. D. E. Piper et al, "Corrosion Fatigue and Stress Corrosion Cracking in Aqueous Environments," Metals Engineering Quarterly, p 50, August 1968

25. D. W. Hoeppner et al, "Fracture and Fatigue-Crack Propagation Characteristics of 7075-T7351 Aluminum Alloy," NADC Contract N00156-68-C-1344, January 1969

26. A. Hartman et al, "Some Tests on the Effect of the Environment on the Propagation of Fatigue Cracks in Aluminum Alloys," NLR-TN m2182, 1967

27. W. E. Krupp, D. W. Hoeppner, E. K. Walker, "Crack Propagation of Aluminum Alloys in Corrosive Environments," International Conference on Corrosion Fatigue, Storrs, Conn., June 1971, to be published in proceedings

28. R. P. Wei, "Some Aspects of Environment-Enhanced Fatigue-Crack Growth," Engineering Fracture Mechanics, Vol 1, p 633, 1968

29. R. J. Bucci et al, "Very Low Fatigue Crack Growth Rates in Air and Dry Argon for a Titanium 6Al-4V Alloy," Fifth National Symposium on Fracture Mechanics, Urbana, Ill., September 1971

30. J. A. Feeney, J. C. McMillan, R. P. Wei, "Environmental Fatigue Crack Propagation of Aluminum Alloys at Low Stress Intensity Levels," Metallurgical Transactions, Vol 1, p 1741, 1970

31. Ohio State University, Fundamental Aspects of Stress Corrosion Cracking, Proceedings of Conference, Columbus, Ohio, September 1967

32. H. R. Smith et al, "A Study of Stress Corrosion by Wedge Force Loading," Engineering Fracture Mechanics, Vol 1, p 123, 1968

33. B. F. Brown and C. D. Beachem, "A Study of the Stress Factor in Stress Corrosion Cracking," Corrosion Science, Vol 5, p 745, 1965

34. M. P. Kaplan et al, "A Study of the Mechanics of Fracture in Stress Corrosion," *Corrosion*, Vol 26, p 7, 1970

35. F. H. Cocks, "The Separation of Corrosion and Stress Effects in Stress Corrosion Testing," *Materials Research and Standards*, p 29, December 1969

36. M. H. Peterson et al, "Stress Corrosion Cracking of High Strength Steels and Titanium Alloys in Chloride Solution at Ambient Temperature," *Corrosion*, Vol 23, p 142, 1967

37. H. L. Logan, "The Stress Corrosion Cracking of Metals," *Metals Engineering Quarterly*, p 32, May 1965

38. E. T. Wessel, W. G. Clark, W. K. Wilson, "Engineering Methods for the Design and Selection of Materials Against Fracture," Final Technical Report to U. S. Army Tank-Automotive Center, June 24, 1966

39. W. K. Stratton, R. S. White, "The Application of Fracture Mechanics to Fail Safety of Rotor Blades," Vertol Division, Boeing Company, Philadelphia, Pa., 1969

40. P. Packman, H. Pearson, J. Owens, G. Marchese, "The Applicability of a Fracture Mechanics-Non-Destructive Testing Design Criterion," AFML TR-68-32, 1968

41. D. P. Wilhelm, "Fracture Mechanics Guidelines for Aircraft Structural Applications," AFFDL TR-69-111, February, 1970

42. H. F. Hardrath, "Fatigue and Fracture Mechanics," AIAA Paper 70-512, presented at AIAA/ASME Eleventh Structures, Structural Dynamics, and Materials Conference, Denver, Colorado, April 22-24, 1970

43. F. J. Sattler, "Nondestructive Flaw Definition Techniques for Critical Defect Determination," NASA CR-72602, January, 1970

44. D. W. Hoeppner, D. E. Pettit, C. E. Feddersen, "Determination of the Flaw Growth Characteristics of Ti-6Al-4V Sheet in the Solution-Treated and Aged Condition," NASA CR-65811, January 1968

45. D. E. Piper, W. E. Quist, W. E. Anderson, "The Effect of Composition on the Fracture Properties of 7178-T6 Aluminum Alloy Sheet," *Application of Fracture Toughness Parameters to Structural Metals*, Gordon and Breach Science Publishers, Inc., pp 227-280, 1966

46. C. Laird, "The Influence of Metallurgical Structure
     on the Mechanisms of Fatigue-Crack Propagation," Fatigue
     Crack Propagation, ASTM STP 415, ASTM, Philadelphia, Pa.,
     pp 131-180, 1967

47. U. A. Hinders, "F-111 Design Experience - Use of High
     Strength Steel," AIAA Paper 70-884, delivered at AIAA
     Second Aircraft Design and Operations Conference, Los
     Angeles, Cal., July 20-22, 1970

48. USAF-ASD, "Damage Tolerance Requirements for B-1 Air-
     craft," CP 621L2002, January 1971

49. H. Wood, "The Role of Applied Fracture Mechanics in
     the Air Force Airplane Structural Integrity Program,"
     AFFDL TM-70-5-FDTR, 1 June 1970

50. Fracture Control of Metallic Pressure Vessels, NASA
     SP8040, NASA Structures Design Monograph, May 1970

51. G. R. Close, "The Development and Presentation of
     Technical Evidence in Products Liability Litigation,"
     Materials Research and Standards, Vol 10, No. 10, p 8,
     1970

52. Case and Comment, Boncraft-Whitney Co., November 1970